The moral right of the author has been asserted
First published in Great Britain in 2017
by
Ringwood Publishing
24 Duncan Avenue, Glasgow, G14 9HN
www.ringwoodpublishing.com
e-mail mail@ringwoodpublishing.com

ISBN 978-1-901514-48-3

British Library Cataloguing-in Publication Data
A catalogue record for this book is available from the
British Library

Printed and bound in the UK
by
Lonsdale Direct Solutions

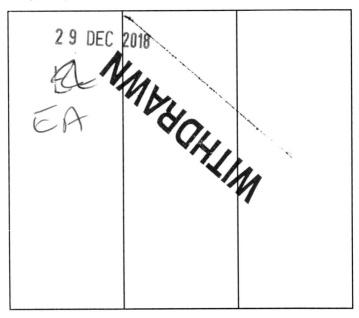

About the Author

Mary McCabe has published dozens of short stories and poems in Scots, English and Gaelic in anthologies and literary journals, as well as feature articles for newspapers. Her longer work includes a psychic novel *Everwinding Times* and an illustrated book *Streets Schemes and Stages* about cultural projects.

Her fictionalised account of scandals in her own family tree, *Stirring the Dust,* written in English, Doric and Glaswegian, was Paperback of the Week in the Herald.

In German translation she has published a children's book *Die zauberhafte Reise,* and her radio plays have been broadcast on mainstream radio in Germany and Switzerland. She is active in the writers' political organisation International PEN.

A political campaigner since her schooldays, she has decades of experience in door-to-door canvassing, attending demonstrations in Scotland and abroad and proposing progressive change.

Now retired from her day job as Researcher/Editor with Glasgow City Council she can devote more time to writing and campaigning.

Acknowledgements

I'm grateful to Gordon Newlands of Planet Ecosse, who located and photographed with his wide-angle camera the close tiles used for the front cover. He had to go into a lot of closes before he found a suitable selection. Also to Eilidh McCabe for her helpful comments on the manuscript and for putting the front cover together.

I'm obliged to Joe Pike for his book Project Fear: How an Unlikely Alliance Left a Kingdom United but a Country Divided. This provided me with valuable insight into the thought processes and experiences of those campaigning on the "Better Together" side.

Thanks also to Sandy Jamieson, Isobel Freeman and the rest of Ringwood for putting their faith in this book. My especial thanks go to Lauren McMinn for her editing and helpful suggestions and Dave Webster for the general production of the book.

Dedication

To those whose commitment to political progress in Scotland
is only intensified by the false summits they reach.

25 Lagarie Drive, Dennistoun

Jan Dvorak Zack Konicek		Ali Akram (Iqbal's uncle) Noor Akram Yasmin 14, Bina 11, Farooq 8
Iain MacLean		Donald Gillies Ewan MacConachie
Lorraine Murphy (sister to Kenny) Angela 16		Iqbal Usmani (Ali's nephew) Catriona Usmani Lena 3, Bobby 1
Agnes Morrison		Rab Gilchrist Marilyn Gilchrist Kirsty15 (Rab's daughter from 1st marriage) Erin 8, Benny 5

77 Wallacewell Avenue, Barmulloch

Elspeth Nimmo Gordo 21, Stevie 19, Malky 16	Wilma Armstrong
Cindy Ross Charlie 4	Abdul Nabi Parween Nabi Habib 10
Kenny Murphy (brother to Lorraine)	Daisy Donnelly

Prologue

Jinty

Our world, blue and white as the Willow Pattern, hangs on the edge of our galaxy where the stars are far-flung and we're not overlooked by the neighbours.

From Earth's moon, 250,000 miles out: no sign of life. No evidence of the millennia spent working the planet to a series of short-term plans: building pyramids, building walls, bridging islands, transmitting signals, exploding nuclear bombs, releasing carbon dioxide, dispersing the ozone layer. Astronauts struggle to discern landmasses below the fluff of cloud.

From the space station, orbiting at 400 kilometres, if you know where to look, you glimpse the Great Wall of China. The Pyramids. Entering the shuttle and travelling towards Earth, more detail. At 217 kilometres the deserts of Africa and Asia Minor present well, golden in the sunlight. Oil rigs appear on the oceans. Roads on the land. By night the globe hovers in a shining net.

Scotland, like the planet Venus, shrouds its assets in mist. For a view of its bare mountains, grids of tenements by day, streets glittering by night, you must duck beneath the clouds, below the level of a Boeing 747, to the level of a Loganair moth.

In 2014, the world did duck beneath the clouds. A world which – at the time I abandoned Scotland – had considered it a fringe of England, or didn't consider it at all, took a hard stare, googled fishy names like Salmond and Sturgeon, checked out flight connections to Glasgow, Edinburgh and Prestwick.

That year, not only the world turned its telescope on Scotland but the very sun shed its grace, scattering mists, drying clouds, bathing natives, tourists, Commonwealth athletes, golfers and political activists on both sides in a golden glow. At the FIFA World Cup qualifiers, Team Scotland gracefully snatched defeat from the jaws of victory, earning the usual faint praise. In Dalmarnock, at the Commonwealth Games, they picked up 30 medals – six golds. At Gleneagles, the Ryder Cup was won by Europe for the third consecutive time. The very parking cone on the Duke of Wellington's head turned to gold.

For politicians and journalists 2014 transfigured the Scottish perspective forever. Ordinary people following well-worn pathways up and down their tenement closes woke up, asked new questions, considered new options. Even from over the border I could hear it. The whinny of the unicorn. The roar of the lion.

25 Lagarie Drive, Dennistoun

Late 19th century tenement of Ballochmyle sandstone, rosy in the winter rays. Four postage stamp gardens, side by side.

First and second gardens: gnomes. On a swing under the crossed stems of a rose. Fishing in a glass pond. Marching with pickaxe to mine in the rockery.

Separating the first and second: a crazy path bucking and jutting like Thomas the Rhymer's road to Fairyland. It leads from a leafless honeysuckle arch to a green door with a cat flap.

Third and fourth gardens are paved with terracotta tiles, sun-kissed the year round independently of the sky. Statuettes covering miles of culture; thousands of years. Athena, the goddess with the clear grey eyes. The Lion and the Unicorn. Urns dribbling last summer's withered nasturtiums, lobelia and petunia out of artistically placed cracks.

Separating the second and third: a concrete path, straight as the Via Appia, pavement to closemouth.

The two ground floor flats have direct portals on to the street.

C/o Morrison: Unlike everybody else up her close, Agnes still pays rent to some corporate factor. There have been no owner-occupiers down the decades to take an interest in passing fads. Agnes's storm doors boast original features which – with original features back in fashion – will raise the price should Agnes's anonymous landlord ever sell. Ancient tirling pin. Embossed cast iron spring-fitted vertical letterbox, shaped for a billet-doux, slim and scented, from a 19th century damsel to her beau.

Internal front door: some master glazier, his craft now as dead as he, created a pale hand trailing in a turquoise stream.

C/o Gilchrist: the tirling pin has been replaced by a brass bell-pull, which still tolls deep within. By now also eligible for promotion as an original feature. Everything else is similar to Agnes's front door except that the stained glass light depicts a different subject: wee boy in lederhosen offering a rose to wee girl in a dirndl dress.

Through the central door into the common close. Art Nouveau tiles, drooping lady (or anthropomorphised flower) in mature colours: wine, bottle, cream. Blank doors without letterboxes to the left and right. On the right, a few steps lead to a secured door which gives on to the shared back court. Slightly uneven stone steps on the left leading up.

The twelve storm doors and six interior doors into the six upper flats have all been affected by their passage through 1960s minimalism.

C/o Murphy: grey cladding on the storm doors. Internal door retains its picture: cornucopia of fruit.

C/o Usmani family: cobalt storm doors. Glass internal door with dinner-plate sized handle, vintage 1965. Letterbox (cursed by postal workers and leafleters) six inches above

3

the ground.

C/o MacLean: Mockintosh nameplate.

C/o Gillies and MacConachie: Small plastic nameplate 'Gillies' and card sellotaped beside it 'MacConachie'.

C/o Akram family: No bell or knocker. Knuckles on the inside door are the only way of gaining attention.

The top left-hand flat has over the last twenty years passed through the accounts of five buy-to-let owners with decreasing interest in the property. Plastic door-bell which doesn't work. Wide letterbox missing its cover. Piece of paper pinned to the door-cheek: Dvorak and Konicek.

77 Wallacewell Avenue, Barmulloch.

Remnant of 1950s Corporation tenement block surviving between wasteland and low-rise redevelopment. Fawn pebbledash. Overgrown lawn on either side of the path leading to the close entry. Six houses to a close, each with its own balcony, a splash of the Med at high latitude. 1980s security entry, no names.

Inside: concrete close, walls dusky pink, odour of stale condensation. On the right, steps lead down to the grassy back court where the bins are housed. Washing billows in the December blast: sheets, pillow cases, a T-shirt printed with a union flag. On the left, the stair up to the half-landing with plain wide windows and a terracotta sill.

Two houses to a landing. Beside each front door is a cupboard which, before the Clean Air Act, used to be a coal bunker. Spiderwalk of enigmatic scribbling beside some of the door-cheeks.

White 21st century front doors in gingerbread style, security peephole in the middle and fanlight in plain opaque glass.

The only nameplates in the close are on the ground floor flats. Murphy on brown plastic to the left, Donnelly on white plastic to the right.

For over fifty years the cooncil hoose was the centre of a dream, the crown in the family jewels. It dominated Scottish aspirations well into the 20th century. In its heyday, two-thirds of the Scottish population lived in one; many who didn't were marking time on the waiting lists which stretched down the years. It was the bait which lured swathes of Glaswegians into new towns of which they knew little. In the post-war period when jobs were relatively plentiful, this prize was at the core of local government corruption.

Once everybody had a bathroom and hot running water, once deindustrialisation had placed grass and fresh air within reach, the council house lost its appeal. It became utilitarian, unimaginative, old-fashioned. The nicer ones were bought at a discount by tenants who let loose their ideas and their purses, creating porches, patios, conservatories.

Malky's close and its neighbours are the remains of that day. Here, individual customisation is still discouraged. Only doormats and levels of dilapidation distinguish one flat from another.

Round and round goes the wheel of fortune. Today, tenants no longer have the right-to-buy and house prices have soared beyond the salaries of the average worker. A whole new generation will never aspire to a bought house. The cooncil hoose is ripe for a comeback. And indeed most political parties have pledged to build more of them.

At some point in the future.

Chapter 1: January

Opinion Poll (*Mail on Sunday*):
YES 32%   NO 52%   DON'T KNOW 16%

Donald

Ewan, Sir Walter Scott and I stand together, watchin the Hogmanay fireworks whitenin the south-east.

Ewan turns up his collar. He shivers.

- Are you cold? Here, take my scarf.

He's so slender – the wind cuts to his bones. He lays his hand on my arm. Gently. Momentarily.

- It's excitement. The home stretch. The coming of the Common Weal.

Walter Scott as a child met Robert Burns and later wrote of his glowin eyes. Ewan has the same kind of eyes.

- Donald, I know politics isn't your thing. But can you not feel it? The stirring of a long-slumbering soul?

Have to tell him. Cannae put it off any longer. How does that hymn go? 'Courage, brother, do not stumble …'

I look round at the late greats. Three politicians, three poets, two soldiers, two scientists, a queen and her hubby. They would likely all have backed me. No sure about Rabbie. Rabbie wrote 'Shall Haughty Gaul Invasion Threat?' That's the poem we Unionists quote as evidence. But I've yet to hear it recited at any Burns Supper. I've been to a few.

No support forthcomin. Sealed lips and hollow hearts.

- I've somethin to tell you, Ewan.
- Oh?
- Don't know how you'll take it.

He smiles faintly.

- You're no gonnae like it.

- You've got me curious now.

- I'm gonnae vote "NO".

Bang. Boom. Bang. Heavenly dancers on high. Götterdämmerung on the ground.

- You jest.

- I'm afraid not. I'm sorr …

My point of view is as valid as his. I apologise to nobody for it.

- What the hell?

- Said you wouldnae like it.

- Why, Donald? Fuck's sake, why?

Please don't step back from me. Peer at me like that.

- Because geographical borders divide the workin class. I've more in common wi a local government worker in Liverpool or Manchester than wi a bank director in Edinburgh. I agree wi Marx: the workin class have no country.

- So why draw the border at the English Channel? Have you nothing in common with a local government worker in Paris or Berlin?

Here we go. Knee-jerk response to everything. Arguin's second nature. Ach well. Be hanged for a sheep …

- I'm no just gonnae vote for them. I'll be campaignin for them an all.

His passion is always beautiful. Even his anger.

- You bastard!

- Don't take it personally.

- You're not who I thought you were.

- What's up? Do I no get to be an activist? Like you

7

are?

- I've always been an activist. You're not interested in politics.
- How do you know?
- Because when I bang on you change the subject.
- Never dawned that was to keep the peace?
- Have you always disagreed with me?
- On politics, yes. Pretty much.

Gurglin in my guts. I look round for a wastepaper basket to throw up into.

- And the 2011 elections when I plastered our windows with SSP posters ... And the 2012 council elections? When I put up the Green posters ...?
- That, Ewan, is why we've got secret ballots.

He slides the gamut from passion into disappointment. He runs out of rage. The skills kick in. His eyes turn aloof.

- You don't have the balls to stand up for your principles.

He's right. Ball-less in Paradise. They're no even 'our' windows – they're primarily mine.

- I wanted to keep ...
- ... the peace ...
- ... the relationship harmonious.
- Where stand peace and harmony now?
- Some issues are non-negotiable. This referendum could reap a bitter harvest. We could end up like Northern Ireland was in the '70s. Even if we save the UK.
- And if we save Scotland instead ...
- If we destroy the UK, unlikely though that looks ...
- We're into the early days of a better nation, small, enlightened and free.

- No much evidence of that.

That's what I say. I think: you naïve dreamer. This is why I want to be with you.

An extra loud explosion lights up Cochrane Street, behind the City Chambers.

- Could be our relationship shattering.

Please contradict me.

- Hope not.
- But if it is?

Ewan shrugs.

- Then it is.

Ewan doesnae look at me. But he pulls my arm.

- Come on into the Counting House. I'll stand you a whisky. We'll drink to the campaign.
- To both campaigns.

Maybe my love and his generosity of spirit can pull us through this.

- And may the bonniest fighter win.

* * *

Agnes

Twelfth Night and Ah'm takin doon ma decorations. Ah'm a wee bit sorry fur them. Aw dressed up an naewherr tae go. Naebody got tae see them but me.

Two foot plastic tree trailin tarnished tinsel. Baubles and trinkets hung fae the branches. Nuts and cones that fruited last century. A draigelt fairy wi nylon hair that's never seen a comb.

Ah got fower cairds this year, same as last. Wan fae Alasdair's faimily. Wan fae ma brither Sandy in Brisbane. Wan fae Lorraine up the sterr. Wan fae the Gilchrists next door. As

9

usual Ah supplemented them wi eight o the sparkliest held ower fae years gone by. A roon dozen. They look lovely strung up above the black marble mantelpiece.

Ah fold up the tree and pit it wi the decorations in the plastic bag. Ah pick oot Sandy's caird and pit it in the same bag in amang the sparklies fae years gone by. Pit the rest o the cairds in the recyclin.

On the coffee table are ten photocopied posters. In the top left-hand corner a picture o Rosie in shades o grey. Fuzzier than Ah'd huv liked. Pity Ali's photocopier disnae dae colour. Mighta been better tae get Lorraine up the sterr tae scan it fur me on hur computer, but Ah didnae like tae ask. Ah know nothin aboot computers an it might huv run hur up a bill.

> *MISSING since December 31st: Rosie. Grey with white and fawn patches. White tummy and four white socks. Red tartan collar.*

Ah've pit ma phone number at the foot.

Ah slip the posters intae polypockets against the rain an roll them up. Ah pit them wi scissors, string and sellotape intae a carrier bag.

Ah check masel in the mirror. Wee, dumpy. Cauliflower heid. Ah'm no expectin visitors. So jist ma blue cardigan an broon slacks. Presentable enough for gaun doon the road and back, but. Ah pit on ma coat, change the auld baffies for ma boots, and let masel oot.

* * *

Abdul

We were bundled into the bus in the night, in midwinter. Driving rain, biting wind. Habib soon fell asleep again. At first he sat with Parween, his head in her lap, but as more families got off a double seat became vacant where he could stretch out full length.

We had no idea where we were going. However, we were used to being taken here and there, our fates in the hands of others.

There were other families in the bus, none of whom we knew. None of them had any more clue than we did of the ultimate destination.

A magical mystery tour. A song I remember from my youth, before corrupting influences were banned.

We had one stop at a concrete oasis, shining garishly into the dark. Here we could sip tea out of a polystyrene cup. I got out to stretch my legs but Parween would not leave Habib alone in the bus.

As dawn spread its grey shafts we entered Birmingham. Interlacing motorways against the sky. We stopped again and some names were called. Not ours. A couple of families got out the bus; stood around the boot pulling out their luggage. The driver climbed in again. Closed the doors and we were back on the motorway.

Liverpool. Manchester. Sheffield. Other cities whose names I've forgotten. At each stop more families disembarked, gathered gear and wandered off into an uncertain future.

We were by then in the middle of the short winter day. Grey sky, blinks of blue, bursts of rain. What we had come to expect in England.

In the smudged light of evening we entered Newcastle. Only four families left including mine. When my name was again not called I went down the aisle.

- Are you sure we are on your list? My name is Nabi.
- You're on my list all right.
- Where are we going?
- Glasgow.
- Where is Glasgow?

- Scotland.

I returned to my seat and told the man in the next seat that we were bound for Scotland.

- Oh, you have my sympathy!
- Why?
- In Scotland it snows all winter and rains all summer.
- What – every day?
- Yes, every day.

Parween's eyes were closed. I did not repeat this to her. The weather in London was hard enough to get used to. And my wife needs cheering up.

However, we have now been in Glasgow two months. And there has only been a little snow. Perhaps the story about the summer was as exaggerated as the story about the winter. I hope so.

* * *

Lorraine

My modern kitchen: white goods along the wall with scrubbed pine table and four irregularly shaped driftwood style chairs. Polished floorboards. Homely overstuffed sofa in the recess with my daughter Angela spreadeagled in it. Head down, thumb busy.

- That's me away, pet. Should you no be on your way too?

No answer.

- Have you got a free period?

No answer.

- What about the tea tonight? Are you goin out?
- Yeah – later …
- I'm goin out too – to my poetry class. Will we just

12

share a TV dinner from the freezer?

- Whatever.

This morning's conference is about protectin young people from the dangers of social media.

Pictures posted in the dawn of early love can haunt you in its night. Your tweet peckin somebody on the bum can fly back at your throat. If you reach for the cup of fame, an ancient posting can fill the chalice with poison.

The fit teen wi floppy hair metamorphoses into a fifty-somethin Lothario.

The presentation before mine: focused on paedos, strong on statistics.

- A cybercrime survey revealed that in the UK 850,000 online sexual approaches were made in IRC rooms and that 238 offences were recorded of meeting a child following sexual grooming.

Well, that wouldnae be my brother Kenny. Cannae switch on a computer to save his life.

But Angela. Blue eyes and blonde hair. Makeup beyond her years. Lamb dressed as mutton – a baby in disguise. Her confidence puts her at risk. Have I warned her enough?

It's my turn. My own theme this time is peer-to-peer online bullying.

I've put in hours of research, timed the talk through. Still feel a charlatan.

I'm always scared at the sea o faces. I'll lose my place in my notes, forget my lists, miss somethin important, freeze. I'll burst into nervous giggles at an inappropriate place – maybe when describin the suicides o victims. I'll lean too hard on the lectern and go flyin into the laps of the folk in the front row.

Of course none o these things happen. As I warm to my topic the talk trips along at its own pace.

- The typical bully isnae a lad wi brawny muscles. It's a member of a group who all turn on an individual. Usually each is scared the next victim might be himself – or herself.

Forty pairs of eyes. Nobody yawnin, whisperin or lookin at a phone. I've passed muster.

* * *

Donald

I circle Blythswood Square twice before I notice it.

The YES HQ is low profile, down in a Hope (that word! How do they always manage it?) Street basement with posters on the windows below eye level. But the Better Together HQ presents no front at all.

No sign. No number – I work out the location from the other numbers in the square. I hover across the road. A young woman approaches, heels clickin on the pavement. She climbs the steps and presses a security button. I sneak in behind her.

She click-clacks into the foyer and starts mountin the stairs. When my eyes get used to the weak daylight streamin through the fanlight I see chandeliers. Marble walls. Cream carpets unsullied by the footfall of activists. Still no posters or signs.

No staff except an elderly lady at a reception desk.

- Can I help you?
- I'm lookin for "Better Together".
- Do you want to volunteer to help?

Doesnae smile. Puts me in mind of one of my teachers, when I'd been talkin in class.

- I'll call Richard.

She picks up the phone on her desk.

14

A young man comes through from the back. Slim, dark-haired. Warm smile. He shakes my hand.

- Come and I'll show you what we've got.

Well-spoken – maybe Edinburgh.

Open-plan back office. Again no staff except another older lady with her back to us workin on a computer in the far corner. Sealed cardboard boxes piled on the floor. Richard pulls one open.

- What d'you want to do? Want to deliver leaflets round the doors in your own area? Or maybe outside a station at the rush hour?

He's so keen. Keen to hold together this battered old United Kingdom. The United Kingdom of Nye Bevan. Of Tom Johnston. Of the Red Clydesiders who recognised no borders in their struggle for the working man. The United Kingdom which gave us the NHS when everywhere else folk were dyin for the price of a doctor. Which alone faced down the Fascists when everywhere else had capitulated.

Answerin the call once more to save old Britain in her time of danger.

Idealistic. Good-lookin. I want to hug him.

* * *

Ewan

I dip in and out the websites – NewsnetScotland, Bella Caledonia and the rest – which cover the suppressed stories.

But I'm still addicted to newspapers.

I buy four newspapers a day even though they make me seethe. The print editions, even though most YES activists boycott them. And even though the only person at home with whom I can share my rage is in the other camp.

This evening Donald and I are together in the same room. Me on the couch, surrounded by newspapers. Him on the recliner, checking his iPad.

Can't resist.

- No other paper has covered this story. Just the *Sunday Herald.*
- What story?
- Cameron using taxpayers' money to set up a branch of the Foreign Office specifically to fight independence.
- Then maybe the story's no true? Where did the *Sunday Herald* get it from?
- Leaked by the Russian press.
- Ah.
- He's contacted heads of state (including Putin) to lean on them to speak out against Scottish independence.
- … according to the *Sunday Herald* and *Pravda.*

What's the point. I shut up. Should get on with some bread and butter work. Got a deadline on Friday.

This time it's Donald who breaks the silence.

- Went along today to Better Together and officially joined as an activist.

I conceal my dismay.

- So what does being an activist involve? Better Together don't have enough volunteers to go door-knocking.
- I've to get trainin tomorrow in telephone canvassing.
- Good luck with that. I only tried tele-canvassing a few times this campaign. Dialled 120 numbers and 10 picked up. Nobody uses landlines anymore. They get too many …

I chuckle

- … cold callers.

This'll be us for the next nine months. Jeering at each other's beliefs. Sneering at each other's efforts. A war of attrition on each other's morale.

Every war causes collateral damage.

Que sera sera.

* * *

Kirsty

They don't redecorate much here. Anaglypta walls. There's probably still asbestos in there. Top two metres pristine white. Bottom metre covered in crayon etchings: wee houses with squint walls, people with oval limbs.

Yet another debate on the box. We're all round it. Benny on Marilyn's lap. Erin on Daddy's lap. Me on the pouffe, checking my emails. Cara at my shoulder.

- Ridiculous letting these kids vote. What do they know about politics? (Marilyn)
- They'll just vote the way their mammies an daddies tell them. (Dad)
- You think teenagers obey the old dears? They'll vote for what's cool. (Marilyn)

Phew. No Watchers. I get into the conversation.

- I want to register to vote. (Me)

Cara: What on earth for?

- You? (Marilyn)
- I've been wanting to for a while. (Me)
- Since when? Since we switched on the telly a minute ago? (Marilyn)
- I want to register to vote too! (Erin)
- Me too! (Benny)
- Well, you're all too young. (Marilyn)

- I'll be sixteen on Referendum Day. (Me)

Cara: Don't hurry to grow up. You'll never be a child again.

- You are fifteen. You can't fill up the form till you're 16 and by then it's too late. (Marilyn)
- Is that how it works? (Me – to Dad)
- What – you think they let you register to vote at the polling station on Referendum Day? (Marilyn)
- Dad? (Me)
- Why are you asking him? I'm telling you. (Marilyn)
- If Marilyn says that's how it goes then that's how it goes. (Dad)
- So why did they say they're giving the vote to all 16-year-olds if … (Me)
- You are fifteen. Too young to vote. End of. (Marilyn)
- If she's registering to vote I want to. (Erin)
- Me too. (Benny)

Cara: Politicians are all in it for themselves.

* * *

Lorraine

Despite the plan to share a TV dinner, I don't see Angela between comin home from work and goin out to my Poetry Writing class. When I come back from my class at 9.50 I find her on her phone again. She'll be on it till she goes to bed. But if she goes to the kitchen for a snack, to the toilet, that'll be my chance. Window of opportunity between her exit and her reappearance.

Approach wi caution. That's the key.

I like my Poetry Writing class. I started goin eight years ago, after the SSP broke up and I stopped goin to all the political meetings. Suddenly my own problems came home to roost.

First Stuart split. Then Angela hit puberty like a hurricane hittin a house.

But writin poetry is cathartic. Teenagers at work, teenagers at home: all sublimated in the beauty o findin the perfect word, the perfect phrase.

One of the early sessions was an introduction to writin in Scots. At school the only Scots poetry we'd got was 'To a Mountain Daisy' and a couple of old ballads. Other than that I thought Scots was the way Oor Wullie and The Broons spoke. Didnae realise Glaswegian is also a form of Scots. I thought of that as slang.

So I'd never tried writin Scots before. All of a sudden it flowed like the tide, fitted like a jigsaw. Practically wrote itself. Scots is suited to poetry. More onomatopoeic than English. When I write in Scots my verse turns out more structured, because it's easy to find rhymes in Scots, both internal and at the ends of lines. And it feels more sincere.

Thinkin about tonight's class (our theme was Families and I wrote 'Ode tae a Difficult Dochter' – which she'll never read) I get distracted. Miss the moment. See the blur of her leavin, hear the click of the door. I hurry out. She's in the bathroom. I hover outside.

The shower's runnin. I wait. The toilet flushes. I wait. The door opens.

- Angela, pet, I've been thinkin. I hope you never …

She chimes along with me:

- … get into chats with people you don't know … For God's sake, Mum, will you play a different track? That one's worn out.

- This meetin I was at today made me realise how girls like you …

- Does my head zip up the back?

- No, and paedophiles don't come wi a P stamped on

their foreheads either.

- Just as well. Or Uncle Kenny …
- Kenny isnae a paedophile.
- Is a teenager not a child? Funny – when it comes to me you sing a different tune …
- Kenny never attacked anybody …
- Is flashing not attacking?
- You spend so much time on your phone. Huvnae a clue what you're doin in there …
- What's your point? Do I ask to read your diaries?
- That's different. I'm …

Her bedroom door slams.

- … your mother.

Chapter 2: February

Opinion Poll (*Scottish Daily Mail*):
YES 38%   NO 47%   DON'T KNOW 16%

Ewan

In the summer of 2013 the parties kicked off. Rallies with National Collective aimed at instilling 'cultural confidence'.

When the Soviet Union fell apart, the Estonians started singing all their old folk songs in public, hitherto banned. They said they sang their way to independence.

Scottish culture hasn't been banned. Not in recent times. But it has been disparaged, discouraged, mocked, ignored. National Collective aim to redeem it.

National Collective. Self-styled *'A growing group of talented artists & creatives ... a grassroots campaign which builds the movement for independence from the ground up.'*

They had a baptism of fire. Right at their beginning their website was temporarily closed down and they were threatened with litigation after they published the fact (already in the public domain) that a main donor for Better Together was boss of a company with shady links to Saddam Hussain and to the Serbian warlord, Arkan.

When the Tory Party had benefited from this man's largesse, Alastair Darling had called on them to give back the 'dirty money'. When Better Together received a donation from the same source, it was Alastair Darling himself who gratefully accepted it.

The Herald published the story and was also threatened with litigation.

Best kind of publicity a new organisation could hope for. The author of the article, a 21-year-old rookie journalist called Michael Gray, brass-necked his way into an interview with the new Prime Minister of Iceland before the UK Government got to him. Got him to say Iceland was Scotland's friend.

National Collective are my kind of people.

OK –I was a fraud. Three chords on the guitar is my whack, and not for public display unless I'm on something. I once applied for Art School and didn't get in. But some of the fellow-travellers were no more talented than I was. Others made up for them with their output: art, poetry, music. Witty slogans:

It's not you, Darling; it's me.

Voted YES in 1979 and got NOTHING. Voted YES in 1997 and got SOMETHING. Vote YES in 2014 and get EVERYTHING

Vote YES – make Scottish History. Vote NO – make Scotland history.

Past Imperfect. Present Tense. Future Perfect.

Better a blossom than an eternal bud.

I had supported various political causes since settling in Scotland back in '97. Marched against the Iraq war. Campaigned first for the SSP and then the Greens. Turned out a couple of times for Pride although I tend not to wear my sexuality on my sleeve.

But it was National Collective which drew me into the YES campaign. Idealistic, beautiful young men and women on song.

Their venues were my kind of places. Studios in back lanes. Govanhill Baths. A vegan island in the cool circle behind St Enoch Square. I'm not vegan myself – can't resist Donald's cooking. But I was reared amongst vegans and understand them well.

The parties swayed to the hot guitars. The Scottish lion

growled in time. The wish trees flaunted their gift tags, each leaf someone's dream for a future Scotland. My mind filled with weed and revolution. I tottered home to Donald at 3, 4, 5 in the morning. If at all.

They say if you can remember the sixties you weren't there. My birth certificate tells me I wasn't there. But I can remember them. They started last summer and they're with us still.

* * *

Iqbal

The impossibly handsome young couple gaze into each other's eyes. They have overcome all the barriers to their love. Amor vincit omnia. They draw closer; hold hands. In a moment their pretty red lips will meet.

They spring apart; begin dancing. The screen is filled with scores of their beautiful friends, prancing wildly, joyously, in celebration of the betrothal. Ululating voices approve.

The credits roll. The children start to chatter. My uncle Ali takes me to his bedroom to look at some cars on his computer.

For some time we've been discussing getting a people-carrier. He has three children still at home; I have two. With our wives, our combined families are nine people. Living up the same close, in and out of each others' houses. With a people-carrier we could go for trips to the country with the children. He and I would share the price.

Ali's wife Noor can drive and my wife Catriona's taking lessons. So during the school holidays even when Ali and I are working they could take the children away on their own for day trips. Good weather is rare, so we should get out the city whenever we can. There will be no more holidays in Pakistan for a while.

23

While we're looking at the cars, now that we're away from Noor and the children, I change the subject. Cautiously. Ali used to be a member of the Labour party. A few years ago he made enquiries about getting elected to the council but it came to nothing.

- Tell me, are you still involved with politics?

He laughs. Shakes his head.

- No. With a wife and children, and my work, how could I have time for that?
- So what do you think of this referendum affair?
- Independence, eh? I like what the SNP did, abolishing business rates for small companies. That's already saved me thousands of pounds.
- Me too!
- I'm impressed with this Alex Salmond. He knows what he wants and he goes for it, regardless of the risks.
- He's clever too. Have you seen him in political debates? He always has an answer.

Ali goes out and comes back with a couple of cigars and a cigar-trimmer. I like a good cigar. There are no public places left where you can smoke indoors. You have to go outside. In the Scottish climate, usually unpleasant. They aim to make us healthier, despite ourselves.

- I went along to one of the events they held for the Scots Asians for Independence. I liked what he said. He'll shake them up, our complacent rulers down in London. They won't know what hit them!
- My mother told me about how your grandfather was involved in the struggle for Indian independence.
- Ah, yes. Daada talked about these days a lot. And about the terrible train journey west into the new Pakistan, leaving everything behind.

24

- I wish I'd known him. So are you going to vote YES?
- I think so. And you?
- Me too.

We look at a few cars on his computer until I see a nine-seater I like. We set a date to go down and look at it. It will belong to us both.

* * *

Malky

On the way to school ma thoughts are shattered by a brayin laugh fae behind. Ah consider the pros and cons o turnin roon. On the fourth shriek Ah chance it.

Three stoatirs fae ma year. Three blonde heids, three Barbie-doll faces, three wee totie school skirts showin the world six fandabidosy legs. Two wi bodies skinny as a pencil, wan wi the kinna knockers ye could get a proper haud on an squeeze.

Chantelle McLean and her sidekicks Kelly-Anne Henderson and Angela Murphy.

Time was Ah'd harboured a wee fancy for Chantelle. Mebbe for aw three. Big eyes and red lips, perfume made yer heid swirl.

On a less carnal level Ah admired – envied – Chantelle's gallusness in confrontin injustice. Mrs Urquhart when she gied the haill class a punny because she couldnae find oot who'd drawn a big dick on her blackboard. Mr Fulton when he gied Donna Logan detention for late-comin when Donna wis a carer for her disabled Maw and deserved a medal fur makin it to school at aw.

Ah sent a Valentine last week. No tae Chantelle, that Ah fancied the most. Tae Kelly-Anne.

Weeer an skinnier than Chantelle. Less dauntin. Mair flawed – her skin breaks oot in the occasional plook and her hair frizzes in the rain. Mair workin-class than Angela. Ah thought Ah might huv a chance wi Kelly-Anne.

Ah chose a comic wan with a daft-lookin rabbit. Ah composed a wee poem that took me hours to get right: romantic while cool.

Soft as a bunny

Sweeter than honey

More golden than money

Funny and sunny

My Kelly-Anne.

Ah wrote the poem oot wi ma left haun.

It only took the first period fur ma anonymity to be breached. Ma riddy debunked ma denial. Brayin laughter in every class; wi every teacher.

Come the interval: Kelly-Anne, on hur tod, dragged me into a storeroom. She backed me into a wall, pressed against me so Ah could feel the thrust of her knockers, smell the scent of her neck.

- How lang huv ye fancied me?

Ah could think o nae answer.

- How did ye no say?
- Well, Ah did, but. The Valentine.
- Aha! So ye did send it. How did ye kid oan ye didnae?

Ma brain: as ever, a banter-free zone. Further doon, tae ma horror, the tingle of a boner.

- Wur ye shy?

Kelly-Anne's voice wis gentle. Ah closed ma eyes to avoid lookin intae hers. Ah nodded.

- Nae need tae be shy wi me, Malky. Ye waant a wee snog?

Ah opened ma eyes. Red lipstick exposin white, even teeth.

Ah nodded.

- Gonnae ask me nicely, well?

Ah cleared ma throat.

- Gonnae gie's a wee snog?
- Whit's the magic word?

Edge o suspicion.

- Please kin Ah snog ye, Kelly-Anne?
- In yer dreams!

Three shrieks in unison. Chantelle and Angela on either side of Kelly-Anne. Howlin harpies.

- Kelly-Anne's way oot yer league, son! Tell ye whit – if ye get yer skin cleared up ye might huv a chance wi some lassie that's mair desperate. Whit aboot Donna Logan? (Chantelle)
- Or wee Kirsty Gilchrist? (Angela).
- She's a ginger an she's built like a bus. (Kelly-Anne)
- Her face wouldnae be bad if she pit on makeup, but. (Chantelle)
- She stays up my close and I've never seen her wi make-up. (Angela)
- Thur always a first time. So izzat a plan, Malky? Ye'll go an ask Donna or Kirsty tae lumber ye? (Chantelle)

Ah broke free. Ah shot the craw ahead o Kelly-Anne's partin slag:

- Get Kirsty tae pit the makeup on you insteid o hursel. You're the wan wi the plooks!

Pop went that bubble. Ah've never dared approach ony lassie since.

Noo once again they're bored and Ah'm therr.

- Och it's wee Malky feastin his eyes!
- Gettin a good look, son?

- Come an we'll gie him wet dreams!

Mair hootin. They catch up wi me. Kelly-Anne and Angela each grab wan o ma airms. Chantelle ducks roon in front, loosens her tie, thrusts oot her chest.

- Three steps to heaven! Wan!

She undoes the first button on her school blouse.

- Two!

The second button.

- Aaahhhh!! Wid ye look at that! He's gettin a right riddy noo!

She grips ma cheek. Stab o pain.

- Aw sorry, son, is that yer plook?
- Ye cannae miss his plooks. They're aw ower his coupon!
- Look – that one's burst and spewin custard doon his chin!

Kelly-Anne points at ma crotch.

- Somethin else is gonnae be spewing custard in a minute!

Chantelle shoves her.

- Uch you're disgustin, Kelly-Anne. Sure she's disgustin, Malky?

Ah keep ma heid doon. Chantelle cups ma face wi baith her hauns. Ah go on starin at the grun. Cannae go on forever.

- Ah've heard o Spotted Dick but Ah've never seen a dick as spotted as yer coupon!
- An she's seen five hunner an seventy-two dicks!
- You shut yer geggie, Kelly-Anne Henderson!
- Spotted face and spotted dick – naebody'll ever gie pair wee Malky a snog or a shag.
- Never mind, Malky, nothin up wi yer hauns!

Ewan

When I first came back from Malawi, before I met Donald, I didn't consider living in any other part of town. Only the West End. I'd lived there as a student. My mother grew up there, before she dropped out and went on the ramble.

I was shocked at the rents. All I could afford was a corner of a compact mews cottage, split into bedsits even more bijou.

Glorious view from my one casement window. The back garden was shared into lots (even I had a rug-sized pied-a-terre) and the arty-farty West End tenants had cultivated them in different ways. Herbs, organic vegetables. Ceramic faces, expressions all different, strung along a wall.

However, you couldn't swing a cat and the rent was crippling.

Meeting Donald opened up a new portal. I'd never realised Dennistoun existed. So similar to Dowanhill, so close to the city centre, and half the price. I ditched my West End prejudices.

Donald (stars in his eyes) at first wasn't going to charge me any rent at all. But a gigolo existence is not my style. Although my income's low and uncertain I like to support myself as far as possible. We settled that I should cover part of the mortgage and part of the council tax but Donald would see to the gas and electricity and the shopping for food.

And the cooking – he's right into that. Suits me – I'm right into eating.

Kenny

Ah've hud a skinful. Here's me lyin in ma airmchair sleepin the sleep o the just. Or is it the unjust? Cannae mind.

29

A hammerin invades ma dreams. Comin fae the front door. Ah heave masel up. It's getting harder an harder tae rise fae this auld chair. Don't know if it's ma creaky knees or because the seat o the chair is sinkin lower an lower.

At the front door Ah keek through the peephole. A face Ah don't recognise. Ah open the door.

Skinny bloke in a leather jaiket. Rid nose. Lang greasy herr. Nervous wey o shiftin his weight aboot fae fit tae fit.

- Ah'm supposed tae ask fur Gordo.
- Two up, son. Left.
- They said he wid be in here.
- They telt ye wrang. He's tap left.

The fella goes on starin at me. Radio rental – eyes comin right oot his heid. Ah go tae shut the door and here does he no pit his heid roon an stert bawlin intae ma hoose:

- Gordo! Gordo! Ur ye therr?
- Get the fuck oot ma hoose! Ah'm tellin ye he's no here!

Ah manage tae shut the door an pit the chain on. Efter a bit Ah hear the bloke paddin up the sterr an chappin on Gordo's door. Thur a wee exchange o views an then raised voices.

Ah try no tae get involved wi ma neighbours nooadays. Keep masel tae masel. Ah made a mistake wi Gordo wance upon a time an Ah'm still peyin the price. Ah feel hert sorry fur Mrs Nimmo huvin tae live wi aw thae big ruffians. Must be hell on earth whit wi them inside an the queue o junkies ootside. Ah heard wance aboot a fella steyed in a studio flat wi three rottweilers. That must be whit it's like.

Ah go back tae ma chair an light a fag. Musta dozed aff again because the next thing the fag's burnin ma fingers an Ah'm chuckin it doon an trampin on it. An thur mair thumpin at the door.

Ma sister Lorraine. Ah let hur in.

- I told you never to put the chain on!

She follows me into the livin-room. Sees the cigarette smokin on the carpet.

- You could have burnt the place down! What did I tell you about fallin asleep wi a cigarette in your hand?

Nippin ma heid. Ah'm no in the mood.

- Tell me why you put the chain on?
- Ah stey in this close. You thank yer lucky stars ye don't huv tae.
- Did somethin happen?
- Naw. Nuthin oot the ordinary.

Ah sit back doon, switch on the telly an run through the channels till Ah get tae the fitba. Lorraine goes tae ma bedroom an sterts pickin up ma claes aff the flair.

* * *

Donald

Ewan's beaverin away at the computer as I come in from my meetin. I stand in the study doorway but he doesnae turn round.

He's beautiful in the desk-light. Adonis. And that's with his clothes on.

That moment. When he walked into my life. Two years ten months and two weeks ago.

The room was no different from any of the rooms where I've spent my workin life. Walls local authority puce. Windows facin north into a grey sky. Striplighting off because it was the middle of the afternoon. Three of us middle managers sittin side by side along a table facin a single empty chair.

He brought into that room the sun and the moon and the stars. I swear the very monitors on our laptops beamed more brightly and the temperature rose three degrees. Mine certainly did.

Tall, slender, soft dark hair, glowin eyes and a luminous smile. Enigmatic accent – faintly Geordie at first with a Scottish element growing stronger as the interview continues.

So fresh-faced. I reckoned I'd no hope. I put him at 26, 27. But when he talked about the work he'd done and the countries he'd travelled in since his journalism degree I realised he must be older.

I glanced down at his CV. Old enough for me to be in with a chance. If he was gay (my gaydar had it likely), single and up for a relationship with an older man.

I almost forgot to ask him the three questions I was askin all the applicants and I didnae take in his responses. When it came to the bit, the rest of the panel voted against him and he didnae get the job. I had to vote against him too. There was another candidate with a Dad who was a crony of the head of department.

However, I noted Ewan's phone number and called him up later to commiserate. His very voice when he picked up set me stammerin.

He didnae seem too gutted. Although since returnin from abroad he hadnae been able to land work in journalism he was makin enough to get by. He'd a couple more applications in the pipeline.

I suggested we meet for a drink 'to show there are no hard feelings'. He agreed and named a gay bar in the city centre.

Throughout the next day my feet didnae touch the ground. Each page of the report I was supposed to be readin spent an hour on my screen. Makin my way to the pub I was floatin six inches above the old cobblestones of the back lanes.

During that evenin (the drink stretched to five hours, includin a Chinese meal which I insisted on payin for) he told me that he'd returned the previous summer from abroad.

After university he'd spent three years teachin English in Shanghai. When he came back he spent some more years tryin to get a foothold in the world of newspapers. Then off on his travels again doin voluntary work in Malawi.

Since his return he'd been keepin himself goin on freelance copywritin work but was now applyin for full-time jobs. He owned a car, struggled to pay the rent on his bedsit and found it impossible to save for somewhere bigger.

Our next date ended up at mine and he liked what he saw. The whole package, apparently. I couldn't believe my luck the day he moved in. Even now I keep expectin the bubble to burst.

Last week the Scottish Parliament passed the law allowing same-sex marriage. Wild celebrations all over the Scene.

Ewan's a non-believer. I don't know any more what, if anything, I believe. I no longer attend church. However, if there is a God, the passion I feel for Ewan must surely find favour with Him. Or Her.

My dream would be to have our union blessed by a church. Any church. It would be like God – if there is a God – showin approval. Of us. Of me and what I am. Although it would mean nothin to Ewan, it would mean a lot to me.

However, when I raised the subject of same-sex marriage with Ewan, he saw it in purely theoretical terms. For him it proved that Scotland was in the forefront of progressive thought.

- Only sixteen countries in the world allow same-sex marriage! And Scotland's one of them. That's one in the eye for those who say an independent Scotland would be socially conservative.

- Have you thought any more about formalising our own relationship, love?

- What – us get married?

As clear as if he'd voiced it: Are you out of your tiny mind?

- Wouldnae need to be marriage. Just a blessing. Though marriage would give you rights, if anythin happened to me.
- Nothing's going to happen to you, Donald. I've watched you crossing the road – you always look both ways.

He maybe saw I looked sad, because he took my hand.

- Nor am I about to walk out on you. You know I don't believe in marriage. My own parents weren't married. Nor did my mother marry Phil and they've been together nearly thirty years now. I don't need a bit of paper to make me stay.

That was that.

Anyway.

I go over to Ewan and lay my hand gently on his shoulder. I see his empty plate cast aside on top of some YESMO returns.

- You found your dinner in the microwave?
- Yes.

I made him shrimp verde, for speed, because he said he had little time. I picture him, head low over the bowl, shovellin it in while hittin keys on the keyboard. Fast fuel.

Yet when we eat out together he has the prettiest table-manners I've seen. Remarkable for somebody whose early years were spent squatting in camps.

He doesnae look round. In fact he tilts his screen slightly away from me. A new taboo. Before this referendum business we would have shared our day.

I get a can of beer for myself and take it through to the living-room. I switch on the telly. Put the Scottish news on via the iPlayer. Nothin but discussion of the bloody you-know-what.

A new angle to the prospect of separatism: Jose Manuel Barroso, the President of the European Commission, has said it would be 'extremely difficult, if not impossible' for an independent Scotland to join the European Union.

Up till now, the YES shower blithely assumed that in the event of independence both Scotland and rUK (as they now call it: fairly trips off the tongue) would carry on as separate individual members.

But of course Spain wouldnae want to make separatism easy for Scotland when they've got their own minorities naggin them for the same referendum we've been granted.

I approach the subject cautiously:

- We export more to the EU than we import ...
- Scotland unlike the UK exports more to everybody than it imports. Another well-kept secret.
- Would be awful if we're put out the EU after all this time. Havin to go to the back o the queue ...

Ewan's face shapes into that expression I'm beginning to know so well. Combined incredulity at my stupidity, contempt for my reasonin, irritation at the amount of his precious time I'm wastin. No an attractive expression, even on somebody as naturally attractive as Ewan.

- What a load of old cobblers! Look at your passport! Each of us is an individual citizen of the EU! Are you saying they'd expel us? On what grounds? The EU expands, doesn't contract. Greenland has had a helluva job breaking away and it's thousands of miles away from Europe.
- Any country can veto a new member ...
- We're not a new member ...
- Spain'll no want to encourage Catalunya and the

35

Basques …

- Spain? Spain who spends every day fishing in Scottish waters while our fishermen only get grants to destroy their own boats?
- The very possibility of losin EU membership would make me vote NO, if nothin else did.
- The only way we'll lose our EU membership is if Cameron goes through with this daft EU referendum and the English vote to leave. So another reason for voting YES.

He gets the last word again.

The Governor of the Bank of England came up to Scotland a few days ago and met with Alex Salmond. Naturally the careful speech he made was claimed by both sides as a victory. However, next day all the headlines awarded the victory to us:

Scottish Sun: *Bank's pound threat to Nats.*

Financial Times: *Carney in currency warning to Scotland.*

Scottish Daily Mail: *Don't bank on it.*

We're holdin up well in the polls, especially wi women voters who find the William Wallace undertones a turn-off. Also with the middle classes and the older age groups. The very dynamic who traditionally turn out to vote.

Why then am I sick at heart about the whole business?

* * *

Cindy

Purgatory fur the baith of us.

Peelin wallpaper. Bare flair. Nae lino, nae nuthin. Big broon stain in the corner wherr somebody spilt somethin, or got

36

murdert or somethin. On a school trip when Ah wis a wean, we went tae this palace in Edinburgh. Thur wis a stain therr wherr somebody got murdert. That's whit it's like.

Shouldnae moan. Ah got a cooker, an electric heater an a couple o bits furniture fae the Sally Ann. Table, chair. Couple o camp beds. Lang as Ah keep aw ma appointments an sign on the dotted lines Ah kin get by. Don't huv tae beg on the streets. Jist as well. Couldnae beg on the streets tae save ma life. Kin hardly make it oot the close athoot panickin. Ah've maybe got thon thingmy – agoraphobia.

The wee fella's pesterin me day an night, waantin attention. Gies me nae peace. Cannae blame him. Ah should be playin wi him, talkin tae him, takin him places. Pittin him intae nursery. Stimulatin his development. He's greetin a lot. Sometimes he gets that bored he batters me. Ah'm a rubbish Mammy like Ah'm a rubbish wife.

Ah try tae think o sangs tae sing him but Ah cannae mind the words. Huvnae much here in the wey o toys. Box fae the Sally Ann. Two plastic Marvel Comic heroes. Couple o toy cars – wee wheels aw bent wi his nibs leanin his weight on them. Drawin book he's awready scribbled aw ower. Jigsaw wi some pieces missin. Few wee picture books but he's no interested. He's a wild wee boay – disnae huv the patience.

Thur plenty space here. Three room, kitchenette, bathroom an balcony. Balcony's wastit on me. When Ah go oot therr Ah feel that exposed Ah come right in again. An Ah'm feart tae let his nibs oot on his ain in case he climbs ower the rail. He's that wild.

He could run aboot aw he waants here. Use up his energy. Wish he would. But just runnin aboot's pointless. And we cannae play hide-an-seek when thur nothin tae hide behind.

Ah don't deserve a wean, neither Ah dae. Lots o fowk waantin wan an cannae huv them an here's me huvnae a scooby whit tae dae wi the wan Ah've got. Sometimes Ah'm feart the Social come an take him aff me.

* * *

Abdul

It's been a year since it happened, and still Parween weeps every day. She tries to hide it from me; goes into a bedroom or locks herself in the bathroom.

She refuses to talk to me about it and I no longer want to ask her.

Of course it's not perfect here. I can't work at my profession. We're poor now and have to be careful with every penny. Although we're far from the city centre we walk everywhere instead of taking the bus.

Our flat here is smaller and clammier than our home in Kabul. But the electricity supply and the water are never cut off without warning.

The woman upstairs is a vulgar person. She gets drunk. When she's sober she looks at us with anger in her eyes. One of the boys in the flat across from her sells drugs so there are sometimes addicts wandering up and down the stairs. I tell my son to keep away from these people.

However, the rest of the neighbours are quiet and friendly. And we're safe here, away from the guns and air raids. In the early evening I sit out on the verandah and marvel at how quiet it is.

I understand Parween's grief. I also grieve for Fareiba. Her light voice, her laughter. Her eagerness to keep up her studies at home once it became too difficult for her to attend school.

A mother's grief is special. She bore her; she suckled her; she caressed her; she taught her the skills a mother passes on to her daughter.

In many ways the worst thing is not knowing. That terrible

38

moment when, in the crush on deck, we looked around for Fareiba and could not see her. Unable to move from our seats for fear of sinking the boat. Scanning the faces of those around us. Calling her name. And, when hope was gone, peering back at the figures on the dwindling, darkening shore.

A seventeen-year-old girl, unused to finding her way about, with no knowledge of Turkish and hardly any English. It is impossible that she made it on her own. She is almost certainly with God. If she is not with God, the alternatives are worse. I try to keep my mind off these alternatives. It's better to think about what we still have.

We still have our Habib. I take him to school every day and there's never any trouble. Habib's teacher is impressed with his progress and says that his English is much better than what you'd expect. He seems to have made some friends. The boy who could no longer look after the dragon chose to give it to Habib. It's a source of great interest to him. I'm glad he has this for diversion since I can't afford to buy him many toys.

I tell Parween to concentrate on being a proper mother to our boy. To talk to him, teach him, love him.

But still she weeps every day.

* * *

Ewan

YES Scotland HQ have produced another edition of their propaganda newspaper. I pick them up at the printer and bring them to our campaign rooms. Margaret and Duncan are there and help me pack them into the satchels.

The newspapers weigh a ton. Keep bursting the satchels – I'm darning them night after night. Delivering them, you can only carry so many and have to keep returning to the car for more.

Now, after nearly two decades of leafleting and canvassing, I'm an expert on Glasgow architecture.

Victorian villas. The interestingly decayed grandeur of Dennistoun's Conservation Area. Detached, semis, townhouses. The abandoned dream of Alexander Dennistoun for a garden city east of George Square. Always a mystery what you'll find within a walled garden. Front doors leading through glass conservatories, at the end of paths, at the top of winding stairs. Flowery back lanes rambling past stables converted into recording studios. 10, 15, 20-room family homes; unlicensed multiple occupancy; Giro drops where the leaflet joins a paper mountain behind the letterbox.

Four-in-a-blocks. Built by the Corporation between the wars, romantically called 'cottage-style'. Broad acres of Glasgow are covered with them. Behind the two front doors are stairs leading to the upper flats, while the two side doors lead into the ground floor flats. The paths to the four doors can be treacherous in the dark: broken paving, broken steps with no handrail, slippery with mud. Every time I've fallen while campaigning it's been in the four-in-a-blocks.

High-rise. The go-to place on days when the rain is turning the newspapers into papier maché. Once you've gained entry the flats almost leaflet themselves. Up all the way on the lifts. Then it's galloping down the sweaty concrete stairs, zooming round the landings, or in and out the pot plants along a balcony of doors. The view to base camp rising to meet you as you descend.

Last year I came across some high-rises where most of the residents were Polish. Most could speak no English. At least half were Jehovah's Witnesses, who are forbidden by their religion to vote. Yet, bizarrely, all of them had found their way on to the voters' roll. For the benefit of the monoglot Poles who were not Jehovah's Witnesses, I collaborated with a Polish friend to produce a leaflet in Polish. Eventually the YES machine produced one of its own. Every sixth baby born in Scotland is born to Polish parents.

Living up a close: since the industrial revolution the most common residential experience in Glasgow. Designs becoming less elaborate down the decades as labour costs rise and public provision replaces private investment.

19th century sandstone: Because of the spacious interiors the height of these four-storey buildings dwarfs tenements of later vintage. Until the 1890s local 'grey' (honey-coloured) sandstone was used. Later they used red sandstone from Lockerbie or Ballochmyle.

The poshest tenements are a paean to the art of stonemasonry. Pillared close entries, plaques with versions of tree, fish, bird and bell, personifications of the virtues. Bow windows with 180 degree outlook, turrets with 360 degrees.

Indoors: whimsical cornicing and a central rose. Shutters for the big windows, servant's bell by the fireside.

Further down the scale are the flat-faced tenements built above shops. Tenements with no tiles in the close entrances. Three doors to a landing, no bathrooms and sometimes a shared WC.

In the 1970s, after wreaking havoc amongst them to clear space for the ring road, the City Fathers looked again at these relics. Squalid yet solid. Slummy yet stately. In a last minute U-turn the surviving tenements were saved from the wrecking ball and given a facelift.

Maroon became terracotta. Black became blonde. Ginger Spice and Marilyn Monroe as edifices. Corner recesses with a stool and pot-plant in the landings where the shared netty used to be.

Inter-war tenements built by the Corporation, also red and grey sandstone. Plainer than before, no carvings outside or cornicing inside. Nevertheless constructed to twentieth-century expectations with kitchenettes, bathrooms, grassy front gardens and drying greens. Red sandstone blocks smart and solid to this day; grey – poorer quality from the start and let to poorer tenants – beginning to crumble.

The 1950s swung away from indigenous stone. Labour costs were high and utility was all. Harled brick tenements, uniformly clean and fawn, walls too jagged to loaf against. Dotted in patterns up and down the braes and glens of Glasgow's greenbelt. Drumchapel, Castlemilk, Easterhouse. To the 20th century innovation of bathroom was added the Continental touch of wire balconies. The planners provided plenty of garden space but forgot about schools, shops, pubs and places of employment.

Out in the fringes these giant schemes have fallen before the bulldozer. No rejuvenation for them. Nature abhors a vacuum: the mounds and hollows of mud, the wide prairielands are acquiring a fuzz of grass. And new-build.

Islets of terraced houses, semis, detached. Individual front doors – much easier to leaflet. Constructed in man-made materials to an Anglicised design. Hobbit-scale by the standards of the tenemental canyons of old.

Glasgow city centre looks like Newcastle. But out there it's more like Gateshead.

Chapter 3: March

Opinion Poll (*Daily Record*):
YES 37%   NO 47%   DON'T KNOW 16%

Iqbal

As I put my key in the security lock my breath floats white before me. However, the air in the street is no icier than the atmosphere in the living-room.

Catriona is rocking Bobby on her arm. Her gimlet expression makes me want to slide back unnoticed into the kitchen and fetch and gobble my own dinner, cooked or not.

She's seen me. Maybe it's not me she's angry at.

- I do not want to live like this.

Ah. The old problem.

- Another fight with Noor?

- I get up at seven. I'm out all day trying to make education attractive to 25 ten-year-olds. Many reluctant learners. Some aggressive. A couple of downright nasty wee buggers.

- Noor doesn't have it easy either. She …

- I come home, fagged out. Desperate for my half hour snooze. And Noor expects me to come straight into her kitchen and make Channay Ki Daal Gosht. To her instruction.

- If you'd rather cook something else …

- I don't want to cook anything. I want to take a ready meal out the freezer and stick it in the micro for ten minutes. I bet you wouldn't notice the difference.

- Home cooking's …

43

- The ingredients in that stuff! And each one has to be fussed over separately. Noor says "It's a great way of combining the proteins of meat and of channa daal." Sure, and if I sat day and night I could knit you all socks – but why should I when we've got the Barras? Life's short and I want to spend it on other things.

I mind my own childhood. The house in Pollokshields. My grandparents presiding. My father and my uncle discussing history, politics or sport in the living-room. My grandmother, my mother and my uncle's wife chattering or sometimes singing in the kitchen while they cooked something. Lots of things. They always tasted scrumptious. We children – myself and my brother and sister, my four cousins – climbing trees or playing volleyball in the garden or riding our bikes in the streets until we were called in at sundown. A blissful childhood. The kind of childhood I want for my own kids.

- Where's Lena?
- Still up the stair.
- Ah. Playing with her big cousins.
- I tell you. I don't want to go into Noor's kitchen again.
- But we need her for looking after the children. She doesn't ask for payment …
- This is her payment. Dragging me into her territory to boss about and lecture on the art of housework. Well, I've had it, Iqbal. We've tried living your way for five years. Now it's my turn.

This is the third time she's raised this subject. Ominous.

* * *

Donald

Sittin in Richard's mother's flat over a few drinks some of us watch the latest BBC debate, with Jim Sillars defendin YES and George Galloway defendin NO.

Both ex-Labour MPs. Lots of water. Different bridges. I'm thinkin so much about Galloway's and Sillars's pasts that tonight's debate passes me by. All I notice is the recurrence of the strange phrase 'stupidity on stilts'. At the end I'm no sure which of them first used the phrase or what it refers to. And after six whiskies it doesnae matter.

Richard's mother, Alice, says

- What a speaker yon Sillars used to be. When I was young I could have sat at his feet forever. If he'd stayed with the Labour Party he could have been a Cabinet Minister. Maybe even Prime Minister. What a waste.

Richard's father says:

- I blame the blonde bombshell.
- She was a good speaker too.
- Saying the wrong things.
- Peddling snake oil.

It's good to watch this with like-minded people. If I was watching with Ewan we'd be sniping at each other all the time. And he would get the last word.

* * *

Lorraine

I'm gettin addicted to political programmes. Turnin into a right anorak.

I was quite the activist. In another life.

When I was a student it was marchin for the miners. Ma and Kenny would still be in their beds when I slipped out and took the lift down with my banner and poles. I didnae believe them when they told me I was wastin my time.

Later it was anti poll-tax demos. Weekend after weekend: marchin up the middle of the streets from Charing Cross to Glasgow Green. Singin and chantin: Maggie! Maggie! Maggie! Out! Out! Out! I was young: I went out angry and came home hoarse.

Tommy Sheridan got lifted time and again. Defendin families getting their furniture confiscated for no payin the poll tax. From his prison cell he got elected as a Glasgow councillor. I saw it on the telly: all the candidates lined up on the platform with Tommy's mammy clutching a big iconic portrait of him to her bosom. For dramatic impact it beat an empty chair hands down.

When Angela was three I joined the Scottish Socialist Party and started attendin meetins. The meetins all happened after work. With an obligatory endin in the pub, they lasted into the night. A bone of contention with Stuart. He didnae like it when I left Angela with him. He liked it even less when I left her with my mother and Kenny, what with Kenny's past transgressions.

I mind the 2003 election when we won six seats on the lists. Colin Fox dancin and skippin all over the count. Rosie Kane in her glad rags promisin us 'madness and craziness' in our new Parliament. Writin her 'oath to the people' on her hand when she was supposed to be swearin her oath to the Queen.

I truly believed the revolution was come.

Then the guy – the very guy whose charisma had built up the party from nothin, who had sown the seeds and watered the shoots of hope, who actually had us believin an independent socialist republic of Scotland was possible – brought the whole caboodle crashin down.

For no reason that I could see. Certainly wisnae about policy. Stuart said it all:

- See thae far-left parties? First thing on the agenda's always the split.

The SSP broke up in acrimony about the same time as my relationship. Stuart found himself a new squeeze whose life revolved round him rather than a political vision. Since then I've been politically inactive, tryin to spend more time with my daughter.

Lockin the stable door.

* * *

Ewan

I reach Hogganfield Loch as dusk is falling. We've met here to suit Anne-Marie, a young rookie who lives in the houses just across Cumbernauld Road.

I park the car. The moonlight gleams on the backs of scores of swans and geese which bob gently on the water, heads hidden under wings. Roll on the light nights. I join Anne-Marie, waiting at the gate. Nobody else. My heart sinks.

We give them ten minutes more.

- Right, Anne-Marie, looks like it's just you and me.

Anne-Marie beams. I think she has a crush on me.

We get back into my car. Drive up and round a bit of the perimeter of the city. On Red Road the high-rises rise high.

- You hear the latest wheeze of our great Council Leader? He's going to blow up the Red Road flats as an overture to the Commonwealth Games. A fun event for the tourists.
- Boys and their toys!
- Obviously itching to be Secretary of State for Defence.
- Or even just an American cop.

Balefully they loom out of the gloom. They've received death warrants before but this time there will be no reprieve. No penthouse plan. No student digs. No YMCA. We who are about to die salute you.

We park outside a row of closes, fawn pebbledash with balconies, six houses to a close. Survivors from a 1950s scheme.

- Ah've been leafletin before but this is ma first time oot canvassin.
- I'll carry the bag of leaflets and you take the clipboard and record the answers. If we need leaflets you can look for them in the bag while I go on with the talking. You don't need to speak if you don't want to but if you do …
- Anythin Ah say can be used against me!

I push the security button and talk our way into the close. Together we climb the stairs.

- When the data comes in from YESMO all the flats in a close are mixed up. Before I print the sheets I rearrange them in order from the top down.
- D'ye no get fair wrecked runnin up aw the sterrs in a wanner?
- I like to work from the top down because of the dogs. You don't get as many dogs in the flats as in the four-in-a-blocks, but I once got bitten by a staffie.

I show her the scar on my forefinger.

- Aw, Ah love staffies! My uncle's got wan and I take him for walks, so Ah dae. Awfy cute – pinky spots and wee piggy eyes.
- Most of them are OK but you get the occasional one that's territorial. And then you don't want it between yourself and the street.
- Nothin barkin up this close.
- They don't always bark first. So never put your hand in the letterbox along with the leaflet. Roll it up so it's firm enough to go in on its own. Some people use a spatula.

The right-hand door two up has a faded Union Jack doormat. Tiny Red Hand of Ulster transfer at the corner of the fanlight. I glance at the door on the opposite side. Where you get one Orange family you sometimes get a cluster.

Some biffs and bangs coming from the left-hand door, the first household at the top of the canvass sheet. Maybe furniture being moved about. I knock and a middle-aged woman opens.

- Mrs Elspeth Nimmo? Hello. My name's Ewan and I'm here from YES Scotland. I've just got a couple of quick questions about the referendum.

Doorstep smile.

Mild blank gaze.

- On a scale of 1 to 10, where 1 is NO I don't want independence for Scotland and 10 is YES I do want independence for Scotland, where would you place yourself?
- Aw son, ma heid's nippin wi it aw. Whit's that ye're sayin aboot wan tae ten?
- One is NO, Ten is YES. To an independent Scotland.

I demonstrate, drawing an imaginary line across her doorway.

- Where are you on the spectrum?
- Gie me a four. No, mebbe a five. Or …
- So you're undecided on independence for Scotland.
- Well, Ah don't know …
- Have you got worries about it?
- Well, whit aboot the … thingmy … the …

I wait.

- Whit wis it they were goin on aboot …? Wis on the telly …

I wait.

- The pound an that?

- The currency. Nobody can stop us using the pound. Lots of countries have become independent from Britain and usually use sterling at first but eventually go over to their own.
- Zat right?
- Ireland, Australia and Canada used the pound for years. Gibraltar still does. Hong Kong used the pound then went over to the dollar. Denmark has its own currency but ties it to the Euro so it's always worth the same.
- So whit ye sayin? We'll no find wursels wi nae money in wur poackets?
- That won't happen anyway. Look, going for independence is not a new idea. It's been the trend for many years. In 1900 there were 79 independent countries in the world. In 2009 there were 194.
- Zat a fact?
- Currency has never been the main sticking point. It's only become important during our campaign because the telly and the Press have made a mountain out of a molehill.
- OK, well. Make me a six.

Anne-Marie scribbles on the clipboard. I glance over her shoulder:

- We've got a Gordon Nimmo, and a Stephen Nimmo registered here. Are they at home?
- Gordo's oot. Never know wherr he is. Stevie's at his work. Ah've goat a son Malcolm an aw, but he's too young tae vote.
- What age is Malcolm?
- 16.
- Then he can vote in this referendum.

- Zat a fact?

- I'll give you a form for him to register.

No response at the door with the Union Jack doormat. With some relief I shove a 'Sorry we Missed You' through the letterbox.

Middle landing, right, listed as McTavish. However, the person who answers is an unlikely McTavish.

- McTavish gone away.

- So you live here now? And your name …?

- Abdul Nabi. From Afghanistan. No allowed to vote.

By his elbow is a young boy. Big bright eyes and shiny black curls. He pipes up

- You want to see my bearded dragon?

Room draped with coloured cloth. Cloth on the floor, cloth hanging on the walls, cloth on the couch. Lady seated by the electric fire, lifts her shawl over her head and turns slightly away from us as we enter.

The lizard lies brooding in a brightly lit glass tank. Blank, hooded eyes. Same colour as the sand which surrounds it. A breathing piece of the desert imported to soggy Scotland.

- He's amazing. What do you feed him on? (Me)

- Vegetables. (The boy)

- I thought lizards ate crickets. (Me)

- He eats everything.

- What's his name?

- Taki.

- Did you catch him in Afghanistan? (Anne-Marie)

- They come from Australia! (The boy, scornfully)

At the door across the landing we think nobody is at home and are turning away when the door opens a chink, on the chain. A young woman, thin-faced. The arm of a toddler round her leg.

- Hello. Are you Jean Lavery?

Looks too young to be a Jean.

- Naw.
- Does Jean Lavery still live here?
- Whit's it aboot?

She looks from me to Anne-Marie and back again. Unsmiling.

- Sorry. It's about the referendum. My name's Ewan and this is Anne-Marie. We're from YES Scotland. It's just a very quick question. Do you want Scotland to be an independent country?

Narrowed eyes wash over Anne-Marie and her clipboard and her various YES badges: 'Aye', 'How NO?' 'YES Please', 'Generation YES', 'Bairns not Bombs', 'Women for Independence'. Over me and my blue and white saucer-sized YES rosette.

Indisputably a NO.

- Mebbe.
- Can I get your name? You don't seem to be on the voter's roll.
- Dae Ah huv tae?
- Do you have to what?
- Gie ye ma name.
- No, of course not. Tell you what … Anne-Marie: get the forms. Here's an application form to join the voters' register. The address to return it is on the …
- Dae Ah huv tae?
- Do you have to what?
- Fill in the form.
- Well, you do if you want to have a vote in this referendum.

Still unconvinced.

- You said you might like Scotland to be independent. Well this referendum coming up is likely to be the very last chance in our lives we'll get to vote for it.
- Ur ye mebbe still registered tae vote at yer last address? (Anne-Marie)
- Mebbe.
- So will you be gaun back there to vote on September 18th?
- Naw.
- Where were you staying before?
- Dae Ah huv tae tell ye?
- Of course not.
- Ah'll no bother, well.

She shuts the door.

Anne-Marie and I look at each other. Shake our heads and turn to go downstairs. Clatter coming from behind. Large woman, Union Jack tattoo, wild wiry mane. 'Sorry We Missed You' in her fist.

- You the clown that woke me up fae ma sleep tae shove this piece o shite through ma door?
- Yes. Sorry, I …
- Here's me on the night shift, tryin tae catch up, an you, ye wanker …
- We're terribly sorry …
- Ye English wanker!

She threw the 'Sorry We Missed You' in my face. She missed.

- Here, ram it up yer erse. Ah don't waant ma hoose durtied wi it.

We hear the door slam from above.

- Will Ah pit hur doon as Undecided? (Anne-Marie)

From the ground floor left-hand door Kenneth ('call me Kenny') Murphy, unsteady on his feet, vodka on his breath, says he's a one or a two.

- Don't know much aboot it. But ur we no too wee?

I start listing the independent European countries which are smaller than Scotland:

- Norway, Denmark, Finland, Ireland, Estonia, Latvia, Luxembourg …
- Ah've never been tae thae places. Maybe they're aw gone tae hell.
- Most are prosperous. Scandinavia, for instance …
- Aye, so you say. But Ah've never been there. Am Ah tae take your word?
- You can look them up. Do you have a computer?
- Naw. Onywey, Ah don't like thon smug bloke Salmond. Far too up issel.
- Do you think confidence is a bad thing in a country's leader? Would you want a shrinking violet for the UK Prime Minister?
- Prime Minister? Whit Salmond waants is tae be King o the Scots, heh heh!
- Well, it's not about Salmond anyway. Independence is bigger than any one individual …
- Don't like yon wee sidekick o his either. Salmon an Sturgeon, eh? Something fishy therr, heh, heh!

Across the close from Kenny, Daisy Donnelly opens the door wide.

- Come away in!

I tell our canvassers not to accept invitations into people's houses. I don't take my own advice.

Homely living-room, couch covered in a hand-crocheted throw. Above the hearth a large Tretchikoff print: green

54

Chinese lady in a pink and gold gown. Photos on the walls and mantelpiece of young people graduating, getting married, carrying babies. Three ducks fly diagonally across the left-hand recess towards the top right-hand corner of the ceiling. The telly's on loud but Daisy mutes it.

- Cauld night fur yese tae be oot. Could yese go a wee cuppa tea? It's just masked.
- Sorry – we'd love to, but we've a lot of houses to get round yet.
- That's aw right, son.

Daisy goes through to the kitchenette and returns after a few minutes with a cup of tea for herself. She settles down in the rocking chair.

- Questions aboot the referendum, ye said?
- On a scale of 1 to 10, where one is NO …
- Never mind aw that. Ye waant tae know if Ah think Scotland should be independent.
- Yes …
- Ah'm glad ye asked me that, son. Ah've been thinking ower that question ever since this referendum thingmy sterted up.
- Do you have any particular concerns about it?
- Ur ye English yersel?
- I was born in Scotland. But a lot of my childhood was spent in England.
- Wherraboots?
- All over. But I went to secondary school in Gateshead.
- That near Newcastle?
- Yes. Across the Tyne.
- Never been therr masel. But when ma man wis livin he wis a lorry driver an he did a loata deliveries doon thon wey. Newcastle struck him it looked very like

55

Glesca.

- Yes. Glasgow's got the same sort of buildings …

- … as Gateshead.

- No. As Newcastle. Anyway, about the referendum …

Daisy lowers her voice.

- Ah used tae know everybody up this close but ower the past few years some new fowk have moved in. They mostly keep theirsels tae theirsels. Him next door takes a good bucket …

She jerks her thumb, raises an imaginary glass to her mouth. She points at the ceiling.

- Thae Arabs ur aw right. He says hullo when he sees me. Hur up the sterr goes: thur too many immigrants. But it wis aye emigration wis the problem when Ah wis young.

- Scotland's not full up. There's room to spare.

- Ah learnt in the school the population o Glesca wis a million an a quarter. Whit's it noo? Boot hauf that?

- Probably. But the population's been on the rise again since we got the Scottish Parliament. To get back to the referendum …

- You'll be too young tae mind the £10 wan-way ticket tae Australia. Ma haill faimily went oot on that. Ah woulda went an aw but they wouldnae cover ma fare because Ah wis deef in wan ear efter the measles. So that wis me on ma ownio an no lang left the school. If ye were in perfect health ye were encouraged tae leave the country. If thur wis somethin wrang wi ye naebody waanted ye and ye got left behind. Ma brither an ma sister mairried oot therr an Ah never seen them again.

- Net immigration's a sign of a healthy attractive country.

- Better fowk think Scotland's a good place tae come to reyther than a place tae get the hell oot o.
- And we shouldn't forget the asylum seekers are running away from …
- Mind you, they're no nice tae their weemin. That lot up the sterr: it's only the man ye ever see. He goes the messages, gets oot an aboot. The wife disnae step ootside the door. The man walks the wee fella tae the school and back. The wife's a prisoner.
- If she can't speak English maybe she doesn't want to go out. Anyway. Can I ask you – on a scale of 1 to 10 where …
- Thon wumman across the landin fae the Arabs – she's hidin fae somebody.
- We shouldn't speculate …
- She's anither wan never gaes oot. Belts across to the supermarket wi hur wee boy in his buggy. Roon the lot in a flash and back hame. Sits at the windae aw day looking up an doon the road. Hur wee boy looks aboot three or fower but he never goes tae nursery or nuthin. Thur disnae seem tae be onythin wrang wi him but she still keeps him tied intae thon buggy. And when Ah chapped on hur door wi a wee cuppa tea she couldnae get away fast enough. An she wouldnae tell me hur name. Whit d'ye make o that?
- Who do you think she's hiding from? (Anne-Marie)

I nudge her to shut her up, but too late.

- Who dae fowk hide fae? Money-lenders? Drug-dealers? The polis?
- We really have to crack on.

I stand up. So does Anne-Marie. She goes:

- Are ye still undecided aboot independence? On a scale of 1 to 10 where 1 is NO and 10 is YES …

57

- Make me a wan, hen. It's the London Government gies me ma pension.

On auto-pilot I reach into my bag.

- Got a letter here from the Department of Works and Pensions …
- Pit it away, son. You say wan thing, they say the ither. Ah'm takin nae chances. Onywey, cannae staun yon Alex Salmond. He waants tae be King o the Scots, him.

Chapter 4: April

Jan

I'm sitting among the cables trying to keep the dust out of my coffee when a burst of laughter comes from the next room. Zack's telling jokes again. His English is so much better than mine.

Zack's the younger brother of my wife, Eva, and I love him like my own brother. It was his idea to come out here. See the world, improve our English, earn better money. I was less keen at first because I'm settled with a family. Zack is still footloose and fancy-free – and, believe me, takes full advantage! Then I saw the wages. Not big money, but considerably better than we would get back home. We pay our way, save a little and I send some back to Eva.

Zack's a hit with the girls. His Central European looks and accent draw them like moths to a flame. Mine too, up to a point, although I'm older and emit less semaphore. That is, I don't present myself on the market. But if a pretty girl makes me an offer, no ties, no consequences – where's the harm? Eva's 1400 km away.

Up till now we've been working in building sites but our hope is to set up in business for ourselves. Building sites are all right in a fine summer, and the other guys are good for a laugh, but when in Scotland can you rely on the weather? Working indoors in factories, shops or even private homes is more dependable. And no worker becomes really rich while employed by someone else.

We're skilled electricians, but we can both turn our hands

to other crafts: basic joinery and plumbing. Going round the building sites, we've got to know several tradesmen who might throw their lot in with us once we're established. A lot of Scottish electricians say they'll only come out for a big job. Or they promise to come out on a job and then don't turn up. Maybe they would rather sit on their backsides. That's fine: all the more scope for us.

Eva runs her own clinic in Karlovy Vary. Typical spa stuff: oxygen therapy, magneto therapy, myostimulation. But there's too much competition. Although she trained in Karlovy Vary, she doesn't need to be based there – her particular therapies don't depend on the hot springs. She would like to bring them to Glasgow, where they would be a new idea. Eva's English is good – 20% of her clients are from the UK. If she were over here, her business skills would be useful when Zack and I strike out on our own.

And it would be wonderful to be back together as a family. Anna and Janinka are growing up so fast. Last time I went home Janinka didn't remember me and I hardly recognised her.

So that's the plan, when we've saved enough capital.

till now, I've contented myself with work, drinking with my mates, following the football and the occasional flutter at the bookies. I take the world as it comes, whether in Czechia or in Scotland. None of my business who they elect to run their government. Zack's different. He's young – still imagines small men like us can change the world for the better.

But we're both interested in this referendum. If Scotland became independent, it would be kicked out of the European Union. It would have to go to the end of the queue for readmission – if it got in at all. And where would that leave Zack and me and our plans to set up on our own?

I'm angry that the Scottish Government is destabilising things. Spoilt children who don't appreciate their luck. They should be careful what they wish for. Slovakia thought it could do without the Czechs. I haven't been over there but I read a report that they're floundering. Running a Government, balancing a budget, providing services, making trade deals: none of it's as easy as they'd imagined. The day may dawn that they'll come crawling back to us, cap in hand.

* * *

Ewan

I pull aside the glass door. Donald's already in, face tilted towards the shower rose. The water rushes over his face, down his cheeks. I push in.

- Move over. I'm in a hurry.

Donald laughs.

- Time for corporal punishment for dead horses!
- There's a journalist coming. The YES office just told me half an hour ago. Have to contact folk. Get a turnout to impress him.
- My, my. The media circus. Sheer hell. Where's he from this time?
- *The Economist.* We've had them from Germany, France, Catalonia, Belgium. The only place I've not had them from is Scotland.
- A prophet in your own land. No even really your land – my land. The Sassenach for YES and the Teuchter for NO.
- It's not where you come from …

We chime in together. Singing at last from the same hymn sheet.

- … it's where you're going to.
- Thoughts of Chairman Salmond. (Donald)

At my computer after making a couple of phone calls, I send out an email to the rest of the dozen people who sometimes turn up to campaign in my constituency. The gist for all is

'There's a journalist coming tonight from the Economist. He wants to observe us canvassing. If you don't want to canvass there will be leafleting available as well. But please come along. It's really important to impress him with a big turnout.'

However, I tailor it to each activist:

'Hi, Sheila – I know you were out with us just on Monday. But it's particularly important to get a big turnout tonight as there's a journalist ...'

'Hi, Bernie – It's OK if this doesn't fit in with your shifts. But if you can possibly make it, please come tonight. There's a journalist ...'

'Hi, Caroline –I know it's hard for you to find time these days. But if you could come out tonight it would be great. I promise I won't bother you again till your exams are over. There's a journalist ...'

While I'm typing a Facebook message pops up:

'Alison Lindsay wants to be friends'.

Alison Lindsay. Do I know her? I get lots of offers from strangers. Still, the name's faintly familiar.

Alison Lindsay's page comes up. Curses. No picture. Not of her, anyway. Unless she's a newborn baby.

These parents who use their baby's picture for the profile instead of their own. Personal modesty? Pride in the bald, bland sprog? Do they never consider their remote contacts, reaching into cyberspace to extract one particular Alison Lindsay from all the other Alison Lindsays?

Many YES campaigners use a flag, a banner, or a crowd of fellow activists as their Facebook profile. Strange sort of bashfulness, to proclaim to the world your political views, even what you had for breakfast, but hide your face away.

Alison is a YES supporter. Banners, flags, shared and liked promiscuously. Her profile picture, though, is a baby.

Maybe Alison Lindsay is the baby. Maybe her self-esteem is so low she thinks that's the last time she was photogenic.

Poor thing. Here on the YES campaign, it's a time for reaching out. And her name rings vaguely familiar.

I click *'Confirm'*.

Canvass bags: How many? On Monday night only three turned up including myself, but today with the attraction of the journalist ... maybe make up 10 bags. If we're swamped with workers they can double up.

Ten bags surrounding me as I sit spread-eagled on the floor. Reach for the sealable plastic pokes.

The A5 leaflets just fit in there if you bend them.

A4 sheets go in the Poly-pockets.

By this stage of the game I have a leaflet for every major question which has arisen at the door. If YES doesn't supply them (who designs the YES leaflets anyway? Does s/he ever actually darken a doorstep?) and none of the myriad leaflets produced by the myriad wee groups fit the bill (Davids for YES?) then I write my own.

The contents of each bag:

> Postal Vote Forms. Voter's registration forms. Blue Survey cards. Window posters. Car stickers. Badges.
>
> Leaflets produced by various YES groups:
>
> NHS
>
> Labour for Indy
>
> Green for Indy
>
> Britain is for the Rich: Scotland can be ours *(Radical Indy)*
>
> Renewable energy *(Powerful Scotland)*

Economy *(It all adds up)*

Aye Right *(List of pro-YES Websites)*

Democracy *(Where is Scotland on UK Radar – not getting the Govts we elect)*

I don't want change *(focussed on the fearful)*

Polish leaflet

How to Disarm a Nuclear Bomb *(anti-Trident)*

Reassuring Pensions letter from the DWP

Info sheets printed by myself:

McCrone Report

Moving the Sea Border

Oil only 15% of Scotland's Economy

My favourite Women for Indy leaflet: comic-book woman discussing divorce:

FRONT Speech bubbles:

Him 'I'll be different this time. I'll change. I promise'

Her 'Britain is an Unreliable Partner'

REVERSE ... We had some good Times Together ... This isn't working out for me anymore ... Your family is great and we share loads of friends ... But we've grown apart ... we want different things ... You want expensive toys to keep up with your rich pals ... I want my kids to grow up in a better country ... We'll still be here for each other ... but I can't wait around anymore hoping you'll change ... It's time for me to do my own thing ... We'll always be friends. But it's over. Vote YES.'

Whenever I see it I'm reminded of my relationship with Donald. But which of us is the Unreliable Partner?

* * *

Kirsty

They wake me at 8.00. Erin pulling the duvet off me, bathing me in freezing air. Benny whacking me with a wooden spoon. Both of them jumping on the bed, on my legs, on my head. Note to self: buy a snib for the cupboard door and put it on. If Marilyn lets me.

- Get up! Get up! Lazybones!

I hang on to the wisps of my dream as I push past into the living-room and out to the bathroom, dragging the duvet with me. I bundle in, shut the door and snib it. Curl up in the bath.

Cara perched on the toilet seat: At least they're too wee to do you serious damage. Not like my big brothers.

Hammer hammer at the door.

- Come out and play!
- You're not allowed to hide in the bathroom!
- Come out!
- We're telling!

I open the door again and they rush in on me. Benny has upgraded his wooden spoon to a claw hammer. I pull the duvet right over my head. The hammer gets me on the back. I go into their bedroom and look out my clothes.

Three packages on the breakfast table. One each for Erin, Benny and me. Easter eggs from our shared grandfather. Must have arrived yesterday.

Uh-oh. Mine slightly bigger than theirs. Or presented in a bigger box.

Erin sets up a wail.

- Don't want this one! Want Kirsty's!

Without being told, I shove my egg across the table and take hers.

We all open our packages.

Uh-oh. Once they're out of the brown paper, my original egg, the one Erin has ended up with, is smaller.

- Swap back!

I do.

Benny looks at each of the eggs in turn. The picture of disgruntlement.

- Want Kirsty's egg too!

I wait to see what happens.

- Kirsty's too big for Easter Eggs! Sure she is, Mummy? (Erin).

Benny sets up a roar.

- Want Kirsty's egg too!

Marilyn tries to reason with him.

- If you take both Kirsty's egg and your own, then poor wee Erin'll only have one and you'll have two!

Erin sets up a roar.

- I want Kirsty's egg!

Two of them chanting.

- We want Kirsty's egg! We want Kirsty's egg!

Laughing now. A power game.

- All right, keep your hair on! We can split Kirsty's egg in two.

Marilyn gets a knife out the drawer. She reaches for my egg.

- All right, Kirsty?

For a moment too long I cup my hands round my present from Grandpa. I try to remember what he looked like. Soft white stubble. Bald head.

- You're too big for Easter eggs. (Marilyn).

Marilyn takes it and saws it in two. Inside: a wee cellophane poke of chocolate buttons.

I reach.

Too late. Erin:

- Sweeties!

Marilyn laughs.

- Aha! Madam here was thinking she'd keep them all to herself! You're too quick for her, sausage!

She takes the buttons, opens the cellophane and shares them out. Twelve buttons. Four each for Erin, Benny and me. Benny bawls.

- More buttons!

Marilyn groaned in mock exasperation as she takes away my four and gives Erin and Benny two more each.

- See you two – you're going to get fat!

She reaches out and tickles Erin's waistline. Erin giggles in glee.

- So you are! You'll end up fat like Madam here!

Benny and Erin nibble at their buttons. Benny holds one out to me.

- Want one?

I make a move to reach but he laughs and puts it in his own mouth. Erin also holds one out.

- Have one of mine!

I rinse out my cereal bowl and stay out in the kitchen to check my postings. Another message from Watcherinthesky. I contemplate. What I read here might shadow the rest of the day.

Cara: Best to know if you've to be on your guard.

I open.

'Go roll on the motorway, U bag of pus. When the lorry hits U pus will explode all over. '

Cara: Well, that's OK. No direct threat.

* * *

Wilma

Ma granny brought up ten weans, so she did. Everybody hud big faimilies back then – no jist the Tims. Ma maw wis the youngest, an the only wan born in Glesca efter ma granda came ower wi Harland an Wolf.

Ma childhood wis magic, so it wis. We wurnae wealthy – didnae even huv an inside lavvy – but ma two brothers an me wur oan the randan mornin noon an night. Fair heidbangers we wur. Booked by the polis time an again.

Ah wis a right wee toerag. Furst oot the gang tae ride ma bogie across a dual carriageway at the rush hour. Jist shut ma eyes an done it. Ah swerr tae this day that Ah passed under a lorry gaun at full speed, between its front wheels an its back wheels. The wee hardmen waatchin me said it didnae happen. It couldnae huv happent. They were jist scunnert because a lassie done somethin they couldnae.

Ah got the belt in school mair often than ony o the boays an Ah wis the last lassie tae get the belt afore the heidie banned it. Ah'll ayeways be proud o that.

We hud a rerr cairry-oan. Chuckin snawbaws at the muppets comin oot the Tim school. Ah used tae pit a wee stane inside ma snawbaws – got a right yelp when Ah hut the mark. Puir brill bein wan o a big team up agin the enemy. Them an their hokey-cokey – as if Goad boathers his erse aboot aw thon bobbin up an doon an him wi the universe tae run. Whitever Pope invented aw thon, it'll be a comfort tae him doon in Hell that they're aw still daein whit they're telt.

An whit aboot aw thon chastity shite! They ban priests huvin sex wi weemin but gie them power over altar boays. They ban nuns huvin weans o their ain but gie them power over wee orphans. Ye couldnae make it up.

They kept everythin in Latin so that even efter ordinary fowk could read an write – we've John Knox tae thank fur that, bi the wey – naebody but the priests hud a clue.

When Ah wis bigger, ma mammy sent me tae learn the flute. Ah practised fur hoors – spent faur mair time on that than on ma schoolwork! Ah got good at it an got oan the band. Fancy rig-oot hud tae be waashed an pressed the night afore. Sky-blue an snaw-white like the flag o Scotland. Ah played on five big Walks in ma time; fower in Glesca an wan in Larkhall. Great stirrin tunes – ma hert fair beat in time wi the big drum.

The West End luvvies look doon thur noses at the Ludge. Caw us ignorant bigots. But whit aboot thon fella made it his mission tae pull fowk oot the Clyde? Saved hunners o lives – never goat a penny fur it. Didnae ask if they wur Prods, Tims or fuckin Hottentots – a life wis a life. As weel as pair droonin sowels he pullt oot lotsa bits o rubbish an he built them aw intae a statue o King Billy. Big-hertit, brave an artistic.

Chinged days. Noo we've got the Muslims tae contend wi as weel as the Tims. Thon Islamists are worse than the fuckin IRA. Blawin up buses, schools an hospitals. Their beliefs are even dafter. They think if they kill enough o the infidel – that's us, bi the wey – they'll get presentit wi 72 virgins in Paradise. An whit did thae pair virgins dae tae deserve that in *their* efterlife?

Thae wankers cannae see weemin as people at aw, jist sex objects. That's how they don't let them oot the hoose unless they're under a blanket. Imagine tryin tae cross a busy road werrin a burqa. Ah blame the weemin in thae countries for lettin the men wipe their feet on them. Widnae be me. Whit Ah say: if the men cannae control their willies the problem lies wi them. Take the burqas aff the weemin; blindfauld aw the men.

Ma ain life's no bed o roses, neither it is. Ma man never seen fifty an ma three weans live in England. Ah'm still workin awey on the phones wi a taxi company. Permanent nightshift. If they hudnae moved the goalposts, Ah coulda retired in fower year but noo it looks like Ah'll be deid afore Ah see ma fuckin pension. The Scottish Nasty Government blame it on London as usual but if they waantit they could soart it. Gie us weemin that huv loast oot some o the dosh they're wastin on foreign aid. Charity begins at hame.

But laugh an the world laughs wi ye; greet an ye're oan yer ain. Thur twice a year we get thegither, ma weans an granweans, ma brithers an their faimilies, an aw the cousins in Belfast. The Scottish time an the Ulster time.

See Christmas decorations? Nothin but Papish idolatry. But at Hogmanay Ah dae up ma hoose Scottish. Get oot the auld Scottish CDs. Pit swatches o tartan roon the picture o King Billy. Ah huv a mini-kilt Ah can still squeeze intae – makes me look like Fran withoot the Anna. Shortbreid oan the table an steak pie in the oven. An mair bevvy than ye could find in Campbeltown Loch.

An here they aw roll up tae ma wee hoose, aw the kith an kin, fae Scotland, England and fae ower the Irish Sea. We rant an we roar an we bring in the bells like they were never brung in afore.

The Ulster time faws in July. Ma crowd meet up at Ardrossan an we near sink the boat wi the swally and the shindig. Ower in Belfast it's ma son Jason noo that bangs the drum. Gies it a special wallop if we pass by a chaipel or a Tim school – reminds them o 1690. The banners are works o art wi aw the colours – orange, rid an gold. Fancier than onythin ye'll see at Kelvingrove. Ah'm too auld an ugly tae play in the band noo but Ah take ma place proudly mairchin wi the crowd at the back. Ah still huv the sash ma father wore.

Ah've never bothert ma erse aboot politics. Politicians are like priests – oan a power-trip oot tae take whit they can fae them that's saft enough tae gie them it. Ah've never even voted afore. Gie them nae fuckin encouragement's whit Ah say.

But Ah've registered tae vote noo. This referendum's important. Thae Scottish Nasties make oot they're aw fur the Queen, but no that lang ago they were waantin a referendum oan the monarchy. An wur Prodestant Queen is wur guarantee of a Prodestant Britain.

If Scotland goes separatist it'll be a feather in the cap tae the Taigs ower the watter. Next thing Ulster'll be under the heel o the Pape an we'll aw be oan wur knees wan wey or anither. Wursels in the Chaipel an wur weans behind the curtain wi the priests.

Home Rule is Rome Rule on baith sides o the watter. Nae Surrender Tae the Whore o Rome. Ah'll live by it an if Ah huv tae Ah'll die by it.

* * *

Donald

I worry about it gettin so nasty. The news is full of stories of Unionists puttin their heads above the parapet and gettin trolled on social media.

I myself get dragged into somebody else's political blog and before I know what's happenin I'm bein called terrible names. A traitor. A racist against my own people. Other names I cannae repeat. Names that haunt you.

I mention this to Ewan. Scant sympathy.

- The Unionists already control the airwaves and the newsprint. This faux outrage is them discrediting the social media which they can't control.

- Seriously, Ewan. The SNP are gonnae have to do somethin about these cybernats. They're out of order ...

- The SNP don't control the cybernats. They're lone nutters. Anyway, you should see the trolling that emanates from the other side.

- Doesnae seem as bad …

- Doesn't get reported, you mean. Some misfits allegedly call a few Unionists names. Banner headlines. Even if the victims have deleted the evidence. Salmond and Sturgeon get regular death threats and there's no mention.

- Have you been trolled?

- I wouldn't waste time swapping insults with folk who've made up their minds.

Ewan has years of activist experience behind him. Years of political arguin. I cannae come up with the slick answers. And I'm boxin with one hand tied behind my back because I want him to go on lovin me. A consideration which doesnae hinder him at all.

I bring in both our meals. For once we'll get to eat together.

I love watchin him eat the meals I cook. This time it's chicken cordon bleu, made to my own recipe. He eats daintily, never droppin a crumb.

Cut out for a gentleman and wasnae needed.

- Fancy watchin a movie tonight? I've been addin to the DVD collection and now there's quite a range to pick from. It's no fun watchin them on my own.

- Can't. I've to enter all these returns into YESMO. That'll take all evening.

- Tomorrow night?

- There's a public meeting on tomorrow night – one of Tommy Sheridan's Hope over Fear things.

- So you're a Sheridan acolyte, now?

- He's a useful catalyst. Donald, even you must admit the referendum's revived interest in political rallies. Every community hall, in every housing scheme:

standing room only.

- Preachin to the converted.
- Not by our choice. If the NO side would only have the balls to take part. Make them proper debates.

I gather up the plates. Ewan says:

- Thought you were supposed to be an activist too. Doesn't seem to take up much of your time. Has Better Together given up on grassroots support? Is it openly top-down now?
- We're gettin there.
- How's the tele-canvassing going?

He asks me, no like he's interested, but like he's preparin to sneer at my answer. Of course my response sets him to do just that.

- It's not. They've told us to concentrate on high-viz stuff.
- Such as?
- Handing out leaflets at stations.
- Ah. Same old, same old. So how do you get feedback on voting intentions?
- We're hirin commercial polling agencies.
- Three cheers for the Tory millionaires.

He's typecastin my side as plutocrats. Bloated capitalists grindin the faces of the poor. Yet it's all Labour leadin Better Together. Alastair Darling. Blair MacDougall. Johann Lamont.

My parents wanted to do the best for us. When my Dad inherited the family croft, he sold it and sent my brothers and me to private school. Entrance test; leafy grounds; uniform would dazzle the dictator of a banana republic.

My brothers took to the culture like ducks to water. Rapidly upgraded their accents and attitudes. Both sportsmen. Both

73

prefects. Both Tories.

I was a fish out of water. Mediocre academically and, worse, useless at sports. Then I met my Nemesis: they guessed I was gay.

I absorbed some of their philosophy. As a manager I hope people find me strict but fair. No time for slackers. I believe people should pay their bills and do without rather than get into debt.

But when Ewan lumps me in with the Tories it breaks my heart.

* * *

Iain

It was exciting at first. The contrast.

Cold, damp, half-empty streets in pastel shades, cars following each other sedately in their lanes. The chat and banter I'd grown up with. Quiet residential grids with predictability round every corner. The future much resembling the past.

Then! Sizzling, humid, brilliantly-coloured throngs. Shops and stalls spilling halfway across the road. Incomprehensible chatter on every side; illegible script on the posters. Aromatic fragrance and stench and a frisson of undefined danger.

I stepped up to the plate. Got right outside my comfort zone.

Earned respect from my underlings who were pleased with their well-paid white-collar jobs. Who spent their off time practising their English to lend authenticity to their identities ('My name is Kevin'). Who took in their stride the 95% knock-back rate. The night-shift (to suit the destination country timezone). The dangerous (for the females) reliance on late night buses and taxis.

Earned admission to the small circle of ex-pat managers. Most of us work day shifts and pass the balmy starry evenings drinking in one another's apartments. One of them has access to a roof terrace and sometimes we sleep up there, cooled by a dampened sheet.

The yoyo existence damaged deeper relationships. A couple of years of it brought Aileen and me to the divorce courts. Now I've got to shell out every month for wee Logan but hardly see him.

Later I had a short-term involvement with a colleague. Bad idea. We split once it dawned that all we had in common was loneliness. Recurring embarrassment now whenever we bump into each other. And we bump into each other all the time.

The chat's mainly gossip about each other or anecdotes from work. Participation in outside civic life is difficult, cut off as we are by culture from our surroundings and by distance from our homes. Sport is all about the English Premier League; politics rarely gets a mention. I'm the only Scot in our wee circle and so only on my most recent trip back did the significance of the independence referendum hit me.

I've kept up my social media contacts but the postings on my own timelines are about holidays and wild nights out, real or imaginary. My Facebook Friends are a politics-free zone. And now I'm supposed to make a decision without knowing the arguments on either side.

* * *

Cindy

Here's some other bugger chappin ma door.

Few weeks ago it wis yon pair askin me tae sign papers an gie them ma name. Somethin to dae wi the votin. Like Ah gie a shite aboot the votin. Me wi aw Ah've got on ma plate. If Ah ever get roon tae votin it'll be fur the Monster Ravin Loonies. Ah'm a Monster Ravin Loony masel.

Noo here somebody else on ma trail. Ah wid sit quiet an say nothin but his nibs always rushes to the door an starts yabberin away at it. Glad o ony diversion. He's that bored in here wi me.

Ah recognise the postman through the peephole. Whit he brings is never welcome. If it's no junk mail it's the Benefit Office tellin me somethin aboot ma money.

When the bedroom tax wis in full swing it wis a nightmare. Hur up the sterr telt me Ah wisnae entitled tae a separate room fur Charlie an I'd be gettin ma money cut.

I wis up tae high doh. Wisnae ma faut they pit me in a three-apartment when Ah jist hud the wan wean under six. If they'd gave me a wan bedroom or a studio Ah'd huv took it. God knows a flittin wid be nae bother wi the wee bit stuff Ah've got. But there wur a loat of areas Ah hud tae avoid, an this wis aw they hud available.

Onywey, turnt oot she wis talkin shite. Charlie gets tae huv his ain bedroom an Ah get tae keep ma dosh. Fur aw it is.

Charlie has the paper ripped aff in nae time. Chocolate Easter Egg.

By the time Ah gaither ma thoughts his nibs has broke intae the egg. Ah goes

- Wait till efter yer tea.

Ah pick up the torn wrappin paper an piece it thegither. The address is wrote in capitals. Cannae be sure. But who else could it be?

* * *

Lorraine

On the way out to my poetry class one night I run into Ewan, one of the guys from two up. He's hurryin down the stairs, laden with bulgin satchels. Navy blue, YES in white across them.

- You've some load there!

He smiles.

- Here's hoping for lots of folk out there waiting to take a bag each.
- Can I come along sometime? I'm YES and I want to help.

His face lights up. You'd think I'd made a declaration of love. And he is, in fact, a gorgeous guy. Unfortunately he swings the other way. So many good-lookin blokes do. Nature's irony.

- Great! We're always needing more activists.
- It's no use sittin at home growlin at the telly.
- That's right. Far too many growling in harmony with other YES supporters. We need folk who'll engage with the voters!

No just a pretty face. Poetic turn o phrase.

- I've done leafletin before but these newspapers look awful heavy.
- Heavy? They're light as a feather!

He jerks his shoulder up. A couple of the satchels hit him on the back of the knees and nearly knock him down the stairs. We both laugh.

- Or you could canvass: you'd just be carrying a few leaflets and a clipboard.
- I've never done canvassing before. I'm scared I get asked a question I cannae answer.
- You don't get asked questions that often, unfortunately.
- You don't?
- They've all got visitors in, or a pan on the stove, or a baby in the bath. Some grab a phone and clamp it to their ear whenever they answer the door.

77

He smiles again. I could look at that smile forever.

- But they are starting to ask more questions. If I don't know the answer I tell them I'll check it out and come back. It's allowed.
- They don't think you're daft?
- On the contrary. When I come back to them with the answer they're delighted I've gone to the bother.

Delighted he's come back again to their door. No kiddin.

- Anyway, if you want to try canvassing you'll go round with somebody experienced – you don't need to open your mouth.
- What's the point o me then?
- Having somebody to take notes and look out the information frees up the canvasser to talk. It's fun when there's two of you.

Goin round the doors with him – fun all right. As I open my door I'm hummin a happy tune. Chattin to a good-lookin guy can fair put a spring in the step. Even at my age. And even if he swings the other way.

* * *

Kirsty

We get leave off school to study for the new National exams. I shut myself in the cupboard and spread my books, notes and laptop all over the bed. I lie on the bed myself. Cara hovering to give what help she can.

Not an ideal arrangement but adequate as long as Erin and Benny have something to occupy them. Otherwise …

Erin drifts in.

- What you doing?
- Maths.

- Can I watch?
- No.
- Uch please? I'll be quiet.
- Get out.
- What's that wee squiggly thing?
- A square root sign.
- What's a square root?
- Out! Out! OUT!

Erin's just bored. But Benny thinks it's exciting to annoy me. He spreads his hands over the page I'm looking at. He switches my laptop (which has no working battery) off at the mains before I've saved my stuff.

Cara: Smash his face in.

- I'm not prepared for death at the hands of Marilyn.

Cara: My brothers threw all my jotters out with the recycling. And I'm not allowed a computer.

I wait till I get Dad alone. Marilyn in the kitchen making the dinner.

- Dad. Could you fit a snib on to the inside of my bedroom door?
- You want to shut yourself away from us? That's no very friendly. Erin and Benny don't have a snib on their door.
- That's different.
- Marilyn and I don't even have one on our door.
- That's up to you. But I need peace to study.
- Can you no just explain that to them?
- Doesn't work.

Marilyn comes in. Rats.

- What's this about a snib?
- I'm off on study leave from school.

- Well! that's a fine wee holiday for you. And you just new back after Easter.
- It's not a holiday. The exams start next week.

I can't believe the resistance I'm meeting here. Why do I need to explain this? Surely every 21st century parent realises we need peace to study? Most parents nag themselves ragged trying to force their teenagers to study.

- I don't think locking them out sends a good message. You don't want them to feel excluded. If you explain I'm sure they'll leave you alone.
- They don't listen to me.

Marilyn calls Erin and Benny over.

- Kirsty has exams coming up. She wants you to be good and give her peace to study. Will you be good?
- Yes, Mummy. (Erin)
- Promise? (Marilyn).
- Promise. (Erin)
- What about you, Benny. Promise to behave and give Kirsty peace?
- Promise.

Marilyn grins at Benny. She ruffles his hair.

- Butter wouldn't melt, eh? I believe you, thousands wouldn't.

Benny giggles.

- Who wants to come for a lick of the custard bowl?

When they're all out Dad gives me a wry smile.

- It's always the same. Generation after generation. We were more crowded – four of us in a two room and kitchen.

Don't want to go into competition with Dad over whose childhood was more deprived.

- My wee sister wouldnae give me peace to study either – and I couldnae stop her pesterin me. I used to call her my "wee blister" and she called me her "big bother."
- Sure. Right hoot.

I go to the hardware store in the Parade and buy a snib with my pocket money. When I get home I realise it won't fit on the narrow bit of door cheek. Whoever designed the cupboard never foresaw that the clothes, books, crockery or whatever would want to lock themselves in. Back to the hardware shop for a hook and eye. After a struggle (my first ever attempt at DIY) I get it screwed on.

When I use it to exclude the wee darlings of course Marilyn gets on my case.

- Thought we'd agreed we weren't going to fit on a snib?
- I need peace to study. I'm not getting it. Dad? Please, Dad?

For once Dad backs me, in his mild way.

- I guess it does no harm for her to snib herself in when she wants to study.

The Wrath of Marilyn is suppressed. I get away with it.

Life after the hook and eye has a better quality. Now I've only got the Watchers to worry about.

Chapter 5: May

Opinion Poll *(Sunday Times)*:
YES 40%   NO 47%   DON'T KNOW 13%

Ewan

We've come a long way. Further than I would have thought possible. Considering the starting point, Glasgow's East End apathy …

- No interested.
- We're aw Labour.
- Ah don't vote.
- Ssh – ma Ma's no well.
- Ah've got visitors. Kin ye come back later?

… has been reinforced by a hailstorm of headlines:

The Telegraph: *The Home Secretary – "Britons would need passport to visit an independent Scotland." (25 March 2012)*

The Telegraph: *The Defence Secretary – "Scottish independence: Warning over 'weakened military.'" (14 March 2013)*

Scotland On Sunday: *Scotland to face pension timebomb after independence. (7 April 2013)*

Scotland On Sunday: *Alert over passports following YES vote. (14 April 2013)*

The Scotsman: *Michael Moore Secretary of State for Scotland – "Scottish independence an irreversible step." (18 September 2013)*

Every initiative of the Scottish Government is headlined 'SNP Government attacked for …' Then follow two columns of attacks by Labour, the Tories and the LibDems. After that a short description of the new initiative. The report finishes with a single-sentence rebuttal by an unnamed spokesperson for the SNP.

Gradually public interest perks up. Doorstep discussions lengthen:

- Ah support independence! Independence fur Shetland! Then they'd take away aw the oil an the SNP would drop this independence rubbish.
- If the UK Government stopped giein us the block grant where would we get the money to run the country?
- Ma hert has always wanted independence. Ma heid says we're too wee.

It's easier to demonise an individual than an idea and by 2014 the mainstream media Unionist consensus is focused on Alex Salmond. 'Fresh Blow for Salmond.' Independence is presented as his personal vanity project.

I go to a reunion with some folk from my old journalism course. A few of them have managed to get jobs in journalism. They tell me the oft-repeated headline 'Fresh blow for Salmond' is a standing joke amongst them. The buzz is that the Scottish editor of one of the English newspapers has been promised a personal bonus of £10,000 if NO wins. £20,000 if NO gets over 60%.

By the time 2014 storms its way in, the media has succeeded in personalising the debate. One way or another.

- Alex Salmond's never stuck.
- Too smug.
- Runs rings roon them aw.
- Mair charisma in his pinkie than …
- Too up issel.
- The newspapers fair have it in fur Salmond. Tall poppy syndrome – eh?

- Jist waants tae be King o the Scots.

John Curtice becomes a familiar figure on the screens, domed head and tight mouth, revealing the latest poll, analysing the latest poll, declaring what the latest poll might indicate. Or might not.

Four months to go. And all to play for.

* * *

Agnes

The flourish on aw the trees reminds me spring is sprung. Cherry trees bubblin like strawberry milkshakes; pink and white apple trees; crisp hawthorn.

Here's me oot ma front gairden plantin ma annuals.

Ma fingers ur no awfy green. Cannae grow nuthin fae seed. They've got tae be well on afore they're in the soil or they just never come up at aw.

So Ah buy the annuals in pots oot the gairden shop and set them oot in baskets an tubs an roon the borders in May when the risk o frost's past. Unless Ah waant tae shell oot fur a taxi it takes me fower different return trips on ma bus pass afore Ah collect aw the flowers fur even a perra totie wee squerrs like mine. Ah fill up wi wee gnomes and a crazy paving path tae add a bit colour ither times o the year.

The Gilchrists next door huv fancy containers. Terracotta vases that pit me in mind o the Mediterranean holidays Ah used to go wi pair Willie and wee Alasdair. They look right lovely in summer wi all the trailers growin oot o them.

Rab makes nae attempt tae plant flooers in the ground. He covers his two patches wi statues o Greek gods and the like. The ground itsel is tiled over. So he'll no be bothered wi snails the way I am.

The snails are uncontrollable. It's the damp climate. They

84

eat their wey through everythin. Their favourite's lupins but they also munch their wey through pansies, chrysants an dahlias. Ah used tae find them inside the hoose, tuckin intae pair Rosie's supper.

At night when Ah go oot wi the bins Ah'm crunchin wi every step. Ah feel sorry for them. Their wee horns and heids go in fast wi danger an then slowly oot again when they imagine the danger's past.

Ah've tried everythin: gravel barriers, traps made wi copper (copper gies them wee electric shocks even if it's no connected tae onything), traps made wi beer. Ah don't really want to kill them, but. They need the pansies for food. Ah only want them for decoration. So their need is greater than mine. Ah'm bigger, but. Might is right.

So Ah go roon the gairden every few weeks an pick aff aw the snails an pit them in a cairrier bag. Maist times Ah get aboot forty snails in wan go. Ah take them doon the railway embankment an turn the bag inside oot an shake them ower the wall on to the ground that runs by the track. Nae flooers there – no much herm they can dae. But if they're hungry enough there's grass an a few wee bushes. New life for them in a new country. Emigration.

Rab Gilchrist comes oot an sterts workin in his ain gairden. Plantin lobelia an tom thumbs an black-eyed susans in the Grecian urns. We exchange pleasantries aboot the continuin sunny weather. He says:

- Were you watchin the European election results?

- Eh … how wis it again?

Ah'm too ashamed tae say the European elections last Thursday passed me by. Forgot tae vote.

On ither Votin Days Ah ayeways turn up an dae ma bit fur Labour tae keep the Tories oot. Women an men huv died fur the right tae vote. An of course thur nae way onybody could help noticin this referendum that's on the noo.

But the European elections never seem as important. Couldnae tell ye who they all ur.

- In Scotland, two SNP, two Labour, one Tory, one UKIP. In the UK as a whole UKIP got more seats than anybody else.
- No logical, intit no? The Pairty that waants tae take us oot o Europe wins the European election.
- It's logical when ye see the amount o publicity they've been gettin on the box. UKIP that never saved a deposit in Scotland got 14 times the airtime of the Greens that have two MSPs – and 4 times the airtime o the SNP that are supposed to be runnin the country.
- Ye know a lot aboot it!
- I know, I know. I should get out more!
- Somebody musta went tae the bother o measurin aw that airtime.
- Some bunch of academics worked it out. It wis Alex Salmond that was sayin.
- Well, he's no unbiased hissel, is he?

That pits Rab's gas at a peep. Didnae intend tae kill the conversation but that's whit happens.

We go on diggin an delvin a bittie. The sun's that hot Ah'm wearin a straw hat. Ah'm lucky ma front gairden faces the West – gets the afternoon an evenin glow.

Ah try to think o somethin else tae talk aboot. No sae often Ah get the chance. Although the Gilchrists stay right across fae me Ah don't know them as well as Lorraine up the stair. Ah used tae babysit fur Lorraine when she wis workin irregular hours. Ah mind wee Angela wis a bit of a handful. Widnae dae a thing she wis telt.

But Ah'm runnin intae Rab mair these days since he got made redundant.

- Ye still workin up at the Citizens' Advice?

He's been daein that since gettin his jotters when they closed doon the bank. He gets tae advise fowk on debts an that. But Ah don't think he gets peyed fur it. He's probably runnin up debts of his ain.

- Aye. But I've somethin else on now. I've been taken on for the Commonwealth Games.
- Och Aye. Ah heard there've been a lot of jobs gaun therr.
- It's no exactly a job. It's for the Launch ceremony. I'm a dancer.

Ah straighten up an take a good look at Rab. Burly, bald, no much taller than me. Wee Glesca bachle. Ah picture him daen Nijinsky leaps aroon his Grecian urns.

- You know Marilyn and I go to the country dancing.
- So is she daein it at the launch an aw?
- No, she hasnae the time with workin an lookin after the kids. You've to go for rehearsals every week.
- Is it the kinna dancin ye've been daein? Country … ceilidh dancin?
- Nothin like it. I could show you. Though we're supposed to keep it secret so it's a surprise.
- Ah'll no tell onybody.

He pits his trowel doon an stauns up on his toes. Nose in the air. Waves baith his airms tae the right, then the left. Does it ower again, higher. An again, higher still.

- That's one of the steps. But I'll be wearin a rainbow coloured jumpsuit. Here! Is that no your cat? The one that got lost?

Ah look roon quickly. Fower month and aw thae posters an never a squawk. Ah've gave up on pair wee Rosie.

Paddin across the grassy bit towards us. Same colourin, right enough …

- Naw. That's no Rosie. Too fat.

- Well, that cat certainly seems to know you.

Sure enough. The cat lifts its heid. When it catches sight o me, it says 'Meow!' an picks up speed. The patches o grey an peach on its face are the same pattern as Rosie's though Ah cannae be sure.

You might look a cat or a person in the face every day for a year but it's still hard to keep the image in your mind once they're gone. Ah'd be nae use at an identity parade.

The cat comes through ma gate up tae me an winds itsel in aboot ma pins. Ah bend tae clap it an catch a glimpse o the collar. It's rubbed an faded but it could jist be red tartan. Afore Ah kin check if there's a name-tag the cat runs up ma path an jumps through the cat-flap intae ma hoose.

- Ye could be right, sez I.

* * *

Cindy

Ah go oot intae the lobby an keek through the peephole. Ah open the door on the chain.

- Got a parcel here for a Charlie Ross.

The postman again.

- Me! Ah'm Charlie! 'S mines!

He tries to squeeze his wee airms through the openin in the door.

- Haud oan.

Ah haud him back, shut the door, slip the chain aff an open it again. The postman makes me sign fur it. Ah hate signin papers, but ye cannae get by in life athoot it.

By the time Ah shut the door Charlie's awready tryin tae rip the paper aff. Ma hert's awready stertin tae thud. Ah look at the address and recognise the writin.

We get the box open. Fitba. Full size wan. Charlie's over it. Sterts tryin tae kick it aboot the hoose. He's still wee an no very good at it. He waants me tae show him how tae dae it. Play footie wi him. Gie him a gemme.

Ah make masel get up an kick it at him. But ma hert's no in it.

Ah keep gettin this panicky feelin, runnin tae the windae an lookin oot baith ends o the street. Ah'm livin on borrowed time.

* * *

Lorraine

Ewan has asked me to lead the leafletin team tonight because he's goin to a meetin of YES coordinators up the town. I gulp half my tea and pour the rest down the sink. Heave the bags that Ewan's handed in over my shoulders. Five on each shoulder. They're all navy blue wi the words 'YES Scotland' in white and they weigh a ton.

One's particularly heavy. Turns out it's no a YES bag at all. It's Angela's schoolbag, also navy blue. As I unfankle it from the others I see, stickin out of a jotter, an envelope addressed to myself.

Dear Ms Murphy

There will be a Fourth Year Parents' Night on Monday 7th April from 7.00pm until 10pm. This will be the last such event before the National Examinations.

We hope you can come along to discuss your child Angela's progress with her teachers.

James Reid

Head Teacher

- What's this? A Parents' Night six weeks ago!
- Sorreeee. Forgot to give you it.
- Now I've missed it!

Angela turns round. World-weary. Sweet sixteen goin on forty.

- All right! Don't get your knickers in a twist.
- But I wanted to discuss …
- Don't worry your wee self. Wouldn't have made any difference. The teachers in that school are all cretins.
- The letter was addressed to me! You had no right …

She's back on her phone. I want to have it out with her. I want to … Actually I want to chuck all the bags at her. But I'm already late for the leafleters. They'll all be waitin.

As they are. Four of them. Paul, Duncan, Margaret and Anne-Marie.

Anne-Marie asks

- Ewan no comin?
- It's me instead.

I heave the bags out of the boot and share them out. They're excited.

- Is it no magic the *Sunday Herald's* come oot supportin independence? (Anne-Marie)
- Nice front page too by Alasdair Gray. (Paul)
- Did you think they were gonnae come oot in favour? (Anne-Marie).

They look at me, their leader for the night. Their resident expert. I have no opinion. Don't read the papers, except occasionally online.

- Well, Ah'm no surprised. *Sunday Herald* wis the first to come oot and support the SNP back in 2007. The very weekend before the SNP won the election by one seat. (Margaret)

- D'ye think other papers'll come roon tae it an aw, noo? (Anne-Marie)
- It's diabolical that every single daily newspaper is against independence. Even though our Government and so many of the electorate want it. (Paul)
- Why d'ye think that is? (Anne-Marie)
- It's not just the bad headlines. It's the good reports they suppress. (Duncan)
- If we had the Press support for independence that Catalonia has, we'd be home and dry. (Paul)

We turn towards the tenements. Two of us on one side of the street, three on the other. Leapfroggin doesnae work wi closes. So Anne-Marie, Margaret and I keep count, every third close. Because we're no 100% reliable at counting, as we each enter a close we lay a copy of the newspaper somewhere around the close door. A sign to others we're inside.

The travellin people also left each other signals, to advertise the lucky doors.

Once inside a close I dump the heavy bag at ground level and mount the stairs. Leafletin is a mindless job and my thoughts drift to Angela.

Are all teenagers so hostile? So full o contempt? The ones I deal with at work are, but most o them come from unfortunate homes.

Here's me. Experienced social worker. I put the effort in: read the child psychology books, try to second-guess her every need. Prioritise bein a lovin mother to my only child. And I'm still a bloody failure.

Wish I had family to share the load. But my own mother died years ago. Angela's Dad jettisoned his first family. My brother Kenny takes; doesnae give.

Worryin about Angela, I forget to pick up the bag again on

my way out. The close door clicks behind me and I have to start ringin the bells all over again. They're no pleased.

* * *

Iqbal

Catriona pushes the printout at me.

- What do you think?

Terraced house in Scotstoun. Two reception rooms, three bedrooms. Front and back gardens.

- It's kind of far away.
- You're a grown-up. Time to cut the ties to Uncle Ali.
- I mean it's far out from the city centre.
- It's close to my parents.
- It's far from the Forge Market.
- It's not too far from my school.
- But it's Noor who looks after Bobby and Lena while you're working.
- My Mum can do it. She was saying she wants to see more of the children. I'm sure Noor would welcome a break from changing nappies.

I read the description. Estate agents make the most dismal slum sound like Balmoral. 'Truly stunning'. 'Rarely available'. We'd have to nearly double our loan.

- Are there no big houses in Dennistoun? What about the Conservation Area?
- They hardly ever come up. They really are 'rarely available'. Too many converted into bedsits.
- We've newly bought the people-carrier. How are we supposed to share it for outings if we're eight miles apart?
- Because of a car we're to go on living on top of each

other?

- Ali and Noor brought up three children in their flat.

The next stage in the journey looms. The journey which started when I drifted away from going to mosque. Stopped observing Ramadan.

That caused a stooshie. But not as much as marrying outside the community.

I think what hurt my Dad most was that by the time he got to know of Catriona's existence, I was already long-established as her partner to her family and the rest of the world. I'd kept my own family out the loop for years. Lied to them, even.

Just didn't know how they'd react. In fact the reaction would have been worse if the flat up Uncle Ali's close hadn't come up for sale at just the right time. My mother's younger brother would keep me in line. Leave me with a toehold in the culture.

Noor and Ali love their Bollywood movies. They go as a family to Asian events like the Kelvingrove Mela. They still speak Urdu to each other and sometimes to their children and mine. So Lena and Bobby get the chance to absorb it.

If we flit to Scotstoun what happens to their Pakistani side?

It's already diluted down the generations. My grandmothers spoke no English and my grandfathers only enough for business purposes. My parents were fluent with a strong accent. Ali, 12 years older than me, is comfortable in both languages. But my own spoken Urdu is shaky and my written Urdu non-existent.

- Listen, Iqbal. You Pakistanis want to live in each others' pockets. Women sharing kitchens. In amongst the third cousins four times removed. I want our children to grow up with space for them to bring their friends home and gardens they can play in.

We stare at each other. Two Glaswegians, glowering across Time and Space.

93

Kirsty

Bulk of exams over. Back to auld claes and parritch as my Grandpa used to say.

The Modern Studies class. Two dozen of the newly enfranchised and Mr MacQueen.

- What does it mean if somebody takes the Fifth Amendment?

At the back of the room, Nathan passes his phone to Sasha who looks into it, giggles and passes it on to Ashleigh.

- Come on, now! This has even become a saying in this country. "I'll take the Fifth Amendment." Who can explain what it means, and why?

Some look out the window. Some look into phones or at each other. A few look at Mr MacQueen. A couple look at the clock on the wall.

- Kirsty?

All eyes on me. I feel myself redden; fight it in vain.

- Sur? Mr MacQueen Sur?

Malky Nimmo has his hand up.

- Good. Somebody's done his homework. Well, Malky?
- How dae we get so much American politics?

Brief titter.

- That's not what I expected to hear! Anybody? The Fifth Amendment?
- Ah mean, how dae we no get Scottish politics?

Mr MacQueen turns his attention back to Malky.

- Are you serious?
- Aye, sur.

Malky frowns slightly.

- American politics are the most important in the world. The USA is the leader of the Western world. If you want to bury your head in Scottish politics go and read the Sunday Post ...

Chuckles from a few who've heard of the *Sunday Post*. Indifference from the rest.

- There's no place for xenophobia in the 21st century. Nobody out in the real world gives a Jings, Crivvens or Help ma Boab about Scottish politics.

He writes 'xenophobia' on the board.

- What's xenophobia? Anybody? Good Scrabble word! Starts with an "X"!
- But sur, we're huvin this referendum ...
- Gillian?
- Please sir, not liking foreigners.
- Good, Gillian. Did everybody hear that? Hatred or fear of foreigners.
- ... an some of us are gettin tae vote ...
- That's enough. So back to the original question. Malky and Kirsty don't know. Somebody tell them. Fifth Amendment?

At the back of the room Ashleigh and Sophie giggle together at Scott's phone and pass it back to Sasha, who passes it back to Scott.

* * *

Agnes

Ah'm sittin on the bed lookin at the wardrobe. The wardrobe door's ajar but no enough to see in.

Not a squeak. Right wee soldier.

Pits me in mind o ma ain time, doon the Rottenrow. Ah never made a fuss neither, but then Ah had human privileges. Gas and air. An Ah wis lookin forward to the wean at the end of it. Rosie husnae a clue whit's happenin.

Please don't let there be mair than two. Three at the maist. Ah picture my wee hoose wi four of them, countin Rosie, aw gettin under my feet. Five, even?

The tension's gettin to me. Ah dial Alasdair's number. Then Emma's. Baith go ower to voicemail. Ah dial Sheena's.

She picks up.

- It's me. How yese aw daein?
- We're good, Agnes. How are you?
- Fine. Could ye put wee Emma on?
- I'll see what she's up to.

She's gone a while.

- Emma's busy on her computer.
- Gonnae pit her on for a wee minute?

She's gone for a longer time.

- She's doing her homework.
- Gonnae tell her Rosie's huvin the kittens the noo? Ah mean this very minute. In the wardrobe.
- I'll let her know.
- She wis awfy keen for me to gie her a blow-by-blow account.
- Best not take her away from her work. Her GCSEs are coming up.
- Oh. Right well. Ah'll phone back when they're born?
- Well … OK then. Good night.
- Tell her …

Click!

- Ah'll post her oot pictures when they're born.

Silence.

Apart from the thrum thrum thrum o Lorraine's lassie up the sterr wi hur loud music.

* * *

Donald

Seven o'clock. The train whistles, starts movin. As it chugs under the bridge beneath our feet we position ourselves on each side of the stairs. Leaflets in hand.

The passengers are generally carryin something in at least one hand. A briefcase, a carrier bag, a phone.

No use offerin a leaflet to somebody with no hands free. It's counter-productive. If one person doesn't accept the leaflet, neither do those comin immediately after. Herd instinct.

Chris offers the leaflets in silence. I like a bit of flourish: a winnin smile and

- Save the Union.

Or

- No more borders.

Or

- Stop separatism.

Hard to judge which method is more successful.

The last stragglers emerge, accept our leaflets or don't. Chris says:

- That wis the 7 o'clock. Come an we'll call it a day. Nothin but total workaholics still on their way.

We stuff our remainin leaflets into our bags and make for my car.

- Can I give you a lift?
- I could murder a pint o heavy.

Because of my car, I'm on the orange juice. However, Chris's tongue loosens and he takes me a trip down memory lane.

- Biggest mistake: right at the start. Whit wis Cameron fuckin thinkin of, lettin Salmond choose the date? Huge advantage, man.

- Yeah. We were at 70:30 in the polls. We needed a quick campaign and an early date while we were still up there.

- It wis clear to all except him. Cameron knew fuck-all aboot Scotland then and he's learnt nothin since.

- Salmond's been obsessin about this independence game all his life. He worked out his strategy decades ago. The idea only crossed Cameron's mind when the SNP got their overall majority.

- Assumin he's got a mind.

- What he needed were better *minders*. They should have made him stick to his script.

We drink in silence for a few minutes. The wag-at-the-wa – a period feature – ticks away the minutes and the hours towards September 18th. Tickin away our lead, tick by tick, trickle by trickle.

- And wherr ur the folk we were lookin to for donations? The wan time the Tories coulda helped us oot and they've turnt their backs.

- You don't stay a millionaire by givin your assets away.

- Megabuck salaries to chancers wi big talk an good connections.

Obviously neither Chris nor I are on the Better Together payroll.

- Same story with the YES lot, though. I've heard Ewan girnin about it. Huge salaries wasted on managers who didnae even stay the course.

- Bonus culture. Nothin changes.

- For all they position themselves on the left.
- Hypocrites.
- An then you've got YES posturin as the arty side of politics.
- How d'ye mean?
- Yon National Collective crew – what are they like?
- Aw them! Up their ain arses.
- They wouldnae know a fiscal policy if they tripped over it on their way to the rave.

The irony. YES posturin as "creative and artistic".

I mind my first visit to London. I was overwhelmed by the colour. The joie-de-vivre. The cosmopolitans: five continents millin about the pavements. A million miles from the grey and black city I'd left. A city where joyless folk embraced a Christianity that would have made Jesus weep. Where they cleared the pubs at ten and tied the weans' swings up on a Sunday. Forced their own hypocrisy upon me and my kind.

Imagine turnin the clock back to all that.

We both sip moodily. I wish I'd taken Coke or Irn-Bru instead of orange juice.

- See yon White Paper?
- Ach. Facile crap from beginnin to end.
- Aye. When it came oot, the UK Government analysed it fur us and telt us wans in Better Together tae use the analysis as a basis tae attack it.
- And did you?

I wasnae involved last November when 'Scotland's Future' came out. I couldnae mind much about it after the initial build-up which went on for weeks. Damp squib, was my recollection. Useful as a door-stop.

- We hud a plan tae take the mickey. We wur gonnae pass it aff as a work o fiction. Gie it fake covers wi titles like 'The Lying, the Which and the Holyrood' and leave it lyin aboot in libraries and bookshops. It wis a brill idea.

- Imaginative. And humorous.
- Pure magic, man. Didnae happen, but. There wisnae the fundin. But they've the fundin tae promise big bonuses tae aw the BT staff if it's a NO vote.
- Wouldnae lose sleep over it. The White Paper sank under its own weight.
- Heh – could ye go anither?

Reluctantly I get him another round. I'm still on my first. This is Chris's third.

Chris grasps his fresh glass.

- Here's confusion to wur enemies. Smug Salmond and the SNP. Thae wee Greenies on their weird planet. Tommy rent-a-mob Sheridan.

He raised his glass towards me.

- An aw Tory cunts.
- Confusion to our enemies.

I clink glasses with him and drain the last of the lukewarm juice.

* * *

Kirsty

A wasp buzzes at the inside of the window-pane. With an ostentatious 'Waaaagggghhhh!!!!' Chantelle backs away from it, waving her arms, and colliding with Siobhan in the next seat.

- Any areas you'd like to go over?

Malky put his hand up.

- Sur, can we huv a debate aboot Scottish Independence?

- We're plunging into the Higher work and you're wanting to spend time on a debate. Well, here's hoping your grades in the Nationals reflect your confidence.

I put my hand up.

Cara: Just you keep out of it.

- But, Sir, we're all soon going to be voting about it for the first time in our lives and some of us don't understand the issues.
- If you want to know the issues switch on your televisions. Goodness knows there's very little else on the box nowadays.

A murmur ripples round the room, rising to a growl.

- We want a debate! We want a debate!

Mr MacQueen shakes his head, raises his voice a decibel or two.

- It's too controversial. We'll have everybody at each others' throats.

The period bell rings and we swarm out. Ahead of me, Chantelle's hanging with Angela and Kelly-Anne. Chantelle's saying:

- Hey. I know where yese can get forms to register to vote.

She spots me and breaks off. As I pass, they turn as one and give me the gimlet glare. I feel it freezing my back all the way down the corridor.

Chapter 6: June

Opinion Poll *(Daily Record)*:
YES 39%   NO 44%   DON'T KNOW 17%

Agnes

Rosie on her side. Eyes glazed in fulfilment. Four kittens suckin away, furry lips clamped. Three o them wi their eyes new opened. Wan still stuck shut. Their wee roond ears stuck on the sides o their heids. Their wee paws wi opposable thumbs. Moggies masqueradin as monkeys.

Another two lyin a bit away fae the heap. One suckin on a bit o Rosie's paw. The other starin into space, ponderin the meanin o life. Or death. Maybe in a coma.

It's the same pair no gettin it as last time. Wee grey fella and wan o the stripeys.

Ah pick them up. They're dull and wabbit. Hauf the size o the fower that are suckin away. Ah phone the vet for an appointment. Pack them wi a hot water boattle in the cat carrier.

She tells me they're 'failing kittens'. If Ah cannae dae somethin soon they'll be 'failed kittens'. She says Ah should bottle-feed them. She sells me some formula milk and a plastic dolly-bottle. I near die at the price. £13.90 for the wee boattle and £150 all told.

Comin up the path, Ah see Marilyn lookin at a two foot high thistle comin up at the corner of hur garden. No often they get weeds, wi it aw tiled over.

She shakes her heid when she sees me.

- Would you look at that. Sprang up overnight.
- Some size. Be a job pullin that oot.

- I'm not going to attempt to pull it out. I'll get Rab to clip it off at ground level with the secateurs.

Back hame Ah sterilise everythin in a pan o boilin water. Takes me back to when Alasdair wis wee. Whit a palaver with sterilisin solution, teats and bottles. Like a mad scientist Ah wis. Aw because naebody telt wee Ally he was supposed to suck at the breist. Couldnae get the message ower to him.

Ah fill up the boattle and test the temperature on my wrist, like in the old days. Ah pick up wan o the failin kittens. The grey wan.

This shouldnae be too hard. Craggy auld shepherds an orphan lambs. Last week the Prime Minister hissel did it on the telly wi an orphan lamb.

The kitten's wee arms spread in panic. His eyes bulge and his gumsy jaws open and shut. He acts the way Alasdair acted when I tried to get him to suck on the breist. Only insteid o howls, it's squeaks.

Ah take my chance when the mooth's open to shove in the boattle. He wullnae suck so Ah squirt. And hope it's gaun doon the right way. Droont in formula milk – whit a way for a kitten to fail.

Ten minutes later, here's me covered in bleedin scratches, the kitten covered in milk an still starvin, the boattle empty. A ring at the door.

Nice enough lookin fella.

- Mrs Agnes Morrison? You know there's going to be a referendum on Scottish independence?
- Aye. (Hope the milk didnae go doon the wrong way).
- My name is George and I'm here from the organisation Better Together. Do you have a couple of minutes?

Wis yon a wee gurgle or wis it a purr? Whit does a death-rattle sound like?

- Sorry, son, Ah huvnae the time. Ah'm tryin tae bottle-

103

feed a kitten.

- Oh, I have cats! Have you tried asking the Cats' Protection League? I found them very helpful.

- Here, Ah never thought o that. Ah'll need to get their number.

- I'll find it for you.

He footers aboot wi his mobile phone.

- There you are.

- Thanks. Amazin whit thae phones can dae.

I shut the door and hurry back. Ah write doon the number o the Cats' Protection so Ah don't forget it.

Referendum, referendum, referendum. It's aw ye hear thae days. Crowda nutters. As if Scotland wis rich enough tae get by on its own. Ye jist need tae take a dauner doon the road tae see how poor we aw are in this country.

* * *

Kirsty

Coming out of school, I try not to think about opening my latest emails.

Cara eggs me on: See me? I've got so many enemies I have to keep one step ahead at all times.

I give in.

'U will no get hame the night with Ur rubbish looks intact. No way Jose!' (Watcherinthesky)

'We know what way you go home. We'll be waiting.' (Watcheratyourdoor)

'U watch Ur back coming out of school.' (Watcherinyourbed)

'Naewhere to hide – Ur ginger nut gies U away.' (Watcherinthesky)

I look to all sides. Big dark sea as all the school uniforms spill out across the playground and through the school gate. I wonder who's looking back at me.

Cara's an old hand at dodging danger: Main threat's once you're isolated on the walk home. You might think a public road would be safe but trust me – they'll force you down an alley, through a close, into a back court, down an embankment.

I make for the back lanes. Duck round the corner and hover.

I might take a long detour. Hang out round by the four-in-a-blocks.

Cara: Bad idea. Mind what happened last time.

Two weeks ago I circumnavigated the four-in-a-blocks when I was running away from Chantelle. Or somebody who looked like her.

An old man standing in his path at the side door beckoned me.

- In here. Quick.

I dived in and he shut the door.

- In here.

He led the way into a living room overflowing with ornaments and furniture. Brass or glass plaques with worthy sayings. Photos of his family tree: backwards in sepia and forwards in colour. Children or grandchildren graduating.

I sank on to the sofa. Had Chantelle seen me going in here? The old man moved towards the kitchen.

- I've just made a wee cuppa tea.

Cara hugged in close: No such thing as a free lunch.

He came back eventually with a tray. I sipped my tea and wondered if Chantelle was still out there. I realised the old man was staring at me. Deep wrinkles in his cheeks. Rheumy blue eyes. Mouth slightly hanging, teeth too white, small and even to be natural.

- Ye've awfy bonnie hair, hen.

I laid my cup down and rushed for the front door. I looked out carefully. No Chantelle.

Cara's right. Not the four-in-a-blocks. I turn the other way. The Conservation Area.

If I'm too late home the Wrath of Marilyn will descend. She might even say there's no dinner left for me. She's pulled that one before.

Cara: At least you generally expect a dinner every day. I get fed last in my house and as often as not it's all gone before I'm served.

But if I go back to the street too soon I could run into … Even if I go back at all.

I don't want to go back at all.

Here it's quite pretty. You'd almost think you were in the country. Bumpy ground – hard packed earth with pebbly stones pushing through in places. Garages on both sides, lined with a mixture of wildflowers and escapes from various gardens. Clumps of foxgloves in full bloom. Masses of rose bay willow herb and orange day lilies ready to bud. Tangles of what will soon be brambles.

Was there something about '… the flowers that bloom in the lane …?' My mother's face. Her high voice singing.

A figure looms in the distance. Manky grey hoodie over torn denims, shambling towards me. Thank goodness; definitely not Chantelle and co.

Definitely male.

* * *

Ewan

In tenements you have to get past the security buttons on the

106

close before you ever see the bells on the houses themselves. You can leaflet in the mornings before work when some of the security buttons are still off but you can't canvass. Nobody wants to discuss politics while dashing out to the office.

I vary my preamble.

> 'Hello. I'm carrying out a survey about the referendum. Could you let me into the close, please? …'

> 'Hello. I'm delivering information about the referendum. Could you …?'

> 'Hello. I'm gathering people's opinions about the referendum. Could you …?'

Only very occasionally does someone refuse to allow you into the close. The stock response to a refusal depends on the reason given:

Scenario 1

- We're no allowed tae let strangers in because of security. Jist shove yer leaflets under the door.
- I can't do that. It would cause litter.
- Well, Ah cannae let ye in, son.
- OK. Thanks very much anyway.

Wait a few seconds and then press another bell, and if necessary a third. Someone will eventually open the door.

Scenario 2

- We're no interested.
- This is an important referendum. People are saying they want information.
- Well, Ah'm no caring.
- Maybe some of your neighbours want information.

At this point the door might open. If not, wait a few seconds and then press …

Scenario 3

- Whit side are ye fur?
- The YES side.
- We're aw "Naw" up this close.
- Really? You can speak for all your neighbours?
- Aye.
- OK. Thanks very much anyway.

Wait a few seconds and then press ...

Once inside you leave the heavy bag of leaflets at ground level taking care that it is neither near anyone's door nor likely to trip up folk passing through to the back court. You remember to lift it again before exiting the close.

Letterboxes. I could do a PhD on their ergonomics.

- The high, which make your satchel slip off your arm and scatter the leaflets on the landing.

- The low, which buckle your back or dirty your knees.

- The vertical, the horizontal.

- The embellished cast iron set into 19th century storm doors: slender slots shaped to the belle lettre, elegant copperplate and a whiff of old scent. These only take small stiff cards. Anything larger you have to roll up. Much easier to slide them under the door. There's plenty of room to slide stuff under time-warped storm doors.

- The letterboxes with draught excluders which chew up all mail. One technique is to roll the leaflet into a stiff tube. But this can make you drop all the other leaflets which blow away over the neighbours' gardens, losing you votes for every lawn they mar.

- Letterboxes sellotaped shut. These are found in the front doors of new builds exposed to the elements. One theory is that behind such doors lurks a Garboesque type who wants to be alone but can't afford the price of a desert island. Another theory is that it's just to stop them rattling in the wind – the resident would rather have silence and no mail than mail and noise. Acting on this second theory I soundlessly peel the tape back, insert the leaflet and stick it back.

- The storm doors which stand open, revealing inside front doors with no letterboxes. These doors are flush tight with no space to slide something underneath. You can leave the leaflets in the space between storm door and inside door (which is often already full of boots, shoes, telephone directories and junk mail) or trap them on the inside of the storm door's letterbox.

The dogs behind the letterboxes: the ambitious high yapper, the dangerous low growler, the silent surprise snapper. All ready to do their duty, to put the mail through the shredder, to take the fingers off the burglar, postman or canvasser. Some garden gates have a sign 'Beware Dogs Running Free.' Is this to stop you opening the gate and letting the dogs escape, or warning you that if you do go in you might be eaten? And if you get eaten will the owner still be prosecuted despite the fact that he warned you?

Doorbells. I know them all.

- The brass bell-pulls pealing from the entrails of the house, from long ago and far away. Alpine cows, village schools.
- The electronics: a few bars of 'See the Conquering Hero Comes'.
- Social work standard issue with a two-way speaker.
- Silent bells which leave you wondering.

The signs on doors: No hawkers. No door-to-door sales. No cold callers.

Is a canvasser a hawker if selling only a vision?

* * *

Malky

Gaun intae toon fae school, by ma usual folk-remembered pathways, Ah rounds a corner and sees a lassie hingin aboot in the lane. She goes neither back nor forward. Close up Ah see it's Kirsty Gilchrist. In ma class fur Modern Studies.

Passing, Ah take a shufty. She avoids ma eye. Turns away towards the hedge.

I mind whit Chantelle said.

- Ye waitin fur somebody?

She looks up at me in surprise.

- No.

I hover. She hovers. We baith hover.

She opens her mooth and thinks better of it. Then says it onywey.

- I'm trying to avoid some folk.
- Who?
- Don't know.
- Ye don't know who ye're tryin tae avoid.

A faint smile plays aboot Kirsty's lips.

Ah smile in empathy. Ah move closer. No bad-lookin efter aw. On the hefty side, but could be cuddly. Frizzy ginger hair, but her features are fine. Neat nose wi a cute sprinklin of freckles. Her eyes …

Tears are runnin doon her cheeks.

- Whit's up?

Ah drop my bag and try to put my airm roon her.

- It's just some folk. They're horrible. They send me nasty texts. They keep saying they're coming to get me …
- Who? Who's comin tae get ye?
- I know who they are. But …

- Huv ye telt yer maw?
- She wouldn't be interested.

Kirsty looks up quickly and drops her eyes again.

- She's not my real mother.
- Yer auld man then?
- No.

Show gallantry.

- Ah'll walk ye hame. Ye'll be safe wi me.

Again she shakes her head.

- One of them stays up my close.

I puff up my cheeks and blow.

- So ye're no keen tae go hame at aw?
- No.
- So who ur thae folk ye're talkin aboot?

Silence.

- No gonnae tell me?

Faint shake of the head.

Long pause. Ah go for it.

- Know whit? Ah'm no keen tae go hame either!

Ah've got her to look at me noo.

- Come an we'll run away thegither?
- What – you and me?
- How no?

Under her tears, an incredulous laugh.

- We don't know one another.
- Aye we dae. We've been in the same classrooms fur fower year.
- Yes, but …
- An Ah've fancied ye fur three.

The first porky. But it gets hur full attention.

* * *

Donald

Hurray! J.K. Rowling, who is a friend of Alastair Darling's, has donated £1,000,000 to Better Together. We're out of the woods for the moment.

Ewan tries to burst my bubble.

- You'll be relieved. Puts a gloss over the rest of the NO funders: arms dealers, tax-dodgers ...
- That's no fair. Who's the biggest YES donor? A homophobic bus millionaire!
- Actually the biggest donors are two innocent lottery winners with no personal agenda.

Although YES had film stars and singers at their launch, it seems to me that more of the great and good have come out for NO. Ewan and I argue about this.

- Brian Cox, Allan Cumming, Robbie Coltrane. All these luvvies who would do anythin for Scotland but live in it and pay their taxes into it.
- If you're in the film industry you have to live where the films are. That's Hollywood, not Holyrood.
- Or maybe Spain? Sean Connery?
- The celebrities who've endorsed YES were brought up here and know what Scotland's about. Most NO celebs couldn't find Scotland on the map.
- Ewan McGregor? Stanley Baxter?
- Zoe Wanamaker? Helena Bonham Carter?
- Susan Boyle? Still lives in Scotland.
- David Bowie? Mick Jagger?

In the end we're both shoutin out names and have totally

112

stopped listening.

Ewan shouts one last name at me

- David Beckham!

and runs out the room so he gets the last word. Childish.

I go down to Better Together to get my fix of crack with like-minded people.

Rebrandin can never go wrong. I find the place awash with new badges and stickers. Goodbye Better Together, hello NO Thanks. The 'NO' comes with a wee X inside the 'O' to remind folk that it's all about a vote. To me it's askin for a kiss. If I'm lucky, I'll maybe get one.

The NO Thanks stickers and badges are white on a blue background: Scottish credentials. There are other badges and stickers sayin 'NAW'. In case folk think London's callin all the shots. Patriotism good, nationalism bad.

Wonder what they paid the advertisin agency.

* * *

Agnes

The Cat Protection dame is at ma door in a jiffy. Help ma goodness – I've hardly even hung up the phone. Light o dedication in her eyes.

First she gies me a row. Everythin has a price.

- It was very irresponsible to let your cat get pregnant.
- Costs £100 doon the vet tae get her dressed. Ah've managed the past two year keepin her in when she's in heat, jist.
- Well, you didn't manage this time.
- She wisnae in heat at the time. Ah wis roon the back pittin oot the recyclables an she followed me like she does. But, here, it wis Hogmanay, an a big firework

113

exploded, an she took aff …

- You let her out while fireworks were going off! That's even worse!
- Ah know.
- Pets get traumatised by fireworks …
- Ah know.
- So how long was she missing?
- Fower month. Ah wis frantic – Ah stuck up notices and went roon the doors … Then here she appears walkin up ma gairden path. Ah wis that relieved …
- We offer a service to pay part of the costs of spaying cats.
- Ah didnae know that.
- You can also get her microchipped in case she strays again.
- My! The things they can dae nooadays!
- So as soon as the kittens are weaned, what do you do?
- Get her dressed.
- Right. Now let's see these kittens. This is what you do …

She takes the grey failure an haps him up tight in a dishcloth so only his wee face shows through. Like a nun afore they aw stertit wearin jeans. Airms an legs clamped inside. Swaddlin claes like the Baby Jesus. He opens his wee gumsy mooth tae shriek and she shoves the boattle in.

- You must feed these two kittens every hour on the hour. Day and night. Will you manage that or should I take them away? We've got volunteers who …
- Ah'll manage, thanks.

They're Rosie's kittens. No her kittens or ma kittens. Ah'm grateful fur the help, but she's got a fanatical glint. Ah'm no up fur a tug-o-love battle.

- It's marvellous the way wee Rosie cleaned up efter the birth. An she must be cleanin away aw the ...Ye'd never know there were kittens there.
- That's the idea, Mrs Morrison. When cats wash themselves all the time and clean up after their kittens, it's not about hygiene. It's because cats, unlike dogs, hunt by stealth. They sneak up on their prey individually. So there must be no smells to warn their prey.
- Here, Ah never thought o that. Ah just thought cats were naturally mair fastidious than dugs.
- So they are. But for a reason.

When she's finished, she lays the kittens back doon amongst their successful siblings. It's no clear tae me if they've taken ony milk in.

She draws up a wee chart fur me wi dates doon the left haun side and, alang the tap, the description o each kitten an its weight.

- You must weigh all the kittens every day. You should phone me and tell me their weights so I can keep an eye on them.
- Whit aboot hoose-trainin? Huv ye ony wee booklets...

Ah've hud cats but Ah've never had new-borns. Aw ma cats huv arrived fully litter-trained. Ah half expect hur tae say she'll move in wi me durin the toilet-trainin period.

- Don't worry. They're not like puppies. The mother will handle all that.
- Here, is that no marvellous!
- As I say – it's not about keeping your house clean. It's training them to hunt by stealth.

All this education and she didnae even charge me onything. Whit a service! Ah tell her Ah'll post them oot a wee donation.

After she's gone, Ah study the kittens in mair detail. Rosie's a bonny cat hersel: dilute tortie – grey, peach and white. The Daddy musta been a striped cat, and probably lang-haired.

Rosie's colours have separated oot in the kittens. So we've got Failin Kitten Number Wan in a lovely soft grey. He's ma favourite. Think Ah might keep him if he survives.

Caw him Bertie efter the very first cat Sandy an me ever had. He wis grey an aw. Wur first pet. Followed us hame in the snow fae school wan day. Jist a wee totie kitten. Ma mammy wisnae keen but we persuaded her. He wis a great wee cat. Followed us aboot when we were oot playin. We were that proud o him. Hertbroken when he got run ower by a coal lorry.

Then there's wan wee marmalade boay, a white yin wi a patch o orange that looks like he's gonnae be lang-haired, and three in a broon stripe, wan of them lang-haired. The stripes go different weys – two of them are the thin straight tiger stripes and wan has the kinna stripes that go in a whorl like a bull's eye.

Ah'm no gonnae gie ony o the others names in case Ah get too fond o them.

* * *

Kirsty

We walk a long way east. On the way we stop at a corner shop. Malky buys a big bottle of Irn-Bru and a pie.

- Whit ye efter? Ah'll treat ye.
- I'm not very hungry.
- Ye will be the night.
- Oh. I never thought … All right.

The night?

Implications. Am I ready for this?

116

I pick a pack of tuna sandwiches and a bottle of water.

Malky leads the way. I follow. No idea where we're going. Road leading towards a housing scheme.

On the right, low-rise four-in-a-blocks.

On the left, wire fences of varying heights, mesh and densities.

Notice: **Safedem Demolition Site. Keep Out.**

Behind the fences an open space of rubble: broken stones, broken bricks. Mostly flattened, up at the back rising into a mound. Here and there a blade of green struggling through: slightly more than you might find on the surface of the moon.

Towards the horizon: five cuboids loom into the clouds. Four on end, one on its side. Three concrete grey, two the shade of a blood orange.

Red Road.

- Aye. We steyed here when Ah wis wee.

He points to one block.

- That wan's still full of asylum seekers. The rest are empty. An they blew some up.
- Terrorists?
- Aye, right. Naw, it wis the cooncil.
- Sounds dangerous. Was anybody …
- No this time. An the asylum seekers are still livin in their block, paddin up an doon thon wee path ower err. But we're gaun in a different block.

More notices set at intervals along the fence separating the doomed blocks from the survivor with its curtained windows.

These Premises are protected by Security Scotland Ltd.

- We're not …

I bite off the bourgeois word 'allowed'.

- Trust me. Ah know weys intae everywherr. Ah know

fower different weys intae here. Ye can go roon the back o the church by the Chinese. Or in atween the shops an the bookies. Or roon behind the pub. Or in by the workies' huts. Or in atween the weans' nursery an the auld folks' club.

A jaunty half-smile.

- Ah know wherr the CCTV is an aw.

We come upon a sign: the **Alive and Kicking Club**. Next to the nursery school.

- Auld fowk huvin their tea-dances next door to the weans daein their Wheels on the Bus. Haill lifespan within twinty metres.

I smile. He's funny.

- We sclim the palin here wherr it's lowest.

He leads me to the spot, throws our schoolbags over, makes his fingers into a stirrup. Up and over I go and he follows.

- On this side ye've a choice o scenic routes. Ye kin go ower the grass, ower the boulders, or ower a nice wee path. Comin?

He holds out his hand.

I don't take it.

Round the backs, down the dunnies, through the ventilators, underpasses, flyovers: the secret paths known only to the Concierge and the wee boys who used to help the Concierge. Up close the coloured blocks are structurally grey like the others, only veiled in red netting.

- Like the netting you get on the wee punnets of fruit.
- We never buy fruit. We're neds.

One door is missing some screws. He yanks it open and we squeeze into a dark, dank concrete vestibule. He calls Cuckoo! and the sound bounces back.

- When they first built thae flats there wis nae sterr. No

on the landins, onywey. There wis a sterr comin oota people's hooses but if ye were a visitor ye hud tae use the lifts.

- What if there was a fire?
- There wis, sometimes. Loadsa vandals 'n that. An the flats wur made o steel cannibalised fae the railways Dr Beeching hud jist closed doon. So they wurnae as fireproof as ither blocks o flats. They hud tae stuff them full of asbestos.

I clutch my throat.

- Is it OK tae breathe?
- Naw! Here, did Ah no mention? Ye've tae haud yer breath!

Malky laughs.

- Ach, Ah'm kiddin ye oan. Ah'm in an oot aw the time an Ah'm still here.

Up all the stairs – pech pech pech …

- Good joab thur sterrs on the landins noo – ye cannae use the lifts wi nae electricity.

… to the 31st floor. Up to a flat where the steel seal was peeled back and whose door Malky opened with a key.

- We steyed here till three-fower year ago. The rest o ma faimily throw stuff away. See me – ah keep everythin.

A sleeping bag and a duvet. A pillow. Pieces of crumpled clothing. A camping light. A torch. A camping stove. A pan. A mug. A plate. A pail.

- Right wee home from home.

Cara: He's planned all this in advance. Check the emergency exits.

- Thur aw mines. Ah come here when Ah cannae hack it at hame. Ye can stey aw night. Naebody'll think to look here.

Cara: That's why you should be worried.

He laughed.

- Thur even a cludgie. Through therr. Disnae flush, but. Mebbe ye'll no waant tae use it. See if ye need, Ah kin brekk ye intae wan o the ither hooses. We kin huv wan each. Work yer wey roon them aw.
- I'd be scared to stay here on my own.
- Did Ah say Ah wid leave ye? Ah'm here for the long haul.

He slips his arm casually round my shoulders. Gives me a light squeeze. Takes it away again.

- But they'll wonder where you are.
- Listen. Ah've goat two brithers. Three big boays gaun radge in a three-apartment. Whenever wan of us is AWOL ye kin hear Ma's cheers in China.
- My lot'll wonder where I am.
- Ur they gonnae brekk their herts aboot it?

Malky sits on the floor with his back against the wall. He pats the floor beside him and holds out the bottle of Irn-Bru.

- Waant a swally?

* * *

Donald

Midsummer Day. For once not just maximum daylight hours: blazin sun in a blue sky from dawn till dusk. As have been all the days of this optimistic year. The very clouds in the sky are biased towards YES.

It's Gala Day. Sportin a red 'NAW Thanks' rosette I get caught up in a brilliant line snakin its way along the Parade. Floats. Men on stilts – a giraffe and an ostrich. Weans dressed as animals. Ducks. Conga dancers. Pipe band.

Glasgow City Council, majority Labour and pro NO, have put this on. Funded it, created it, chosen the participants.

But as the parade rocks 'n' rolls its way towards the park my heart sinks. In the park entrance, outside the gates so they don't have to pay for a pitch: a big pop-up YES stall.

Free pens, gonks, wee saltires. YES Balloons on sticks, your choice of colour. Every wean carryin one off is a walkin advert for the rest of the day.

Grinnin activists engagin the passers-by in conversation, offerin a selection of leaflets glossin over all the aspects of independence which have ever scared the shit out of you.

A young girl prancin about with a penny whistle and another on an accordion.

How bloody Bohemian.

I'm tempted to challenge them, to ask them if they've permission, to threaten to have them moved away. But this would label us NOs party-poopers.

How did YES steal all the good stuff? Why has NO let YES align itself with summer, creativity, peace, social conscience, compassion, laughter and music?

There are plenty of positive reasons for keepin the UK intact. It's no about whether Scotland is wee, poor and stupid. It shouldnae be a choice between two evils.

The question should have been 'Do you wish to preserve the integrity of the United Kingdom?'

We should have appropriated YES.

* * *

Malky

We're sittin on the flair side by side. Boattle o Irn-Bru between us. Gettin tae know wan anither. Huvin a lassie here wi me in ma den pits me over the moon. If we hud

121

a chandelier Ah'd swing on it. But Ah keep ma glee under control.

- You said you all stay in a two-bedroom house?

- Ah sleep wi ma brither Stevie in the big bedroom. Ma brither Gordo sleeps in the wee bedroom. An the auld dear sleeps on a camp bed in the livin-room.

- Must be rubbish for your mother. I sleep in the walk-in cupboard in our living-room. But at least I've got a door.

- Ye sleep in a cupboard! Like Harry Potter!

- Probably bigger. There's space for a single bed. It's not under stairs. So a flat ceiling.

- Wherr dae ye keep yer claes?

- I get to use a corner of the wee ones' wardrobe.

- How does yer auld man no buy a bigger hoose?

- When I was wee there was no need. Then after he got his redundancy there was no money.

- Yer Maw's workin, but.

- Marilyn, you mean. She's a nurse but only part-time. I know it's a struggle for them to pay the mortgage. What about you? Could your mother not put in for a bigger house?

- She's on the waitin list, but thur a shortage o five-apartments.

- No sign of Gordo moving out?

- Why should he? A regular landlord wid expect rent. Which he's no peyin the noo.

- Well then, would it not be better for one of you boys to sleep in the living room?

- Whit – an Gordo shares a room? Let me explain aboot peckin orders.

- You're teaching your granny. I passed my Higher

Hierarchical Studies when the world was young.

She rests, eyes closed, back against the wall. Ah take in her profile. Waist could be slimmer, but nice knockers. Her legs ur hauf bent an hur school skirt has slipped back tae show the shape o hur thighs under the black tights.

Ah gie full rein tae ma imagination.

Haud on, but. Wan deviant in ma faimily's enough.

- Whit age ur ye?
- Fifteen. Why d'you want to know?

Whit can I say?

- So ye wullnae huv a vote in this … thingmy … this referendum?
- I will, if my Dad minds and registers me. My birthday falls on the actual date.
- Ye're kiddin! 18th September?
- That's it. Virgo.
- Whit ye say?
- Virgo.
- Och aye. Yer star sign.

Dare Ah?

- Ah thought ye were referrin tae yer status therr!
- Status?
- Naw. Forget it.

Talk aboot somethin else. Back tae politics.

- By the way, ye don't need tae wait fur yer auld man tae register ye tae vote. Ye jist fill up a form yersel, noo. Ah done it last week.
- You know a lot about politics.
- No really. Only got intae it last year. Afore that Ah couldnae a telt ye the name o the Prime Minister. Didnae even know there wis a Parliament in

123

Edinburgh. Ah knew aboot evolution an revolution, but Ah'd never heard o devolution.

- So what changed?

- Ah got intae thae websites. Thur a haill lot o them, noo. Pittin oot the info the London Government waants tae hide fae us. Right eye-opener. Ye heard o the McCrone Report?

- No.

- When they discovered oil in the North Sea back in the '70s the Government commissioned a report aboot it. The report said an independent Scotland would be wan o the richest countries in the world. An ye know whit they did? Slammed a 30 year secrecy order on their ain report. An went on tellin us aw Scotland wis poorer than Bangladesh.

- Who said we were poorer than Bangladesh?

- The Secretary of State for Scotland. Wur Governor-General. Onywey. Last year Ah got the bus to Edinburgh an went on this big independence rally. Pure magic, man. 30,000 therr wi banners an music an everythin. Heid o the mairch reached the tap o Calton Hill afore the back o it stertit aff alang the Royal Mile.

- Edinburgh's a beautiful city. I've been there a few times with my family. We've been to events at the Fringe. You know: the Edinburgh Festival Fringe.

- Ah've heard o the Edinburgh Festival.

- Biggest cultural festival in the world.

- Ah didnae know that.

She turns and smiles at me.

- You teach me about politics and I'll teach you about culture.

Ah slide alang the flair till we're touchin each other. Lightly. Ah'm fully aware o aw the points o contact. Calves, thighs, hips. Ah slide ma airm roon her shouthers. Her hair's saft against ma airm. Ah rub a few strands atween ma fingers.

- Thur loads o things we can learn fae wan anither.

But hur mind's awready back in Edinburgh.

- How many cities have a street with a castle at one end and a Parliament and a Palace at the other? And loads of interesting wee closes up the Royal Mile.
- The Indy Rally wis ma first time therr. Blew me away. Never knew thur wur places like that in Scotland.
- Scotland's full of lovely places. We rent a holiday house every year in a different part. Up the Highlands, Skye, East Neuk of Fife …
- That reminds me. D'ye hear aboot them movin the sea border?
- How do you mean?
- They just done it. Two weeks afore the Scottish Parliament got set up, the UK Parliament shoved the sea border between Scotland and England on the east coast further north. So the haill sea fae Dundee southwards an all its oil belangs noo tae England.
- Is that allowed?
- Who's tae stop them? The SNP tried tae get it overturned. But the Scottish Government is under the authority o the UK Government. They can dae whit the hell they like.
- I never thought of it that way. I mean, we're not like … China or Saudi Arabia. We're a democracy.
- Aye. Rule o the majority. But whit if ye're wan o a permanent minority that votes a different wey? Heads oot a different road? Ye know, wance ye stert seein Scotland that wey, ye cannae see it ony ither wey. Stauns oot a mile. Ye wunner how ye ever missed it afore.

- Like sex.
- Whit?

Sex an politics. We're bouncing them aff wan anither like ping pong balls.

- Can you mind a time when you didn't know sex existed? When you didn't know what happened – how babies were made.
- Wi two aulder brithers? Naw, sorry, Ah cannae.

Ah snigger a wee bit, no sure wherr this is gaun.

- I can. I was late finding out. They were all laughing at me at school. But once I knew about it I wondered how I ever missed it. It's all over the internet, it's in adverts, in magazines, films, books and the theatre. It's all over the telly, it's in jokes and conversation.

Noo that she's brought up the subject o sex Ah shouldnae miss ma cue. Ah've opened her eyes tae the political Establishment an their nefarious weys; maybe Ah kin open her eyes the same wey tae me. Ah squeeze her shouther. Coorie in a bit mair. Bring ma face closer tae hur cheek.

- Shower o ratbags, laughin at ma wee Kirsty. Jist because yer heid's no full o dirt, because ye're a nice innocent …

She pulls away. Turns and faces me. Her lips are temptin. Pink, full an soft. But Ah manage tae look her in the eyes. Grey and grave.

- It was ignorance, not innocence. And sex isn't dirty.
- Ah didnae mean sex wis durty. Ah don't think sex is durty at aw.

She's quiet for a bit. Ah gradually regain the lost ground in squeezin her tight. But when she speaks she's back on the politics.

- What you said the other day, asking Mr MacQueen if we could discuss the referendum …

- Och aye. Here's them rammin America doon wur throats and ignorin this big thing happenin right here right now. They moan aboot low turnoots at elections and then they ban us teenagers fae discussin wur ain politics. 'Sno real.
- Maybe they want us to be apathetic.
- Ye reckon?
- If voting ever changed anything they would ban it.
- Heh, that's brill, man! D'ye make it up?
- No.

The sun glints red through the window. Within the room wur ain two shaddas reach across the dusty flair tae the opposite wall. Ah stand up and reach fur her haun.

- Come an we'll watch the sunset fae the verandah?

Two of the nearby blocks graze the clouds but wur ain block stauns under nothin but the blue sky.

At ground level the people an cars are ants. Beyond, we can see ower the sweep o city roofs and roads and then, further oot, the span o the Erskine Bridge and the jagged peaks o Arran.

- Ye heard o Standin Stanes?
- Like what the Picts and Druids or whoever put up? I've seen them! In Orkney, on holiday …
- Thur Standin Stanes ower therr at Sighthill.
- You're joking! Ancient ones?
- Naw. Pit up aboot 40 year ago as a job creation scheme. Thatcher came in an axed the money but they're still therr. An aw thae auld hippies that think they're magic come crawlin in aboot them on Midsummer's Day.
- Can't make them out. But it's still a great view.
- Fae the verandahs oan the other side o the block ye can see the Campsies, so ye can, an Ben Lomond.

127

- See Dumgoyne, the bumpy one at the end of the Campsies? Well, I've climbed it.
- Didnae know ye were intae hill-climbin.
- I didn't go up all the way under my own steam. Some of it I got a coal-carry from my Dad. Poor Daddy was peching away with the weight of me! And then coming down Mummy and Daddy slid down the grassy slopes on their bums. Dad held me in front of him.
- Sledgin!
- It was when my Mummy and Dad were still together.

She starts to look sad. Ah say

- Waant tae see somethin my brither Gordo done when we lived here?

Ah climb ower the balcony rail. She gets worried. Tries to hang on to me.

- Don't …
- It's OK.

Ah wedge ma feet under the spar on the ootside o the ledge wi my hauns grippin the tap spar.

- Now, look …

I let go my right hand, then grip the spar again. Then Ah let go the left hand and grab the spar again. Then Ah let go baith hands and as Ah fall backwards intae nothingness, quickly grab the spar again wi baith hauns.

- No! Don't! I hate it! Come back over!

She's nearly greetin. Ah feel pleased that she cares so much whether Ah live or die. Ah climb back an gie her a quick hug.

- Only difference: Gordo used to clap his hauns when he let go afore grabbin it again. He could clap three times. Some ither boays managed to get in fower claps. Drove Gordo mental.

- Did you ever do that? Clap?
- Naw, Ah wis a feartie. Ah'd never make a gang leader. The only brave thing Ah ever done wis dreepin doon fae oor balcony tae the wan below. But even then Ah could only dae it if Ah hud two them hauden ma hauns at the top an a couple o them pullin me in at the bottom. An Ah hated it.
- So why did you do it?
- Because if Ah didnae they'd caw me a wee poof.
- You're like savages!

I stop feelin pleased.

- How?
- Holding your lives cheap. Risking everything to show off. No thought for your whole lives ahead of you. Just the thrill of the moment.

She thinks Ah really am a ned. So Ah say

- Never gied me much of a thrill. Much reyther no huv hud tae dae it. Wan game Ah did like wis "Chap door run away".
- That sounds harmless enough. Still a nuisance to your neighbours.
- We used tae tie the opposite door haunles thegither across the landin an chap them baith an then shoot the craw doon the sterr. Neither o them could open their doors.
- That's awful! They could be stuck there for days!
- Na. Maist o them hud phones.

She's lookin at me a funny way. Like seein me fur the first time. No clear if she likes whit she sees. Ah thought aw lassies went fur brawn. Gordo beefs up at the gym an sprawls oot on wur balcony tannin his pecs an he never goes short. As me an Stevie, through the wall fae him, can testify.

But maybe the classy lassies go mair fur brain.

- Ah love lookin at aw thae different buildins. Ah wisht Ah could be an architect when Ah leave school, so Ah dae.
- Why can you not?
- Awfy lang trainin. Don't fancy bein skint fur aboot nine year.
- That's longer than it takes tae be a doctor.
- If a doctor gies ye the wrang pills he kills wan patient. If an architect's buildin faws doon he kills hunners.
- Never thought of it like that.
- Whit aboot you, when you leave school?
- University, I suppose.
- To dae whit?
- Dunno.
- An whit aboot when ye leave university?
- Dunno.

Ah point to the sky.

- Therr's wur sunset.

Wan of the best sunsets ever. Pink and grey and red. Streaky bacon sky. The high rises silhouetted, windows flashin gold. The night racin ower the low-rises fae the horizon.

- The sky's blushing.
- It looks mad.
- What's it mad about?
- Aboot … thae lassies that are efter ye, and aboot yer auld man makin ye sleep in a cupboard …

She smiles. Her lips part. Nice white teeth.

- I'm not significant enough to drive the sky mad.
- … and aboot the teachers keepin us in the dark aboot politics. In case we stert an insurrection.

- I'd like to start an insurrection.
- Aye. Wid be a right laugh.

The wind moans past wur ears. A gust tangles wur herr and flaps wur very cheeks. This is the wey Ah like it. Facin doon the elements. But Kirsty folds her airms and shivers.

- Ye cauld?
- I always feel sad at the end of a sunny day.
- That's Scotland fur ye. We never know if we'll get anither.
- I feel I've wasted it when I should have done something special with it. Something I couldn't do on an ordinary day.
- Is runnin away no somethin special?
- Don't need the sun for that. I've done it on a rainy day.
- Ye've run away before?
- Don't want to talk about it.

Winnin hur confidence. First goal on the Kirsty Gilchrist project.

- Come an we'll dae somethin special again the morra?
- If it's nice.
- It will be.

Ah get to put ma airm roon her. Jist lightly. She disnae pull away. Wi my thumb I stroke the skin on her wrist where it comes oot her sleeve. Smooth as silk.

The wind gets wilder. The street lights aw come on at once, flickery pink then steady yellow. Lights stert to come on in the low hooses. Kirsty goes inside again and Ah follow.

- Did you mean it when you said we could stay here all night?

She looks doubtfully at the raggedy bundles on the flair.

- Aye! Ah'll show ye ...

Ah bustle aboot. Switch oan the campin light. Make it homely.

- See: you can huv the sleepin bag. Ah'm fine here wi the duvet.

She's still staunin there, lookin at the sleepin bag. Lookin at me.

- Jist to be clear …

I feel masel gettin a riddy.

- There'll be nae cairry-oan. Ah'm no gonnae … unless ye waant tae … it's no that Ah don't think ye're … Ah mean ye're a wee babe …
- That's all right, Malky.

She lays her haun on mine and smiles. Ma airm tingles.

- I trust you.

A glow goes all ower me. She trusts me. The glow (ironically, in the circumstances) reaches ma loins and Ah turn quickly away.

Thur nae heatin in the place and so in the event we cuddle up close aw night. She's in the sleepin bag an Ah'm happed in the duvet. Baith fully clothed. Nae body contact. But Ah get tae wrap ma airms roon hur an haud hur tight. Ah keep them that wey even when Ah get pins an needles. It's the best night Ah ever spent in ma life. Even though Ah'm still awake by the dawn chorus.

* * *

Agnes

Into the pan again wi the bottle. Ah turn on the gas. While it's boilin Ah look at the clock. Aye, she'll be hame fae school by now. Ah dial Alasdair's number. He picks up.

- How ye daein, son?

- Very busy, Ma. I'm completing a website that's got to be in by Monday.
- Och, Ah'll no keep ye. Could ye pit wee Emma on? She waanted tae know how the kittens were gettin on.
- Hi Gran.
- Hello, pet. How's things?
- Fine, Gran. I'm busy on Facebook just now.
- Ah'll no keep ye, hen. But ye waant tae know aboot the kittens?
- OK. How are they?
- Ah'm huvin tae boattle feed the two wee yins. The Cat Protection wummin showed me how tae dae it.
- Cool.
- But it's awfy hard. Ah don't know if thur ony mulk gettin intae thur wee mooths …
- Why can't their mother feed them?
- Because thur too many kittens an no enough workin nipples. The wee yins get shoved oot the wey.
- You should take the big ones away sometimes and that would let the little ones get a chance.
- Heh, that's a great idea! I'll maybe dae that! Ah never thought o that!
- OK.
- Ye're a clever wee lassie, thinkin o that. Ah never …
- I have to go, now Gran.
- Right, Ah'll no keep ye. Here, Emma …
- What?
- Ah'll send ye pictures o the kittens.
- But you don't have a computer, Gran.
- Naw, I mean Ah'll take pictures on ma camera and when they're developed Ah'll get copies made fur ye

an post them tae ye.

- Well … that sounds a lot of trouble. Don't bother if it's too much work.
- It's nae bother, hen. Ah know ye'd love tae see them. They're bonnie wee things – wee baby faces an big eyes …
- Cool. I really have to go now, Gran.

Ah get oot my camera. As Ah aim it and try to get an angle that shows their wee expressions Ah wonder what Emma must look like now. How long is it since Ah seen her, or even a picture of her? They didnae come up the past few Christmases – they went to Sheena's folks in Inverness instead. Ah used tae go doon tae them in summer sometimes, but the last couple o summers they've went foreign holidays instead.

Emma must be quite grown up noo. They change so fast over the years.

Ah waste a couple of exposures when the kittens move at the wrang time. Awfy hard gettin aw six to stay still. Except when they're asleep. But Ah waant them wi their eyes open. Whit if Ah take them wan at a time? But that would use up six different exposures. Ah've only goat eight exposures left oan the film.

Thur a knock at the door. It's wee Bina Akram fae up the sterr. She's haudin a covered bowl in her hauns.

- Chicken Biriyani.
- That's lovely, hen. Tell yer Mammy thanks very much but she shouldnae go tae aw this bother.

Her Mammy's always handin in plates o food tae us. It's usually curry but very nice. No as burny as thon curry ye get in the restaurants.

Ah think the Usmanis an the Akrams are the same big faimily. Aye in an oot o wan anither's hooses. The weemin seem tae cook thegither for the haill faimily and quite often thur food left over.

Either that or they think Ah'm a pair sowel needs feedin up.

Wee Bina's wrinklin hur nose.

- There's a funny smell, Mrs Morrison.

Right enough. Soarta chemical.

The boattle! Ah rush intae the kitchen. Lay Noor Akram's curry on the table.

The pan's dry an burnin. The boattle an the teat are black puddles in the middle o the pan. Ah pick it up and rush wi it tae the sink. Ah pit it doon an turn oan the cauld waater. It sizzles. When the pan's full Ah turn aff the tap and belt back tae the door.

- Ah've been boattle-feedin kittens and Ah've went an meltit the bottle.

- Kittens! Gonnae let me see them?

The kittens are lookin their best, all eyes open.

- Why are these two so wee?

- That's why Ah'm boattle feedin them, hen. Tryin tae get them tae grow.

- Can I get one of them? To keep?

- You certainly can, Bina, once they're bigger and if yer Mammy lets ye. In fact if ye waant ye can huv two.

When she's gone Ah go back to the pan an lift it up. Here, does the surface o the sink no come away with it. See thae plastic sinks.

Ah spend hauf an hoor tryin tae scrape the remains o the boattle aff the pan. Don't know if it wid be safe tae use again. Whit if the plastic's poisonous? Ah look back at the sink. Big ring on it where Ah dumped the pan. Ah rub away at it wi a Brillo pad tae nae effect.

Marked sink. Spoilt pan. Destroyed baby boattle that cost

£13. Kittens still famished. No a successful result.

Ah go ben the bedroom and look at the cats again. The usual suspects sookin away. The two failures – wee grey fella and stripey girl – kicked intae a corner, lookin fatalistic. Lookin fatal.

Ah reach in an pluck two o the big wans aff their nipples. They let go wi a smackin noise. Ah pit them in the cat carrier an shut them ben the bedroom wherr Rosie cannae hear them squeakin. Ah pit Bertie an his wee striped sister on their Mammy. They clamp on an stert tae sook.

* * *

Malky

Kirsty's footerin wi her phone.

- It's run dry.
- Gie's it. Ah'll charge it up at hame. Gordo's got loads o different chargers in his drawer.

She hesitates.

- I don't like being without it. Promise you'll bring it right back?
- Swerr tae God.

It's in a pink case, wi wee stickers all over it: hearts and flowers. Ah nearly ask her if there's a password but stop masel in time.

Back hame Gordo's bedroom door's plastered wi threats. Skull an crossbones fae when he wis 12. A radioactive sign fae when he wis 15. Mair genocidal stuff fae noo.

Ah listen at the door. Knock. Wait. Open wi caution. Empty. I go ower tae his drawer an stert rummlin through the fankle o cables.

So many phones. Up-to-date phones, oot-the-ark phones, smart phones an stupit. So many chargers. First few don't fit.

- Whit ye daen in here, ye wee bawbag?

Fuck. Gordo, burstin in on me.

- Whit's that ye've goat?

Double fuck.

- Gie's it.

We struggle, wrestle, roll on the flair and predictably he gets it aff me.

- Heh, this is a lassie's phone. Ye girlfriended up?
- Naw. Gimme ...
- Or is it yer ain, ye wee poofter, ye? You'll never have a burd. It's a bumboay you're efter ...
- Gie's it!

Last hopeless grab. Gordo belts me wan on the gub, sends me intae orbit.

- Ah'm gonnae find a charger for this phone an see whit's on it. Ah'm gonnae find yer innermost secrets, ya wee tranny!

He waltzes oot wi Kirsty's phone in his pocket.

Ah sink doon in despair, blood drippin oot ma burst lip aw doon ma T-shirt.

* * *

Rab

A policewoman and a policeman on the couch. Marilyn and I on chairs with Benny on Marilyn's knee.

- So she's been missing since Friday. Would you say running away was out of character?

Marilyn and I speak together:

- Pretty much. (Me)
- She does have form. (Marilyn)

The policewoman looks from me to Marilyn and back again.

- She's run away a couple of times. (Marilyn)
- But that was long ago. (Me)
- How long ago? (Policeman)
- Four, maybe five years ago. (Me).

The policeman scribbles in his notebook. The policewoman says:

- How long was she missing and where did she go?
- The first time she was eleven. She was only missing for two days. She was found hiding in one of these unused committee rooms in the City Chambers! (Marilyn)
- Well, that's doing it in style! (Policewoman)
- I said to her maybe there was a political career in store for her! (Me)
- Yes, you made her think she'd done something clever. (Marilyn)
- I wis just so relieved to find her. (Me)
- And the second time? (Policewoman)
- I think she was thirteen then. She managed to stow away on the back of a lorry and ended up in Manchester. She was gone four days that time. (Marilyn).
- So each time she was on her own – no other people involved? Can you think of any friends she might have gone to this time around? (Policewoman)

I wrinkle my nose, shake my head.

- She doesnae have many friends.
- None at all, as far as I know. (Marilyn)
- Whit aboot that wee lassie … whit wis her name again … wi the long curly hair … Cara? (Me)
- I don't remember any Cara. (Marilyn)

- It wis afore I met you. At her first primary school … (Me)
- I don't think the police want to go that far back, Rab. (Marilyn)
- What about relatives? I gather she's not your own daughter, Mrs Gilchrist? (Policewoman)
- She hasn't seen her mother in many years. We totally lost touch. (Marilyn)

Benny pulls Marilyn's head down. Loud whisper:

- I thought you were Kirsty's Mummy.
- No, dear. I'm your Mummy and Erin's Mummy. But not Kirsty's.
- Do you know for sure that Kirsty and her mother haven't been in touch? (Policewoman)
- They'd better not. There's a interdict on it. (Marilyn)
- Oh? How's that? (Policewoman)
- When Rab and Sylvia split up, custody was awarded to us. But the very first access day Sylvia did a runner with the child! (Marilyn)
- I see.
- The law caught up with them after a few days. And we all gave her another chance. The stupid woman took advantage again. This time they were missing a month. They got as far as the Republic of Ireland.
- Do they have connections there?
- Nobody at all. Sylvia had the idea they couldn't be traced there.
- But they were.
- No, but her own mother was interrogated and eventually went to jail for obstruction. Then Sylvia turned herself in. After that they put on an order that Sylvia should have only supervised meetings with

the child. A social worker present at all times. And no unauthorised contact.

- How did that go?
- Very badly. There only were half a dozen visits and they all ended in tears. Eventually the caseworker agreed the visits were too disruptive – were preventing Kirsty settling down with us. So they stopped them altogether.
- What age was Kirsty then?
- That was … let's see … nine years ago now.
- Wisnae as long ago as that, wis it? (Rab)
- It was, Rab. Eight at least. I was pregnant with Erin at the time. I would doubt if Kirsty remembers Sylvia at all.

Benny pulls Marilyn's head down again. Loud whisper

- Who went to jail?
- Somebody you don't know, dear.
- Why did they go to jail?
- Benny, pet, I'm talking.
- What about other relations? Grandparents?
- Rab's Dad lives in Stirling, so we don't see him often although he sometimes sends wee gifts for the children. He hasn't seen hide nor hair – we've already called him.
- Sylvia's parents?
- Her Dad died when she wis young. And my Dad told me her mother died a few years ago too. (Rab)
- My own parents live in Strathaven. No word from Kirsty there either – I did call them. (Marilyn)
- Aunts? Uncles? Cousins?

Marilyn shakes her head.

- I'm an only child. And Rab's sister lives in London. There was a bit of a rift at the time of his divorce – we're not in touch with her.

* * *

Kenny

Ah poke for a bit till Ah see it's no ma key at aw. It's the key tae Lorraine's hoose. Rummle aboot in ma pooches and try again. Inside the close, Ah hirple tae ma ain door. Ah'm openin it when the close door opens again. Thur a shadda ahint me. Gordo.

Ah try an squeeze in an shut the door on him but he's ower quick. Try tae shove him oot but he's ower heavy.

- Whit ye eftir this time?
- Why should Ah be eftir onythin?

Thon lop-sided grin. Few year ago Ah thought it wis charmin. Noo it scares the piss oota me.

- Ah'm here tae visit ye, wee man. Social call, that's aw. No gonnae offer me a drink?

He dauners past me an planks hissel doon on the couch.

- Ah've nae bevvy in the hoose.

He gets up an dauners ower tae the press. Opens the door.

- Ye huv so, ye fuckin liar, ye.

He waves the hauf–empty boattle o vodka. Thon grin again.

- Crafty, eh? Tryin tae keep it aw tae yersel?
- Take it an get oot.

Hate the thought o the evenin withoot it. But hate the thought o the evenin wi Gordo even mair.

- We kin split it. Ye goat two tumblers?
- Jist fuck aff.

- No waantin tae drink wi me? Here, that's no very nice.

Bottle in his mitt, he comes up tae me. Right up so Ah smell the breath in ma face. He tweaks ma cheek.

- Thought we were mates. Ur we no mates?

Ah shove him. Ah catch him aff balance an we baith tummle oan tae the couch. Ah struggle tae ma feet again. Ma knees ur giein me jip. The boattle survives.

He sprawls ower the couch. Legs takin up the haill length o it, left airm flung ower the back o it, boattle hingin fae his right.

- No comin tae jine me?
- Please get oot. Ah'm expectin company.
- Uch, how did ye no say?

He rises slowly. Pats his pockets.

- Here, ye widnae huv a fag on ye, wid ye? Ah'm oota smokes.

Ah footer tae try tae get a couple oot o the packet but he beats me tae it. Pulls the haill packet oot ma pooch.

- That's awfy good o ye. If thur onythin Ah kin dae fur you … onythin at aw …
- Jist get oot.

Tom cat patrollin his territory. Ah shut the door behind him. Ah sit doon tae face the evenin on ma tod wi nae smokes an nae bevvy.

* * *

Agnes

Ah grew up in this hoose. When Willie and me got mairried we moved in wi ma mammy. It wis normal tae dae that then. An it wis a good hoose – three-apartment wi no just an inside toilet but a bathroom. Ma mammy slept in the kitchen bed-recess so Willie and me had the front bedroom and wee Alasdair had the back bedroom. Ma mammy did maist o the housework an cookin so I could stay on at work till Ah fell pregnant. And Ah went back tae work when wee Alasdair sterted at the school.

So this hoose is full o memories. Ma mammy singin the auld Scotch sangs tae me an me singin them in turn tae wee Alasdair. Ah wanted tae pass them on tae him. He never got ony Scottish sangs or stories or even history at the school. So it's up tae the mammy tae pass aw that stuff on. Ah mind his favourite sang wis 'Wee Willie Winkie.' No the twee version ye find in nursery rhyme books. The hail five verses as wrote by William Miller, who lived and died no a stane's throw fae here. But it disnae gae on. Alasdair husnae passed it on tae Emma. An the music Sheena knows isnae the kind ye could sing on yer ain withoot the techno-backin. Madonna or Wham or Boy George. The younger generations urnae participative. They'd reyther switch on somethin than sing a sang thursels.

Wan change Ah'm glad o. Ah kin still hear ma mammy sayin: 'It's ma turn o the sterr.'

I used tae say it an aw in ma time. But wi me it wis a scliff an a promise. Tae ma mammy it wis a work o art. Doon on hur knees on a mat scrubbing. She done the sterr up lovely wi pipe clay – even drew wee stars on it tae mark it her work. Ah doot they don't make pipe clay noo – wi aw the wumman oot workin, they've nae time tae embellish the hoosework like that.

Least of aw me. Up this close we aw pey a wumman tae take wur turns o the sterr. Ah pey intae it an aw, even though Ah'm retired and in the hoose aw day and even though Ah'm the only wan still rentin.

Alasdair tried to persuade me tae buy ma hoose mony's the time. He didnae say but Ah expect he thought he could inherit it fae me and sell at a big profit. It wis temptin, fae that angle. Ah coulda bought the hoose wi the tenant's discount fur aboot £10,000 and by the time Ah popped ma clogs Alasdair could maybe sell it for £100,000.

But Ah didnae agree wi it. If aw the tenants buys up the best hooses there'll be nane left fur the young wans tae rent. It's no as if they're still buildin cooncil hooses. An no everybody waants tae buy a hoose, tae get forced intae debt fur thirty year. Tae sign up tae pey fur aw the improvements the rest o yer neebours want whether ye want them yersel or no. Whether ye've got the money tae pay for them or no. A millstone roon yer neck.

The phone rings.

- Ma? It's Alasdair.
- How are ye son? Lovely tae hear fae ye.

I cannae mind the last time he phoned me, rather than the other wey roon. But that's the wey o the world.

We chat a bit and then he comes to the point.

- We were wondering how it would be if Emma came to stay with you.

Knock me doon wi a feather.

- For a wee holiday?
- At first, but if it works out …
- If it works oot …?
- Maybe for a few months.
- Whit?
- We'd like her to register with a school in your area.

Ah'm dumbfoonert. If he'd telt me the Martians were on their wey doon ma chimney Ah'd huv sooner believed it.

But Ah huv tae be careful here. If Ah ask aw their reasons they'll maybe think Ah'm agin it. Gift horses an aw that.

- That wid be lovely, son. Does she know aboot this?

- It was her idea.

Again, Ah'm lost fur words. A teenager wantin tae stey wi her auld granny? No natural. And a shred o doubt creeps in. Whit aw is Emma expectin fae me? Wid Ah be able tae keep hur entertained? Ah mind Alasdair wis a fair handful in his teens.

But Ah quell it. Magic has led tae this and magic will see me through.

- Emma's very interested in this referendum you're having up there.
- She is?
- She's into all the websites. You know – or maybe you don't. Wings Over Scotland, Bella Caledonia, National Collective. Tweeting and Facebooking and blogging about it all over the place. She wants to cast her vote.

I picture wee Emma, her ribbons, her dolly.

- But she's jist a …
- They're letting 16-year-olds vote in this referendum. Emma turned 16 in …
- In April. Ah know.
- It's not just that. If she joins a Scottish school after the summer holidays, after her GCSEs, it's easier to adapt to their system. She can sit her Highers next year and eventually go to a Scottish university as a Scottish student. So no fees.

It begins to click into place.

- But will she no miss her wee pals?
- She would have to be leaving the school anyway. Doesn't run to Sixth Form. The system hereabouts is they go to a Sixth Form College to do their A levels.
- But won't her pals be goin on there too?

- Yes, that's part of the problem. She wants to get shot of the other girls in the school. There's been a bit of bullying.
- Och, poor wee sowel! Did she tell hur teacher?
- Nothing they can do. They've got anti-bullying strategies galore, all worked out by some committee sitting round a table. None of them work. It's just teenagers. All the schools are the same. Anyway, with being in Facebook groups about the referendum she's already got online pals up where you are.
- But are you an Sheena aw right wi that? Emma leavin ye …
- That's another thing. You know Sheena works from home. Well, since I struck out on my own I've been working from home too. Can't say I miss the two hour commute on the Tube. And do you know, for the sale of our poky wee London flat we could buy a big detached villa somewhere more up country, Milngavie, maybe, or Milton of Campsie. It would be a completely different way of life. We've been seriously discussing it, Mum.
- So when wid you …
- Obviously lots of arrangements to be made. But meanwhile, Emma could move in with you and get adapted to the Scottish school system.

Is this a dream? Ah huv tae sit doon. Ah dae, an thur a big squawk behind me. Ah've went an sat on a kitten. The kitten flies oot tae under the sideboard. Rosie flies at me an sinks hur fangs intae ma ankle. Blood runnin doon ma foot.

Ah don't blame hur. Maternal instinct. It's a powerful force.

* * *

Malky

146

Heard Gordo gaun oot somewherr. Oot the hoose, doon the sterr, oot the close. Ma chance tae find Kirsty's phone.

Ah rummle through his wardrobe, his drawers. Loatsa Buckie boattles lyin aboot, maist empty, a few full. Ah consider takin some back to Kirsty. Get her blootert, huv ma evil way wi her.

Only kiddin.

Under the bed: cardboard box full o souvenir T-shirts for the Commonweath Games. Hauf-finished bottle of voddy rollin aboot. See thae things that fall aff the back o a lorry.

Ah could nick some Buckie with less chance of him noticin, but Ah figure a lassie like Kirsty would see Buckfast as low-class. So Ah'll risk the voddy an see how far it gets me.

* * *

Agnes

They're at thon bonny stage, the kittens. Big heids, wee bodies. Innocent wide eyes, buttoned-up faces. Runnin aboot in an oot o everythin. Front paws doon, bahoukie in the air, gie a wee wiggle an then POUNCE on a sweetie wrapper, an elastic band or thin air.

Bertie an wee Stripey are still totie but catchin up fast. Thon wis a great idea of Emma's, tae make the big wans take turns. Emma saved the wee wans fae a slow death, so she did, athoot ever layin eyes on them. Clever lassie.

Noo they're stertin tae be weaned, they're turnin intae right characters. When Ah pit their food oot they come beltin intae the kitchen, wan efter the ither, skitin on the polished flair. Bertie an Stripey bringin up the rear, wi their shorter legs.

Sometimes Rosie remembers her maternal duties. When Ah gie her a bit gammon, she'll take it through tae them. Ither times she forgets an growls tae keep them aff while she scoffs it hersel.

Ah go round the hooses in wur close with the basket o kittens. Lorraine's the one Ah know best. Ah go to her first.

- Uch, they're gorgeous! But both of us are out all day. Wouldnae be fair on the cat.

Ah turn away, then turn back.

- Ma granddaughter Emma's comin to stey wi me. She'll be enrollin in the same school your Angela goes to.

- Oh, that'll be nice for you! What about her parents? Are they …

- They're comin up an aw, but later. Here, d'ye think it's this referendum drawin them aw up?

Ah laugh.

- Certainly it's drawn the world's attention to Scotland.

- Emma says Ah should advertise the kittens on the internet.

- I'd be careful about that. If you put them on the internet then set a price for them. At least £80 each.

- Och not at all. Ah've hud a cat maist o my life an I never paid a penny for ony o them. Widnae be lookin to make a profit.

- That's not the point. You don't want them goin to men lookin for practice bait for dog-fightin, for instance.

Ah'm stunned. Ah look doon at the wee trustin faces and picture them bein flung oot a sack intae a pack o snarlin dugs. Wee Bertie thrown an kicked like a fitba. Used for tug-o-war.

- Whit a lot o badness is oot there.

- We don't like to talk about badness. But some folk live in worlds very different from ours.

- Nuthin excuses cruelty tae animals.

148

- Tell you what. I'll ask around at work. Apart from my own colleagues there might be clients glad of a kitten for company. I can think of a family who've got a disabled child. It's best to give them to somebody you know.

Ah go roon the ither hooses in the close. The Usmanis an the Akrams ur away somewherr. So's yon chap MacLean. Ewan MacConachie says he's allergic. And fae the rest Ah get nae takers.

* * *

Ewan

Only two people there. I recognise neither. One's taking camera equipment out of his car. The other extends her hand.

- I'm Agnetha, from the journal, *Donder*. This is Rasmus. Would it be all right if he takes a short video of you? For our online edition.
- Feel free.
- Looks like you're "it" for tonight. I understood the people of Scotland were enthusiastic about this referendum.

I dust off my excuses.

- Well, it's a bit of an ask for activists to come out during the week after work. We get a bigger turnout at the weekends. And there's a football match on tonight …
- More passionate about football than about their country's independence?
- Ewan! Sorry I'm late!

Whew. The cavalry. Over the next five minutes they dawdle in. Margaret crossing the road. Mike and Caroline ambling along hand-in-hand. Bernie, Duncan and Paul in Bernie's car. Alima and Khalid in their own car.

Middle-aged matron. Lovelorn couple. Two working men and a First Year University student. Pakistani couple. And me – a gay man. Bi. YES camp diversity. Motley crew.

I share out the canvass bags and clipboards with the YESMO sheets. Send Mike and Caroline one way together, Alima and Khalid another way, Margaret with Bernie and Duncan with Paul. I lead Agnetha and Rasmus myself.

Four-in-a-blocks, thank goodness. No tenements.

Rasmus makes me do the walk three times to the first house.

The first take, awkward and self-conscious, feeling the urge to give the camera a running commentary, I trip on the uneven broken path as it curves round the side of the building and almost fall.

The second take I stride with hope and confidence – but Rasmus's camera gets shaken by the wind.

The third take I move furtively and with bad posture. Rasmus says that's the one we'll go with.

- Could you ask the people at each door if they would mind if Rasmus films the discussion?

No answer at the first five doors. At the sixth, a woman in her pyjamas. Shift worker? Early-to-bedder? Very late riser?

The level of interest in politics has risen steadily over the course of this campaign. The woman at once starts to argue with me about why, in her opinion, Scotland is not ready for independence. ('Maybe in ten years' time.') Or has missed the boat. ('We shoulda went for it in the '70s when there wis aw this oil.')

She's amenable to being videoed, pyjamas and all. She looks into her fifties. Did she vote for devolution in the 1979 referendum? ('Naw. Thought it wid be a useless talkin shop. But it's turnt oot no bad, efter aw.')

At this point, to my horror, she absent-mindedly sticks her

forefinger right up her nostril and wiggles it about. Rasmus's video whirrs silently, relentlessly. I picture this example of the Scottish electorate flashed to millions of Belgian homes. I worry about this so much I fail to notice the point at which the woman gets converted. ('Aye, you're right enough therr. Somethin Ah never thought of. You know, Ah think mebbe Ah will vote YES, efter aw.')

Strolling back:

- A conversion?
- Wonder how long it'll last.

My turn for the spotlight. Agnetha starts up in her clear, slightly Americanised English while Rasmus's camera stares into my face:

- We arrived in Glasgow today and have to fly back to Amsterdam tomorrow night. I'm supposed to interview both sides. I asked Better Together to send me to one of their events but all they could offer me was Inverness today or Cumbernauld next week. Yet YES Scotland gave me a choice of two campaigns both in Glasgow tonight.
- Better Together are struggling for activists. I've heard that in some cases they're having to pay them.
- Who told you that?
- My partner is an activist for Better Together.
- Really? How fascinating. Yet you don't fall out?
- Not so far.
- Do you think you might be able to convert her?
- I doubt it.
- Or she you?
- Even less likely.
- Maybe you can get her to act as a third columnist!
- No.

The point at which I should have corrected the gender has passed by. To do it now would be embarrassing. Like where someone hails you as an old friend and yatters animatedly while you try to place him in context. I steer the conversation away from Donald.

- We're finding a steady increase in volunteers.
- Are you Scottish yourself? You sound …
- I'm a mixture. My mother's Scottish. But she was a political activist who travelled all over, wherever the campaigns took her. Germany, Scotland, England, Ireland. Taking me with her after I was born. First time I actually settled in Scotland was when I came to study.
- Which is …?
- 17 years ago.
- So were you involved in the campaign for the devolved Parliament?

The 1997 referendum was the first campaign I took part in independently. I remembered arriving, the month before the vote. University didn't start till October but some of my friends were setting up a student flat together and we needed to sign the contract.

The campaign was low-key then. You wouldn't have known a momentous decision was in the offing. I was just 18 and rushed down to register. I had never voted in anything before.

A few days before the referendum date Princess Diana was killed in a car crash. The country was plunged into conspicuous mourning. Books of condolences in every school, church, theatre and cinema. Somebody suggested a two minutes' silence on each anniversary, equating her loss with all the dead of two world wars. A pall of rotting bouquets hung over George Square.

Hard to tell, in hindsight, how much was spontaneous and

how much media-orchestrated.

We were ordered to show respect by stopping all campaigning for the next week … the second last week before the vote. Still, the double YES (yes to devolution, yes to tax powers) won with a landslide. I knew then that Scotland held the hope for change.

Maybe the Scots always need two referendums, two campaigns for them to seize the day.

One campaign to expose the suppressed information. That they – we – have a past, present and future. To raise confidence that an alternative political reality is available.

A second campaign to let us act on this information. In which case this current one is doomed to fail. Will there be a second?

- Are you a member of the SNP?
- Yes, for now, though in my time I've been a member of the Scottish Socialists and the Greens.
- A campaigner all your life?
- My mother's long-term CND – you know – ban the bomb? – and she took me on demonstrations. I spent my early childhood at Greenham Common Peace Camp!
- Greenham – could you spell that?

I wrote it down.

- It was set up by women in protest at nuclear weapons being sited at the airforce base there, down in Berkshire. My earliest memories are of taking part in cross-country human chains. We did them in both Scotland and England.
- Fascinating!
- We left Greenham Common when I was school age. Eventually, my mother met a guy from Gateshead and we went to live there.

153

- And you've never been back to Greenham Common?
- Doesn't exist any more. I've been on plenty demonstrations to the Peace Camp at Faslane, just up the road. Where the UK's nuclear deterrent is based.

Faslane. Stumble on to the red-eye bus (usually leaving from the Quaker office at Charing Cross) before daybreak. Everybody subdued. Tumble out into the grey dawn at the roundabout outside the barbed wire fence. On both sides the road is bordered by razor wire reminiscent of a First World War battlefield. Razor wire: not to keep out spies left over from the Cold War, but to keep out our own citizenry.

The object of our protest is to stop the workers getting in for their morning shift and the lorries gaining entry to the nuclear base.

Individually we choose our MO.

Those of us with jobs to go to stay vertical, obedient, shuffle about in whichever direction the police point us. Sheep and shepherds. By the time the regular trains and buses are running we'll be on one of them, heading back to the office. Unless we take up the offer of hospitality, tea, space-cake and spliffs from the Peace Campers.

Those of us taking it (literally) to the wire have undergone full briefing on anti-demonstration law. We sit on the wet ground. We ignore police requests to get to our feet. We focus our efforts on making it hard for them to carry us off. We lie down. Chain ourselves to the gates and sometimes to each other.

Long cardboard rolls from carpet shops are produced and double ended rubber grips inserted. One protester inserts the left arm and the other the right arm. We each grasp an end of the unseen grip, deep in the middle of the roll. The only way for the police to separate us would be for them to saw the carpet roll in two, risking amputating one of the hands inside.

We end up in a police cell. And – particularly if we're nobodies, lacking celeb status – are usually released the same day. But never any guarantees.

Agnetha turns her attention to Margaret. An activist for independence since she was at school in the 1960s.

- Startit when Winnie Ewing won the Hamilton by-election.
- So what makes you carry on, year after year? Do you never lose heart?
- Ach, it's a long-term struggle. The pendulum swings forward, and it swings back. Don't know whit causes the swings – they just happen. Swings back, but never as far back as it wis last time. Next time it swings forrit again and it goes that bit further forrit than before.
- Three steps forward two back?
- Mair like ten forward, nine back.
- You're a patient lady.
- Nothin o worth comes easy.
- So where did this sudden enthusiasm for independence come from?
- Wisnae that sudden. Grew gradually oota devolution. An ye know whit they say aboot devolution: it's like evolution but it takes longer!
- Sorry – I don't fully understand …
- Disnae matter. Onywey – until we got the Scottish Parliament maist folk couldnae credit that us Scots could organise wur wey oot a paper bag.
- What do you mean?
- Ah mean: nae confidence we could run onythin. A community council, a fitba team. The Holyrood Parliament gied us the chance to prove wursels to wursels.

155

- So why didn't you have any confidence?
- If ye don't get taught yer history at school ye think nothing wis ever achieved here.

Agnetha laughs.

- So what has been achieved here?
- Scots invented near everything in daily use the day. Phones, TV, penicillin, bicycles, the steam engine …
- So you're all natural inventors, then?

Agnetha might be expressing scepticism or admiration. Time for me to gallop to the rescue.

- The most important invention was the idea that education should be for all. Men and women, rich and poor. The other inventions followed from there.

The following evening, Facebook and Twitter noise it abroad. President Obama has come out against independence for Scotland. The body language on Youtube: Obama slightly embarrassed. The message not forceful:

'There is a referendum process in place and it is up to the people of Scotland. The United Kingdom has been an extraordinary partner to us. From the outside at least, it looks like things have worked pretty well. And we obviously have a deep interest in making sure that one of the closest allies we will ever have remains a strong, robust, united and effective partner. But ultimately these are decisions that are to be made by the folks there.'

David Cameron alongside, looking intently at him. A rare case of the special relationship working for the junior partner.

Just before I shut down the computer I get an email from Agnetha.

> 'This afternoon walking back to my hotel near Charing Cross I came upon a BT leafleting team, being filmed by a BBC crew. They were handing out Obama-leaflets, seemingly in high spirits after Obama's

156

support for the Union.

I spoke to one of them, a young man in his twenties. He admitted not to be a volunteer, but a "hired enthusiast".

Looking at the squad, (there were five of them), I was struck by the differences in appearance and attitude between them and you folks.

Take care.

Agnetha.'

As I undress, Donald is sitting up in bed reading a newspaper. I think: Don't say a word. Just don't say a word.

He does say a word. Hint of a smirk on his face.

- You see we've now got the US of A on our side? Next best thing to God, eh?

I cross the room in one bound. Face up against his.

- I knew about it from the news. Your Better Together friends knew about it before it even happened.
- How d'ye mean?
- This afternoon while Obama was still climbing down from the podium they were giving out leaflets in the street with all the details.
- What can I say? Our side have all the talents. Second sight ...
- They were being filmed by a BBC crew. Another lot with second sight.

Donald's snigger is increasingly irritating.

- Our lot are pounding the streets in all weathers, sometimes twice or thrice a day. Better Together send out a few of their paid staff when the Government warns them something big's going to happen. Which group will appear on the box tomorrow?
- Ewan, Ewan. Mustn't be a sore loser, my dear.

As he turns away I catch the glint of a tear in his eye.

* * *

Malky

Back in the Red Road, Kirsty's crackin up aboot ma burst lip.
Nurse wi a wounded soldier. Moppin wi hur paper hankies.

- Jist a wee family fracas.

Ah pulls out my first offerin.

- A Commonwealth Games T-shirt! Didn't think they
  were on sale yet! I love the wee Clyde character.
  Thistle with a cheeky face.
- See if it fits ye.

She turns hur back but disnae go oot the room while she
pulls aff hur tap and pulls on the T-shirt. Hur bra is pure
white an lacy. Black underwear is supposed tae be sexier but
hur white Primark is sexy enough fur me. She turns hur front
tae me again.

- Perfect fit.

Tighter than the top she hud on afore. No a low neckline, but
the shape o hur underneath … Ah pulls oot ma trump caird.

- Vodka!

Ah try to read the expression on her face.

- You wanting to get me steaming?
- We can get steamin thegither. Got us a mixer!

Ah pull a carton o orange juice oot the carrier. Figure Kirsty
widnae go for straight vodka.

- We can huv a wake fur the Red Road flats. They wur
  gonnae blow them up as a spectacle tae entertain the
  world durin the Commonwealth Games. Thur no noo,
  but.
- So the flats have had a reprieve?
- Naw, they're still gonnae blow them up, jist no the
  noo. Some ither day. Blow them up in a quiet way,

158

like.

- Your childhood home!
- Ach, nothin lasts forever. They've hud thur moments o glory.

Ah pour oot the vodka first while she watches like a hawk.

- Thanks.

Ah sneak in wan extra wee glug.

- I said thanks! Enough!

Ah fill it tae the tap wi juice.

- You are trying to get me drunk!

She looks at me wi the kinda gleam in hur eye that says she's no really angry. Time tae distract hur wi a story.

- A Frenchman wance tried tae walk the tightrope atween two o the Red Road blocks.
- Did he manage?
- Naw! He'd awready managed it atween the Twin Towers o New York, but.
- The ones that blew up in 9/11?
- Aye. But the Scottish weather done for him.
- Too much wind? Did he fall?
- Nut him. He walked backwards aw the wey tae the stertin blocks!
- How far was it?
- Come oot an Ah'll show ye.

We dauner oot to the verandah wi wur cups in wur hauns and take a deck at the brutes. Under the moonlight they look forlorn. Grey on grey. Unloved.

Ah mind when they were ma world. Late for the school and the lifts broke – clatterin doon aw the sterrs. Pechin back up aw the sterrs at the end o the day. Skateboardin back and forth aw roon the entrance. Up an doon the braes. Comin hame in the winter, skitin in the tramped-in ice. The January gales, the buildin swayin so ye thought it wis comin doon.

Noo it really is comin doon. Nae mair court o appeal.

Kirsty goes:

- Prisoners on Death Row.
- It's no their fault they're ugly.

Ah pit ma airm roon her shouthers. Gie her a wee squeeze. Keep it therr. Wan finger lightly oan hur diddy. She's thoughtful. Disnae notice.

- They've had a hard life. A short life, for buildings. And they've faithfully performed every duty. Giving poor folk their first chance of a bathroom and hot water.
- Giein me an ma pals places tae play.
- Giving everybody fine views all round.
- An a wee bit thrill when the wind blew strong.
- Could you feel the place actually swaying?
- No hauf! Sometimes Ah could be lyin still in the bath wi the waater splashin like the Atlantic.
- Were you not scared?
- Na.

Ah haud her close. Tight. She rests hur heid on my shouther. I rest ma cheek on hur hair. Ah move slightly. Look at hur face. Hur eyes are hauf shut. Then she raises her heid, clocks me and pulls away fae me.

Ah go on wi the tale.

- And they gied a hame tae students.
- Was this a students' residence? It's not close to any university, is it?
- North Glasgow College wis jist up the road.
- Would most of their students not be local?

160

- YMCA wis here an aw. They jist hud tae get the bus like the rest of us.
- And the flats are still sheltering asylum seekers running away from wars and torture.
- Hah. So they say. They're no aw runnin away fae wars.

Kirsty turns and frowns at me.

- How would you know?

Uh oh. Didnae mean tae rattle hur cage.

- Ma ma reckons they're jist here fur whit they kin get.
- That's right. A safe place to bring up their children.
- They've no aw goat weans. Maist o them are jist young guys. Ma auld dear's been waitin years on gettin a bigger hoose wi a bedroom fur each of us. Then thae chancers turn up fae naewherr an go right tae the heid o the queue. Get handit a stoatin hoose and aw the furniture.
- They have to be given furniture. They arrive with nothing.
- Let them buy their ain furniture! We hud tae.
- But they've got no money.
- Let them work fur their money.
- They're not allowed to work.

I don't know whit to say. Ah'm stymied by the fact that Gordo is allowed tae work and … well …

Ah try tae see it fae hur point o view.

- Right enough, thae asylum seekers steyin up oor close are nae bother. But why should they get the same size hoose as us when they've only got wan wee boay?
- So are you in favour of the bedroom tax?
- Naw, of course not.

161

Ah've never met onybody in favour o the bedroom tax. An we're aw glad the Scottish Government's compensatin the folk that get their money cut.

- The bedroom tax was specifically to help people like you, that are overcrowded.

Hur face looks kinna shut. Defo no the moment for that kiss. Ah finish aff ma voddy an orange and so does she. Ah go in an bring the boattle oot. This time she disnae look at the cup when Ah'm fillin it up.

- Who are the lassies tormentin ye?
- Don't want you to go and accost them or anything.
- Cross ma hert an hope tae die. Ah'll no go near them. Or dae onythin ye don't waant me tae dae.
- It's Chantelle McLean, Kelly-Anne Henderson and Angela Murphy.

Somehow Ah'd known. My dwindlin fancy for Chantelle and Kelly-Anne slips doon a few mair notches. Bitches. Gaun mob-handit against ma wee Kirsty.

- How did it stert up?
- I've always been teased because of my red hair. Never been in the loop.
- Tell me aboot it.
- But it took a vicious turn when we came back after Christmas. See Suzanne Crichton? Wee girl with fair hair? Well, Chantelle heard that she'd shagged a boy that Chantelle's been shagging. So Chantelle got her round the back of the bike sheds and started battering her.

I stop listening. 'A boy that Chantelle's been shagging.' I picture Chantelle up a close, roon a back court, in bed wi some faceless boay. I picture him undressin her, runnin his hands ower her body. Her lettin him. She slags me and she shags him.

162

- Whit boay?
- Boy?
- The wan that's been shaggin Chantelle.
- Does it matter? Don't know if you know him. Left school a year ago. Paul Moodie.

I know him. Big hunky cunt wis given a try by Motherwell. Brawn withoot brain. I picture Paul Moodie wi Chantelle, peelin aff her school uniform, her jumper, her blouse, liftin up her skirt, runnin his manky big goalie's paws …

It dawns that Kirsty's stopped speakin.

- So how did you get involved?
- I just told you.
- Sorry. Run it past me again.
- She was getting right torn into Suzanne. Got on top of her and grabbed her hair and started bashing her head against the ground. The rest were cheering them on and shouting "Cat Fight! Cat Fight!" But Suzanne was no match. When her head split and started pouring with blood, I ran into the school up to the staff-room and got a couple of teachers to come out.
- Ye grassed them in.
- I was hoping nobody would realise it was me. No chance. A few of them saw me with the teachers and told Chantelle afterwards. The rest is history.
- So whit happened to Chantelle and Suzanne?
- They both got three days' suspension. Wasn't fair. Suzanne never wanted to fight with Chantelle – was running away from her, in fact.

I wrap ma airms roon Kirsty. The tap o hur heid comes up tae ma mooth, jist. She tilts hur heid back an looks up at me. Hur eyes are wide an hur lips are pairted. Her face gleams pale in the moonlight. So Ah can be safe that ma ain plooks are in shadow.

- Ah'm no gaun near thae ratbags unless ye waant me tae. But say the word an Ah'll defend ye wi ma life.
- That's nice to know.

The moment is now. Ah press my lips tae hurs, first gently then passionately. We baith close wur eyes. Nae tongues – she's a classy lassie. Wur boadies melt intae wan anither an wur herts beat in time.

The wind whustles aboot us but we're warm on this best of aw summers. The moon an the stars shine oot a clear sky. The doomed relics o the1960s loom aw roon. They wish that they too had a future insteid o jist a past.

* * *

Ewan

Tam Malone from Radical Independence Campaign phones.

- We're hittin the housin schemes on Saturday. Could you print oot some YESMO sheets for us? And clipboards if ye've ony gaun spare.
- How many canvassers are you expecting to turn out?
- Boot sixty.
- Sixteen? You're an optimist!
- I said sixteee.
- Sixty!
- Aye. At least.
- Why can you get sixty and I'm singing Mr Blue Sky when I get six?
- Shoulda went tae ma chairm school.
- I can't print you out enough sheets for sixty canvassers. That would be about 400 sheets. I've got to do them every day for myself as well. And I've got to do boring

things like work, eat and sleep.

- And drink.
- Chance would be a fine thing.
- No worries. You're no the only wan printin them fur us.

On Sunday *The Observer* has a double-page spread about 1000 canvassers from Lerwick to Dumfries hitting the streets for Radical Indy. No Scottish title carries the story.

Only a few of the RIC activists have canvass sheets and even fewer have clipboards. The rest have postcards and mountains of enthusiasm. *The Observer* story goes into a lot of detail. Interviews the organisers.

Apathy still lurks behind some doors in Easterhouse, Gorbals, Wester Hailes and the Raploch. A couple didn't know the referendum was happening. A sullen sprinkling didn't care. A staunch wee band boasted that they'd never darkened a polling station in their lives. And never would. Cross their hearts and hope to die.

But the experienced canvassers have discerned a new spark.

As I have, too. A spark which might be a flame. The spirit which once inspired Thomas Paine, Thomas Muir of Huntershill, Baird, Hardie and Wilson, Emily Davidson and Emmeline Pankhurst twitches its eyelids and draws breath.

Canvass returns from the local RIC find their way back to me. Burning the midnight oil, I feed the responses into the YESMO database. I struggle with the scribbled postcards, many incomplete or illegible. Unless there's a first name, a properly spelt last name, a postcode and a digit on the 1-10 scale the YESMO system won't accept the entry.

If the rest of the information is complete Google gets me the postcode. Eventually.

No digit? Down to conjecture. I give YES an eight, NO a two and DON'T KNOW a five.

Wrestling with Macdonald, Mcdonald, McDonald and MacDonald, as well as Mackintosh, McIntosh, MacIntosh and Macintosh, not to mention   and   … I start to lose the will to live. When McDonagh and McIntyre involve themselves, I call it a day. I plunge my fists into the bag of useless postcards carrying a sole first name, Mr, Mrs or Ms and start feeding them, three by three, into the shredder.

* * *

Kirsty

Last night when he came over he'd been in the wars. I got into Angel of Mercy mode, drank his vodka and forgot to ask him. But today I remember.

- Did you charge up my phone?
- No. The port was wrong.
- Rats. I hate being without it.

He planks himself down beside me and slips his arm round my neck.

- Ye've got me. Isn't a real pal better than virtual pals?

Cara: An invisible pal is the best of all.

I shift a bit away from him, conscious I'm maybe starting to honk. Too long away from clean clothes and a shower.

- Anyway, give me it back then.
- Whit d'ye need it fur? It's no workin. Ah'll get you a better phone.
- I need my own phone back. The SIM card. All my contacts.
- OK.
- OK … what? Give it to me now. D'you not have it?

Silence.

- What have you done with my phone?

166

Cara: What did I tell you?

- Don't worry – I'll get it back …
- Where is it?
- Gordo took it.

Gordo. His ned brother. Gang battles, Buckie and chibs. Drug-dealing. Organised crime. My pet pink phone in the middle of it.

I start to cry.

- I'll get it back for you.

Cara: What did I tell you? He's got you trapped up here and now he's cut your link with the outside world.

- I want to go home.

He tries to put his arms round me again. Holds his face close to mine. He has a new plook beside his nose. Red volcano with a yellow head. I push him away as hard as I can.

Chapter 7: July

Opinion Poll *(Daily Record)*:
YES 41%   NO 46%   DON'T KNOW 13%

Walter

Doon the Wallace, Ah see my old china, Archie Reekie, sitting over a wee goldie. Ah get one for mysel.

- Ah wis surprised tae see the "NO" poster in your window.

- Wondered when ye'd notice.

- Aye. Well Ah'm glad you're seein sense. But Ah'm surprised.

Me, Ah've voted SNP for forty year. Livin in Stirling, Ah've watched the Bannockburn marches year on year, stridin through the toon. Ah watched them in the '70s when there were mair o them gaithered on the field of battle than there had been on baith sides back in 1314. Ah've watched them when they were low in the '80s. Ah've seen them jaunty in the sunshine, trauchlin through the rain. Ah've come rushin oot the pub with the gless in my hand and toasted them in a good malt. Ah've joined them and finished the march wi them and listened to the speeches and clapped and cheered. Ah've smiled at the fanatics in their mediaeval gear wavin their dirks and bawlin their slogans at the sky.

- So this you changed party? Gone Labour – just when Labour's doon on its uppers?

- Not at all. Ah think the SNP Government's progressive. Ah think the Labour-Tory coalition on the cooncil is an indictment on them baith. Ah voted SNP last time and Ah'll be votin SNP again next time.

- So … why … ?

Ah enjoy ma moment. Dirl my whisky, look through it at the light fae the window. Turns everythin golden. If only it were as easy to change the future.

- We've missed the boat, Archie. The oil's nearly all squandered noo, whatever gloss they pit on it. Wur industry's shut doon and wur decision-makin jobs huv decamped to London.

- Aye, well, Ah agree wi ye there. If we'd got devolution in 1979 we might have got independence in the '80s when the oil wis gushin away. But it's too late noo.

- Don't get me wrang. Ah'm ragin at ma fellow countrymen – includin you, by the way – for wastin their chances time and again. You lot don't deserve independence. You deserve to see your country goin doon the pan. Which is whit's gonnae happen when the NO side get their majority. With help fae yours truly.

- So ye're votin "NO" oota malice? Ye're a thrawn bugger, Gilchrist.

- Ah like to be unpredictable.

- Aye, you are that.

We think wur thoughts. Ah could go a puff at my pipe but Ah cannae be ersed gaun ootside and staunin in the cauld. We finish wur drinks and Archie goes to the bar for anither round. He comes back and lays them on the table.

- By the way, yer neighbour, Bill Jamieson, wis jist in here earlier. He telt me the polis were roon at yer door yesterday.

- Musta been when Ah wis oot. Wid be aboot ma granddaughter.

- Yer granddaughter in Glasgow?

- Aye. Rab's lassie. Kirsty. She's missin.

169

- How long's she been gone?
- Good few weeks.
- That's bad! Whit age is she?
- Ah huvnae seen her in years, ken. Ah'd been picturin her still aboot ten or eleven. But she's actually almost sixteen.
- Ah, teenagers. Do they think she's ran away?

Ah mind last time Ah saw her. At teatime Rab an Marilyn an masel were aw bletherin away but naebody wis peyin her ony notice except when Marilyn telt her aff for spillin hur juice. Efter dinner, Ah'd played a caird game wi her an Rab. Marilyn wis busy wi the ither wee lassie. The wee laddie wisnae born. Struck me ironic at the time that here we were playin 'Happy Families' an yet there wisna an awfy happy atmosphere aboot the hoose.

- Nae idea how she's gettin on. Last time Ah saw her she didnae say very much. She mighta said mair if we'd been on wur ain. But Rab's wife Marilyn was aye there.
- Stepmother, eh?
- Ah don't care that much for her. Got the impression she hudnae muckle time for Kirsty.
- Rab'll mak sure the lassie's taken care o.
- Rab's … he's a bit saft. Ah ken fine thon dame Marilyn'll wear the breeks.

Back hame there's a chap at the door. Polis are back. Policeman and policewoman. The policewomen aye look so wee, and their hats so big. Ah take them in and offer them a cup of tea.

- Not for us, Mr Gilchrist. Are you aware that your granddaughter Kirsty's missing from home?
- Aye – ma son Rab phoned.

- Any idea where she might have gone?
- None at all. Huvna seen her in years.
- What about her own mother?

Ah.

Just a few months to go. Then …

- Do you know where she lives?

Better no get caught oot tellin whoppers to the polis.

- Sylvia moved around a bit.
- Any chance Kirsty would be in touch with her?
- Doubt it.
- We heard that Sylvia ran away with Kirsty a couple of times. Maybe she'd want to get in touch with Kirsty.
- Aye well, she's no allowed. There's an interdict.

The wee police wifie's been sayin nothin, just starin at me steadily. Now she speaks.

- What was the relationship between Kirsty and her mother when they were in touch with each other?
- Normal, as far as I know …
- Why was there an interdict? Was there any hint of abuse or ill-treatment?
- No, nothin o that kind at all.

After they leave Ah lift the phone and dial.

- Sylvia? It's Walter.

* * *

Ewan

I flop down at the table. Donald brings my dinner in. Lamb shanks with ancho chili honey, he announces proudly.

- So? Mission accomplished?
- It was OK. 17 YES and 14 NO. Everybody else out or

watching River City.

- Weegies are thick as two planks. I'm pinnin my hopes for NO on the East Coast academics.
- You're a Weegie yourself.
- My parents were teuchters.
- Some teuchters. Too ashamed of their language to speak it.
- They spoke it all right. Whenever they didnae want ma brothers and me to understand what they were sayin.
- If they'd passed it on to you, you could have landed a nice job in television.
- Aye, well, they didnae have a crystal ball.

After dinner I start submitting tonight's results into the YESMO database.

Alison Lindsay messages me on Facebook.

'Hi Ewan. You might be interested to know you have a son, Calum, born on 13th March. I don't want you to interfere with his upbringing. I won't contact you again. But I thought you should know in case he tries to trace you once he's grown up.'

I read the message over three times. I go back into Alison's page. Check her photo album. Only six pics: two groups of young women, none of whom look familiar, and four of the baby. Check her friends. Only 25 – none ring a bell. Check her postings. Not a heavy user of Facebook. Only a few postings before 13th March. Around 13th March a flurry of conventional congratulations and gooings, all from women:

'The wee man's gorgeous!'

'Well done, you!'

You'd think it was parthenogenesis.

I cast my mind back to 13th March. No, silly me – nine

months before. What exactly is the human gestation period? Into Google. Right. What was I up to first week of June 2013?

I've swung both ways on occasion. AC/DC. Though for the past three years or so Donald and I have been faithful to each other.

As far as I know, anyway, in Donald's case.

In mine – more or less.

Well, up to a point.

Still. The more I think about it. Summer 2013. National Collective events. Parties.

It could be true.

* * *

Agnes

Ah watch the Commonwealth Games openin ceremony on the box. Ah'm no really interested in sport an in fact, wi the cats takin up aw ma time, Ah'm no watchin as much telly as Ah used to. But thur's been such a hullabaloo about the Games – how it's gonnae mean the entire rehabilitation o the East End – or at least Dalmarnock. They've been gaun on fur years aboot it. An maybe Ah can pick oot Rab Gilchrist in the chorus line.

He never said he wis gonnae be dressed up as a Tunnock's marshmallow biscuit. So Ah don't look too closely at them. Original idea. Ah loved them when Ah wis younger. But they're a bit sweet fur me noo. Ah've aye got ma ain teeth an Ah want tae keep it that wey.

I expect Rab's wan o thae wans waving their airms aboot. Aw dressed in floral colours. Aye, he'll be wan o them. Cannae pick him oot, though, thur too many o them an the camera only steys in the wan spot a moment at a time.

173

The bit Ah like best is the wee Scottie dugs that lead in every fresh national team. Ah don't think it's the same wee Scottie every time – sometimes it's a black wan, sometimes white. An sometimes the dug gets cairried roon – maybe because that wan's no very obedient. The owners urnae aw the same either, though they're dressed kinna similar. Bunnet an tweeds. Cross between a gamekeeper an an auld jakey. No like an athlete, onywey.

It's good that Scotland takes an original angle on things.

Life wi seven cats in a three apartment is fair hectic. Ah cannae thole the wee sowels greetin ootside ma bedroom door at night so they get the run o the place. The electric blanket draws them tae the bed. Usually Ah've got three o them under the duvet, lickin and kneadin an sometimes scratchin ma belly, three o them on tap o the duvet pouncin on ma knees an feet every time ah move, an wee Bertie that wis the failin kitten, mairchin endlessly ower ma pillows roon ma heid.

So Ah try tae stay still an no let ma hauns dangle ower the side o the bed. When Ah wis a wean Ah used tae keep ma hauns in under the covers because Ah wis feart o the crocodile under the bed. Things turn full circle.

Come six a.m. they reckon Ah've been lazy enough an they stert up their meowin in ma face. They claw at ma hair, they shove their wee faces intae mine, bumpin noses wi me.

Ah cannae get peace tae waash ma face an get dressed till Ah've went tae the kitchen an gien them their breakfast. Then it's a race – me gettin brushed up an ready an them gulpin their food doon their thrapple.

Then Ah go tae make ma ain breakfast but Ah get nae peace if Ah don't share some wi them. They're no awfy good at sharin wi wan anither – they run aff wi bits o gammon an bacon tae different corners an growl.

They're good aboot the litter tray – Ah didnae even huv tae

show them whit tae dae. That's when Ah'm glad they're no dugs. But Ah'm cleanin it oot aw day long an humphin bags o litter alang fae Ali's shop aw week. Hurts ma sair knees.

It's fine an cosy at the twilight's last gleamin when Ah draw the curtains, make masel a cuppa tea an toast, pit oan the telly an sit wi ma feet up. Ah get Bertie snorin it aff behind my neck an two on ma knee. Somethin fair relaxin aboot a sleepin cat.

Still, they never sleep fur lang. Whit'll happen if Ah cannae get onybody tae take the kittens on? Ah've no got a wide social circle. The folks that waant cats already huv them. Cats urnae that difficult tae acquire.

A rattle at the door. Somebody usin the tirlin pin. Who can it be at this time o night?

Bina an her wee brother Farooq. This time they're carryin a tray atween them. Big hunks o watermelon.

- This is leftover from our dinner.
- Och, hen, that's far too much for me!
- It's not all for you. One each for the neighbours.

Silly me thinkin it's aw fur me. Daft. Ah'm that embarrassed Ah make anither faux pas.

- Here, is it no awfy late fur yese tae be huvin yer dinner? Youse wee wans should be in yer beds.
- It's Ramadan. We huvnae eaten aw day.

Ramadan. Of course. Whit a time o year tae be haudin their Ramadan, when the daylight lasts aboot twenty hoors. Wid they no be better haudin it in winter? But religion's never aboot makin life easier for yersel.

- Can we come in now and pick the kitten we want?
- Did yer Mammy definitely say you could have one?

Both nod vigorously. In they troop. They lay their tray doon and I pit my hunk of watermelon in a bowl. They sit doon and Ah pit a couple o kittens in each o their laps.

- Ye can huv ony o them except the wee grey wan. Ah'm keepin him.

Over the next ten minutes, they play with the kittens. Throw them sweetie papers an the kittens obligingly retrieve them. Bina wants the white long haired wan wi the orange patch. Farooq wants the marmalade boy. Bina wins.

Efter they're gone, Ah look doubtfully at the watermelon. Ah like a slice o honeydew melon or Galia melon but Ah usually find thae rid watermelons a bit tasteless.

Here, it turns oot the juiciest thing Ah've ever sunk ma teeth intae. Ah eat ma wey through it over the next three days.

Guid-herted, thae Akrams.

* * *

Kirsty

I don't go home. It's kind of atmospheric having the whole block to ourselves.

We get into a pattern. Malky brings in supplies stolen from home or bought – he gets money from his part-time jobs. He does my washing along with his own in his mother's washing machine. A few afternoons a week he smuggles me into his own house for a shower.

Occasionally, I sneak home while they're all out.

I know their movements. Marilyn's shifts at the hospital. Dad's school run with Erin and Benny. Since losing his job Dad's been doing voluntary work with the Citizens' Advice Bureau where his financial background comes into play.

I charge up my old Kindle (unlike my laptop it has a working battery) and download some more free novels. The Kindle, laptop and phone were all presents from Grandpa. It's amazing that he's technologically aware enough to send me all these digital gifts. As I recall, he's pretty antiquated. Maybe not 100 but near enough. Most folk his age hardly know computers exist.

I check my emails. Clear and present danger from the Watchers. Returning not an option. I bundle spare clothes into Marilyn's case and trundle it out to the bus stop.

To mislead the search, Malky suggests I send my folks a postcard saying I'm going away.

Cara: You're your own worst enemy.

It's been a lovely summer and we spend a lot of time outside. Sometimes the three of us and sometimes just Cara and me. There's lots of empty ground and nobody knows me round here.

Commonwealth celebration. The only really wet day of what's shaping up to be the sunniest summer in my life. Big queue with full airport security just to get on to Glasgow Green. They make Malky and me remove our YES badges! Weird.

The Green's full of folk draped in scarlet plastic ponchos, like giant tomatoes on grass. Usual razzmatazz: bouncy castle, face-painting. Ferris Wheel jammed up against the Napoleonic monument.

The big marquee's selling souvenirs. We wander round it, looking, not buying. T-shirts with the Clyde character; but Malky and I are each wearing one of those already. Mugs and travel rugs in the specially designed tartan of bright green and lilac. Stuffed dollies of the Clyde character in different sizes. But even the wee ones cost a fortune.

Malky asks me if I want to race against Usain Bolt.

  - What's a Sin Bolt?
  - A Jamaican runner. Even you musta heard of him.
  - I'm not into sport.
  - Wis aw ower the papers the other day. Wis supposed

177

tae huv said the Commonwealth Games here were shit. Ah think he maybe meant the weather.

- This has been the best summer I can remember!

- Me too. But probably worse than the Jamaican winter.

I look around.

- So is he here?

- Who?

- That runner you mentioned. The one I'm to race against.

Malky bursts out laughing.

- You really meant it! Ye urnae intae sport!

- Of course I meant it.

I don't show I'm offended. He points.

- It's just a ride.

A screen running alongside a short track. On the blue background a figure in vest and shorts trailing a streak of shocking pink repeatedly sprints from end to end. On the track a motley crew: boastful young braggarts, hopeless fatties, Paw, Maw and the weans all try in turn to beat the Bolt.

Nobody comes close.

- Uch, it's not for me. You go ahead.

Malky pays his money, goes to the start, crouches down, gets set, goes.

Gives it all he's got. He doesn't beat Usain Bolt. He returns to me, peching.

- Whit dae you fancy daein yersel? The Big Wheel?

Sitting in a puddly seat, rising high over it all. Up level with the top of the Napoleonic monument a few feet away. The monument was struck with lightning soon after it was built in 1806. Probably on a rainy day like this.

\- Come and we'll try the ceilidh dancing.

I grab his hand and drag him into the Spiegeltent.

Inside it's lovely wood, stained glass fitments, mirrored walls. Incredible detail for a temporary structure. A band is playing and a thin throng of couples, from old to very young, are doing a Gay Gordons.

Ceilidh dancing is the only part of PE I enjoy at school. But we just get it in the run-up to the Christmas Party. And if the teachers don't pair us up, I sometimes don't have a partner.

Dad and Marilyn go every week to a ceilidh dancing class up the town. There was three weeks one time when Marilyn couldn't go because she'd sprained her ankle and Dad took me instead. They gave us much more complicated dances than the ones we got in school. Eightsome Reel, Black Mountain Reel, Trip to Bavaria.

I like the complicated set dances best. Trip to Bavaria: OK as long as everybody keeps on the move. Mairi's Wedding: you abruptly change direction to rescue the corners and bring them home. I love the structure of set dances. You and your partner work in halting stages up the set into lead position and then blaze your way down. An allegory for life.

Sometimes Cara and I practise at home but we can only do the couple dances and I don't like them as much as the set dances. And when Dad and Marilyn and the wee ones are in the house I just have to hum the music under my breath.

Cara enjoys it as much as I do.

Malky doesn't. But he rises to the occasion. I pull him on to the dance floor, grab his right hand and loop it round the back of my neck. Forward one-two-three-four, backward one-two-three-four. Same again in reverse. Birly, birly, birly birly, polka.

There are so few dancers braving the floor that we've space to give it laldy, pour our young energy into it, overtake them.

179

I wish I was wearing a dress instead of jeans for the birly bit. A birly, swirly dress that would rise like a lampshade and flatten like a disc. The kind I don't possess.

The usual numbers. Gay Gordons. Canadian Barn dance. Strip the Willow. Virginia Reel. For the Dashing White Sergeant we need a third dancer. Cara's made herself scarce and I'm too shy to ask a stranger. All the other dances I know are too obscure to offer this crowd.

Coming out, I've worked up a sweat. Although it's rainy, it's not that cold. Warm enough to not mind sitting in a puddly seat on the Big Wheel. The gondolas have wee canopies over them. And we can always sit on our carrier bags.

From on high we look down. Green expanse and moving tomatoes.

When I was in primary seven we did a project on the history of Glasgow Green. The first project I ever researched on Google. I got a prize for it. Just a bar of chocolate, but I was that proud. Didn't tell them at home – ate the chocolate before Marilyn got the chance to make me share it round.

Women bleached their linen on the Green and dried them on lines slung on the washing poles which are still there. The 1820 Radicals trained there for their insurrection. Criminals – their names still displayed in the People's Palace – were hanged on it. Suffragettes and other protesters right down to today made their speeches on it.

I look down on the People's Palace with the Winter Gardens glinting in a shaft of sun. The big imperial fountain in front of it. The River Clyde with a few kayaks weaving along. The tomatoes on the green. These are my people, about to make a huge political decision for our country.

Cara: Trust me. They'll make the wrong one.

I feel warm and loving. I want to hug all the tomatoes. YES voters and NO voters alike. Scots, English, Poles, Pakistanis and Africans. My family, even including Marilyn.

My classmates, even including Chantelle. I want to hug the whole human race.

I hug the only example within reach.

And immediately regret it, because he hugs me back with gusto. He has kissed me before but this time the squeeze goes on for days and the kiss is invasive. His bristles scrape my chin and his warm palm lightly cups my breast. His eyes are half open, as if he has been transported to another plane. Scary, but somehow thrilling. The very gondola birls with passion.

I've taken an irreversible step.

* * *

Ewan

Fraught meeting in the YES HQ.

Not well chaired: usual suspects hogging the spotlight, shouting down the more reserved (like me).

Complaints about the YESMO database: the computer won't accept any of the information if some of the responses are missing. So if you didn't get a response to the question 'Where are you on a 1-10 scale where 1 is NO and 10 is YES?' you have to assign a number in accordance with the general tone of the conversation.

Sometimes when you try to submit a street the computer wipes the information and you have to start all over again.

Some people haven't even started submitting the results – they've just let the canvass returns mount up.

Some coordinators are boycotting the YESMO system. They prefer the SNP's own ACTIVATE program (incompatible with YESMO) which asks about party allegiance as well as attitudes to independence. To them this indyref is a staging post to the main event: their own personal campaigns in the

2015, 2016 and 2017 elections.

Coordinators from every constituency in the city reporting back on their activities, vying with each other over doors knocked and percentages. Everybody reports a majority for YES.

At the end, four of us – Gillian from the Greens, Andy from the SSP, Wendy and I from the SNP – all go for a drink to the YesBar in Drury Street. Independence is now so mainstream that a pub can openly align itself with it and still get enough custom. Maybe even increase its custom? I hope this is a commercial decision rather than a principled one. We need more head-support, less heart-support.

I order Irn-Bru as my car is parked in St Vincent Street. Andy goes to the bar to place the orders. Gillian and Wendy get into chat over the latest NO propaganda in the media.

My attention is caught by a group seated in the far corner. One of them in particular looks familiar. Not so much her face as what she's wearing: a T-shirt with the slogan

When sleeping women awake, mountains will move.

The slogan takes me back to the summer of 2013. A National Collective event. Precursor to this year's wall-to-wall YEStivals.

Her face looks increasingly familiar. I strain my ears to hear their conversation.

- Your Irn-Bru.
- Ta, Andy.

The girl in the T-shirt stands up.

- I'm heading.
- No want one for the road, Alison? We're just orderin.
- No, the wee fellow's got to get to his bed. And the baby-sitter's to get to hers.

That clinches it. As Alison makes her exit I dive out after, ignoring Gillian's 'No wantin yer Irn-Bru?' at my back.

Alison hurries up the road and I hurry after. Stalking.

Alison goes for Buchanan Street subway. I follow at a distance.

Step into the shadows when she stops to look up at the statue of the Duke of Wellington in front of GOMA. In honour of the Commonwealth Games medals won by Team Scotland, the fly-by-nighters have replaced the orange parking cone he wears on his head with a golden one. I chuckle into myself. Maybe she does too.

In the station, I lose myself in the queue. Board the opposite end of the train and leave it when she does, at Kelvinbridge.

I stalk her to her close and hide in another doorway while she lets herself in. I follow to the close door. Some closes don't have names: just 1/1, 2/1 etc. As an experienced canvasser I know 1 is left and 2 is right.

This close has names. Lindsay is 3/1. Top left. Not ideal for hauling a buggy up all these flights.

My fingers hover over the bell but in the end I pull away and take the subway back into town where I get a bus.

Next morning I look for my car. Up the street, down the street. Round the nearest corner. Try to recall exactly where I parked it last night. Always difficult with Victorian tenements: many cars relating to each close; streets designed for shanks' pony.

Horrors. Disjointed flashes of memory. I parked my car before the meeting in St Vincent Street. I parked it in a place where parking is free from 6pm until 8am but forbidden outside these hours.

What now?

The taxi takes forever. When we reach St Vincent Street, my car is predictably away. The driver (who, like most taxi drivers, is a YES) advises me how to go about getting it back. Taxi drivers know that kind of thing.

The next hour is a blur: the Kafkaesque City Chambers, wandering from one heavily-queued counter to another, getting mixed up in a queue of people complaining about housing, finding no one who could help outside of his own three-word wide margin of bureaucracy. Finally in the toilets, I fall over a cleaner who takes pity on me and shows me a queue for an information desk where, she assures me, they will guide me to the best queue to join.

And so I find myself at the London Road car pound. The office is a workman's hut in the middle of the yard. I arrive at the break between shifts. The new car-releaser doesn't know the password of the previous car-releaser and can't get into the computer. Half an hour later and £60 lighter, I have the release papers for my battered eight-year-old Nissan Micra, but can't get out because a ten-ton lorry is blocking the gate.

* * *

Rab

I awaken to Marilyn shaking me, thrustin a postcard at me.

- Look – does this put your mind to rest?

"Dear Dad

I'm fed up with Glasgow and I'm taking the bus to London. Don't worry about me – I'm fine. I'm going to stay with my pal Cara and her folks. I'll get in touch when I've worked out my plans.

Love from Kirsty."

- Well, Rab? Is it her writing?

I try to recall what her writin looks like. Everybody nowadays writes so little by hand. It's all computers.

- Of course it's her writing. Who else would have written it? We'll show this to the police and they can call off the search.

- She's still a wee lassie, Marilyn.
- Sixteen.
- Still fifteen.
- As good as sixteen. By the time these sluggardly Plods track her down, she'll be well over-age.
- An who's this Cara?
- You were the one mentioned the girl in her old primary school.
- Never thought they kept up. Cannae mind hur surname …
- There are lots of ways nowadays for young folk to keep in touch with each other. Ways that we can't understand, Rab.
- Whenever we see her she's on her tod …
- Maybe she's not as much of a loner as we thought.
- What about her clothes?

I jump out of bed. Hurry to the children's bedroom and open the wardrobe.

Most of Kirsty's clothes are gone.

* * *

Iain

There they are in their favourite corner, nursing their pints. I always feel awkward joining them, forcing them to break into English to accommodate me. On the other hand our ex-pat status – in reverse of each other – is one of the experiences which bonds us. Back in the Czech Republic Jan also has children whom he supports but seldom sees. And of course they're my nearest neighbours.

Zack spots me.

- Well look here! It's Iain! Back from India?
- Couple of weeks, just.
- Only two weeks, eh? What do they say … no rest …?
- For the wicked. That's me.

I sit down, punch Jan on the shoulder.

- You two must be keeping busy too, eh? A real "taps aff" summer. You're both very brown.
- Browner than you, my friend! (Jan)
- Only mad dogs and Englishmen strip off in the Indian sun. And I'm neither.
- Neither …?
- Neither a mad dog nor an Englishman.

They look at each other and laugh.

- Maybe more of a mad dog than an Englishman! (Zack)

We all laugh.

- So what about this independence referendum? (Me)

To my surprise they both get agitated.

- Tell me: why do they want to do this thing? (Zack)
- I don't know. I've been away … (Me)
- They have no idea … have you heard of the velvet divorce? (Zack)

A memory comes to me of Aileen in a blue velvet dress. She wore it one year to Daft Friday at Glasgow University. She was absolutely stunning. I couldn't take my eyes off her. We'd been on the fringes of each other's groups for some time, members of the same circle, attending the same student parties, but that was the first time we really got off with each other. The softness of that velvet … and of her skin beneath.

- It refers to the separation of Slovakia from the Czech Republic. (Zack)

- Velvet divorce my arse! (Jan's English is improving).
- Slovakia's been a disaster since it went its separate way. (Zack)
- I don't know much about ... (Me)
- I'm sure they're sorry they're not still with Prague. (Jan)
- Not that they were ever asked ... (Zack)
- Makes me angry when they talk here about state-controlled TV. You Britons have never lived somewhere where the State really did control all the news. (Jan)
- Have you heard of the Prague Spring? (Zack)
- Not really. (Me)
- My parents still talk about it. In 1967 the Czech leader Dubcek tried to break away from Soviet rule. When the newspapers and television came to him asking what they should print ... (Zack)
- We really did have a State news! (Jan)
- ... he said "print what you want!" (Zack)
- They opened the borders. My Dad's sister was able to go to Edinburgh as an au pair. (Jan)
- Didn't last. Surely you've heard of how the Soviet army invaded Czechoslovakia in 1968 and brought us back under control! (Zack)
- Of course. (I lied. Couldn't go on parading my ignorance about their country.)
- My aunt was ordered back. She made her choice and stayed, all alone, 18 years old. She was sentenced in her absence to two years' jail and didn't see her family again for 20 years. (Jan)
- So don't complain about your British Government. It's nothing like what we had from the Soviet Union.

(Zack)

- I never said …
- Do you think the Soviet Government would have given us an independence referendum? (Zack)
- No, of course … (Me)
- So be grateful for what you have, my friend! (Zack)

Clear enough what they'll be voting.

* * *

Kirsty

When I go out I like to have a destination. When Cara and I lived in Dennistoun, we used to walk to museums and art galleries. People's Palace, Museum of Religion, Provand's Lordship, Gallery of Modern Art. They don't cost anything and it got us out the house.

Now and again we'd push the boat out and get the 38 bus all the way to the Burrell and Pollok House. Or the subway from George Square to the Art Galleries.

When Mummy and Dad and I were together there was a picture on the wall of a lady in a boat with a fancy patchwork quilt trailing in the water. Daddy used to say it was a picture of Mummy. I believed it at the time. It looked like her, seen from the side.

Later I was always hoping to find that picture in a gallery. I never did, although Kelvingrove has some pictures of ladies that look a wee bit like her. If I knew its name or even the artist I could google it. But memories from when you're wee are uncertain. Disconnected fragments. And any topic to do with Mummy is taboo at home.

Red Road involves a longer walk into town and so nowadays Malky, Cara and I turn rather to the north and the east: parks, golf courses. I get to know the places where I can use the facilities. I now understand the old ladies who complain about cutbacks on public toilets.

Malky knows his way around these streets as if he designed them. Trick question.

- Whit's the auldest hoose in Glesca?
- Provand's Lordship.
- Wrang. An you an Eastender. Provan Hall.
- Where?

And so we take the bus the other direction to Easterhouse. Never been there – thought it was just a housing scheme. But here we are in a medieval manor. A garden ablaze with colour by day. One of the spookiest bedrooms in the country by night.

There's a guide. Malky, Cara and I are his only trippers so he gives it laldy. Tells us the history of the house. The life and times of James IV. The short existence of a kitchen boy, scorching slowly as he turned the spit. Attacks by local warlords, with the nobility abandoning the servants and drawing up the ladders behind themselves. The furniture carved in the early 19th century out of a 13th century submerged Clyde bridge.

That night the story of the spectral room with the drowned furniture preys on my mind. Malky prepares to go home and I beg him to stay. In our habitual sleeping position with my back turned to his front I can feel he's aroused. A thrill runs through my body which is nothing to do with the spooks.

Cara goes: give him an inch …

- He's giving me a lot more than an inch!

Still I'm proud of the way Cara and I keep the lid on the situation. Hot breath and fumbling, but I'm still intact in the morning.

Another day, another trick question.

- Whit river's Glesca built on?

189

- The Clyde?
- Some Eastender you ur. Ah'll show ye …

So we go tracing the course of the secret Molendinar. After it flows out of Frankfield Loch, it vanishes around Hogganfield but Malky knows a place it bubbles up again in Riddrie Cemetery. Most of the places where it still bursts out from underground the Council's caged it with a grating to stop folk falling in and suing them. But there's a wee open waterfall near the aptly named Molendinar Community Hall.

- Me an the lads used tae play in that wee waterfall bit. Catchin waater beetles an that.
- How do you know so much about the Molendinar? Did your mother tell you?
- Ye're jokin. Googled it.

It takes us much of the afternoon to walk to the next section, off Alexandra Parade.

- Noo it's easy tae follow because it's the exact course o Wishart Street and John Knox Street. Ye cannae see it. But it's still therr, under the tarmac.
- Bubbling away down the years.
- Deep underground.
- From Frankfield Loch to the Clyde.
- See thon Bridge o Sighs?
- Between the Cathedral and the Necropolis?
- Wisnae originally built ower Wishart Street. When it wis built, it spanned the Molendinar, in full flow.
- Right enough, it looks like a bridge over water. Over a natural chasm.
- Then they covered the full length of the Molendinar wi Wishart Street.
- Why?
- Tae stop the weans droonin in it.

We trot along first Wishart Street and then John Knox Street. Familiar road – Dad or Marilyn has driven us along it many a time going to town. A couple of times going to a concert in the Cathedral. Never realised we were driving along a river.

I sneak a glance at Malky striding along beside me. He's developed a more graceful walk. More confident posture. The shambling hoodie's gone. Or maybe it's because I'm now aware that there's more to Malky than meets the eye. Much more.

He feels my eye on him and turns. I quickly pretend to be admiring the foliage at the side of the road.

Walking's different from driving. You take in detail.

Small detail. Wild foxgloves bursting through the tangle behind the Necropolis paling. The dark under the two smaller arches of the Bridge of Sighs.

Big detail. The ugly back end of the Royal Infirmary to the right followed by the rusty green Cathedral on high. To the left, the Necropolis rising. Malky points up to the entrance to the Bridge.

- Gonnae you read that out?
- What – the bit on the wall there?
- Aye. Read it out in a loud voice.
-- Can you not read it yourself?
- Ah wouldnae sound right. You'll read it better.

We go over to it and I see what he means. I clear my throat. My voice sounds thin and tremulous. I clear my throat again and think myself into the persona of a Free Kirk minister.

It takes another couple of clearings of the throat and a glance round to make sure we're alone before my voice rings out up the winding paths, in amongst the statues and gated mausoleums to the feet of John Knox.

This bridge was erected by the Merchants' House of Glasgow, to afford a proper entrance to their

191

> *new cemetery, combining convenient access to the*
> *grounds with suitable decoration to the venerable*
> *cathedral and surrounding scenery, to unite the tombs*
> *of many generations which have gone before with the*
> *resting places of generations yet unborn, where the*
> *ashes of all shall repose until the resurrection of the*
> *just, when that which is born a natural body shall be*
> *raised a spiritual body, when this corruptible must*
> *put on incorruption, when this mortal must put on*
> *immortality, when death is swallowed up in victory.*

For a moment we're lost in rapture. Neither of us giggles.
I'm thrilled by the authority in my own voice and hope that
Malky is too.

- Come an we'll go back here by night? They floodlight
  the Cathedral wi spooky green light.
- Sounds magic.

The Molendinar escapes its culverts just once more, behind
the old Great Eastern Hotel. Here it's more like a canal,
sluggish between high walls, wild flowers and bushes
dipping low from the banks. But it dives into a tunnel and is
invisible until it pours its load into the Clyde.

A couple of times Malky gives me a ride on Stevie's scooter.
He's responsible – gives me Stevie's helmet to wear. He
says the scooter's top speed is 50mph which he rarely
does anyway as he's usually riding in town. I'm not into
dangerous thrills but it's glorious sitting behind Malky, my
arms tight round his waist, the engine roaring underneath us,
the windstream in front and the sun on our backs. I'm always
sorry when the run ends.

The first time it's just a wee hurl to try it out. The second
time we go for a full day. Up the Springburn Road, through
Bishopbriggs and round by the Campsies. Through
Strathblane to this place called Carbeth where there's an inn.
We splash out on Cokes and sit outside at the tables where

192

we can see wee weekend huts folk keep for themselves.

- Sure wan o them wid dae us fine? Wan that's no lived in. Plenty fresh air …
- The air's fresh enough in Red Road 100 metres up. And the view's better. And the town's closer.

He only takes me out on the scooter twice. It's really Stevie's scooter and it's not fully legal for Malky to ride it. He's uneasy about taking a pillion passenger in case something happens. So mostly we walk about.

Once when we're walking hand in hand along Wallacewell Road a car sitting at lights toots at us. I jump, thinking I've been spotted when I'm supposed to be in London.

Full of young men. Don't recognise the grinning driver.

- It's OK. He's no tootin at you. It's ma brother Gordo.
- Ah! The infamous Gordo.
- Well: it's no exactly okay …
- Why not?
- Disnae own a car.
- Maybe the car belongs to a friend.
- Disnae own a drivin licence either.

The lights change and the car bowls on its merry way.

- He's driving reasonably carefully. Don't think they would pick him out for a joy-rider.
- Bet he's an ace driver b'noo. Loadsa practice.

Sometimes we go to YES events. Malky finds out where they are – he's in with so many websites. Gets the Facebook postings from his contacts. Although he likes to think of himself as a loner, he's well-connected on the political blogs.

There are a few events organised round Tommy Sheridan and the slogan 'Hope Over Fear'. It's a great slogan.

Cara has no time for him: Misogynistic, narcissistic, proven liar. What's to like?

But she never has time for anybody. I can see how he drives the crowds wild. First-class orator and a Man of the People. I can find no fault with what he says at these meetings.

Once we go to a Common Weal meeting. Robin McAlpine explains economics in a way even I – who's always hated maths – can understand. Again, I can't fault the logic.

Our wee squat turns into more of a home. Malky gets everything in for me. He does a Sunday paper round on the moped and delivers pizzas one evening a week. With his hard-earned cash he buys me food to supplement what he brings from the house. Food he's heated in the microwave and a gallon bottle of water. He says Stevie's OK about him monopolising the scooter so much – Stevie owes him for past favours.

I miss having ready access to broadband but I read the books I've already downloaded. My Kindle can stay charged for ages. Malky buys me newspapers so I can keep up with the referendum. It seems old-fashioned reading the papers but Malky and Cara and I discuss them in a way you can't when you're reading online.

Then after eating, we play tig or hide and seek, the three of us, on a grand scale, up and down the different floors. When Malky is het, Cara and I coorie together in some old storeroom. Reminds me of the excitement we shared as children. When I'm het she hides along with Malky and I find them squatting on the stairs. Cara herself is never het.

I think Malky would like to play something else but I ward him off. When we spend the night together we kiss and cuddle a bit but I control the progress and he always backs off. He's a bit in awe of me.

Cara still doesn't trust him. When we're out and about she's forever muttering things like 'Now's your chance! Run for it!' Once when we were all out on the balcony and he was hanging over looking at the ground she went 'One quick shove! Go for it!'

But I'm confident he thinks of me as his secret treasure rather than his pet or his prisoner.

Malky sleeps overnight in his own house a few times a week to allay suspicion. Then it's only Cara and me – real spooky.

The longer I stay away the more scared I am of the row I'll get when I go home. The Wrath of Marilyn. Scarier than any spook.

Chapter 8: August

Opinion Poll *(Scottish Daily Mail)*:
YES 41%   NO 47%   DON'T KNOW 12%

Lorraine

The doorbell's still broken. And him gettin hard of hearing. Keep meanin to get him a new one, but forgettin. I chap the door and when there's no response, let myself in with my key.

Four empty beer cans and a half-eaten fish supper still in its polystyrene on the table. The house is freezin. Kenny still in his parka; asleep in his armchair, pitted with cigarette burns. A lit cigarette still in his hand danglin close to the arm of the chair. His mouth slightly open. His chin, furred with grey, trembling with every snore.

I switch on his gas fire.

Ben the kitchenette, last week's dishes in the sink. As I pull on the marigolds I take note yet again to buy Kenny a dishwasher. For my own sake.

I go back to the livin room. Try to shake some life into him. No point in him sleepin his days away. He wakens with a start, breaks into a cough, pulls out his hankie and spits into it.

- There's a debate on the telly tonight, Kenny. Come an we'll watch it thegither?
- Ah'm no interestit in politics. They're aw the same, thae politicians. In it fur theirselves.
- This debate isn't about politicians. It's about …
- Ah know whit it's aboot. Christ on a fuckin bike, thur nothin oan thae days except the referendum.

- It's important, Kenny. It's the most important issue of our times.
- No tae me.

I perch on the arm of his chair. Pick up the remote control.

- Well, anyway. We can watch the news together. See if there's anything about that wee lassie up my close that's missin.
- Whit wee lassie?
- Kirsty Gilchrist. Stays up my close. The police were round the doors again recently. They'd thought she'd run away to London but now there seems to be some doubt about it.

No mention on the news yet of Kirsty. She's not that wee, old enough to have run away after a fight with her parents. Fights with teenagers can be cruel. And apparently Kirsty's run away before.

Another item takes my interest. A discussion about the recently shelved idea to blow up the Red Road flats as part of the entertainment durin the launch of the Commonwealth Games. Watched by the world, Glasgow was to have publicly discarded its 1960s brutalist phase as it had already discarded its No Mean City Phase, its Slum Clearance Phase, its Industrial Phase, its Miles Better Phase, its Capital of Culture Phase. Reinventin itself yet again as a post-modern, bicycle-friendly, environmental UNESCO City of Music.

Kenny's slumped against my shoulder. I heave him upright.

- Look! Where we used to stay! Mind?

No response from Kenny, but I watch spellbound, returning in my head to my world as it once was. Before the Red Road flats.

Today Bridgeton is a neat neighbourhood of new-build maisonettes. Bridgeton in the Swinging Sixties was light years from Carnaby Street. Dark canyons of tenements

197

officially Below Tolerable Standard.

Gas lighting, lamps still out. Under the shadows, children scurryin and squattin, bouncin balls against the walls and under their legs, changin picture scraps at the closemouths, kickin cans and footballs along the cobblestones, markin peever beds with lumps of chalk. The pavement and walls to a level of five foot are a mass of faded chalk markings. 'PD Loves JF. EJ Loves WT. Garry loves Linda. Brenda loves Davie. True by BP'

A pale blue Hillman Imp turns into Heron Street and pulls up. A man in a brown suit emerges. He's carryin a leather folder.

Curtains twitch. Children swarm. Two come right up to him.

- Hi, Mister! Watch yer motor fur a tanner?

The boys look maybe ten years old. Right enough, his car is the only one in the street. He fumbles in his pocket.

- Each!

The second boy extends a blackened palm.

At the entrance to No. 42 he steps over two girls squattin over books of scraps. They stare up, hangin mouths and passive eyes. Scuffed legs below trailing underskirts. To either side – passages into blackness. Before him on the right the passage to the back court – a mess of ash and burst drains. To the left a crumbly flight of stairs, leading to a half-landin where the toilet door hangs off its hinges and a broken window still filters in the dying day.

He climbs, watchin his feet, holding his breath.

The first floor landin: same dark side-shoots. Front door in the middle of the landin wall has a bit of paper with the name 'McGlone'. The floor of the right-hand passage is a mass of evil-smelling rubbish; on either side he can make out the outline of a door, but no names. One of the doors bursts open and a bruiser swaggers out. Scar on eyebrow, rings on fingers.

- Excuse me, is there a family Murphy?
- Tap flerr, son!

Three up, identical lay-out. No names. Middle door stands ajar.

A room some fifteen feet in length and ten feet across. Ammoniac reek. Opposite, curtainless sash window over a stone sink. A swan-necked brass tap trickles onto the mound of dishes. Corner: press with no door, shelves with enamel plates, jam jars and ginger bottles. Against the left-hand wall the only nod at modernity, a yellow formica table set with a handleless cup and two jam jars, ketchup bottle and a half-full milk bottle. Two upright chairs and a black easy chair, horsehair rupturing from its cracks, set beside the range to the right. In the easy chair, a crouched creature in black, gnashin gums, bobbin pipe, rubbin claws, more Witch of Endor than O.A.P. Mattress with a spreading patch, epicentre of the pungency in the centre of the room. A hackin cough behind; bed-recess, sunken man happed in grey linen. Gurgling, retching, spitting with sudden gusto in the general (not specific enough) direction of the range.

- Aye? Whit ye efter?

Wham! The door is kicked open. Pinched-faced woman, draggin a bare-foot infant, eyeless plastic doll.

- She wis away roon No. 44, rakin the midgie!

Swipe across the wean's face.

- An Ah'll lather ye saft if ye dae it again, so Ah wull, rinnin oot wi nae shoes an you wi the cauld!

The infant stares blankly, trickle of mucus running from her nostril into her mouth, pink mark spreading across her cheek.

- Mrs Murphy? I'm fae the Housin Department. Ye've got a new hoose.
- Wherr?

199

- The Red Road.
- The new high-rises?
- That's right. Come to this address on Monday at 9am an ye'll get the key to one of the flats there.

He hands her a card and looks around.

- How many people stay here?
- Jist the fower o us: me, ma man, ma boay Kenny at the school the noo, and ma lassie Lorraine here. Mrs Malarkey therr – she's fae next door.

The old wife takes her pipe out of her mouth and grins.

- Goat anither hoose up yer jaxie fur me, son?

It's great, at first, stayin on floor 27. Havin the space after the single end. Everythin new and fresh-smellin. No more stink of ash and rot and pee and jobbies. No brimmin middens. No leakin drains. Hot runnin water. A bathroom, a dedicated kitchenette. No more shades of grey, brown and black: all the rooms painted different colours. Big bright windows with the sun and sky so very close.

My tubercular Dad succumbs shortly after his first spell sittin out on the wind-ravaged balcony. At least he got a grand view of the Campsies before he went. My mother, Kenny and I reach the outside world by lift and over rubble-strewn waste-ground. Over the hills and far away – to the shops and school.

The primary school years. We chase one another from room to room. On the balcony most days the wind blows your hair nearly right off your head. It wouldnae do to be wearin a bunnet – you'd never see it again. We love havin a wee bit of outside that's just ours. We hang over the balcony lookin at the world below until Mammy yells at us to keep our feet on the ground.

We play on the lifts. Pushin the buttons to go up to the top and down to the bottom, racin each other on different lifts, is enough for us. The vandalism, the jumpin about to jam the lifts: that came years later.

Mammy says we're in the windy city. I think the song was written about us. We're always bein blown in or blown out, across wild and empty spaces. Sometimes in a force 10 gale wind the whole buildin sways like we're in an ocean liner. Once we're evacuated from the top floors and have to huddle in the bottom until the hurricane dies down.

We don't know then about the dangers of asbestos. The white stuff lyin about outside the flats is great – you can use it as chalk to draw up the beds for peever.

I wrote a poem after I grew up about my changin world.

Up and Doon and Roon

When Ah wis wee Glesca wis black
Canyons windin
Tramcaurs grindin
Chalk oan the was
Clickety cobblestanes
Rickety gallus weans

Noo Ah'm big, Glesca's rid
Rubbit raw
Scrubbit braw
Brassy blonde hooses
Rid Squerr n jazz
Razzamataz.

Up oan the skyline
High-rise an pylons
Wind birlin stour
Roon the fowk faur ablow
Wide yawnin space

Wi nivver a trace
O the tramcaurs and canyons
We knew lang ago.

It's weird being so far away from the shops and traffic. But later they lay on entertainment underground. Tailor-made for the likes of us. Pub, bingo hall and bookies. Folk take taxis from miles around to come to the bingo under the Red Road flats.

I like the Red Road flats.

I like them for rescuin my family from the dirt and stink and smoke and squalor and cold and overcrowding and decay that killed my Dad, exhausted my mother and stunted my infancy.

I like them for raisin all our horizons – literally – beyond Glasgow to the distant hills.

I like them – and all the so-called 'brutalist' blocks of the 1960s – Sighthill, Bluevale, Whitevale, Yoker, Wyndford, Hutchesontown, Shawbridge, Kennishead and the Drum – for givin Glasgow the profile of a multi-dimensional city.

I like them and their surroundings for being created from start to finish for the use of the poor. Schools, community halls, public libraries, local government outposts, plain but well-equipped affordable housing.

I like them, and although my own needs have moved on, I'm sad to see them go and glad they'll be given a solemn end.

The telly topic has also moved on. Another discussion about the Commonwealth Games. I nudge Kenny again.

- They were showin the Red Road flats. You missed it all.

Kenny just grunts.

Time to make tracks. As I pick up my bags and rise, I glimpse something shockin pink sticking out of the corner of the muddy brown couch.

Even Kenny these days possesses a mobile phone, but it's the last century kind, without a screen. Doesnae play music, help you navigate streets, or connect you to the sum of human knowledge.

It's certainly no shockin pink and stuck over with hearts and stars.

On the back there's a word spelt out in alphabet stickers. KIRSTY.

I feel cold.

* * *

Iqbal

Farooq comes downstairs to call me into their house for dinner. As soon as I enter I feel a chill in the air. Ali's in his armchair glaring at Bina.

- What's wrong? Have you been quarrelling?
- The children are so headstrong. They've no respect for their parents.
- That's a stage Catriona and I still have to look forward to!
- Noor's annoyed. Bina's told Mrs Morrison that we'll take in one of her cats. Without consulting her mother or me!

I turn my own frown on Bina.

- What are you thinking of? Something big like that and it'll live maybe fifteen years. You might have left home, be married, and your Ammi still has to clean up after the cat!
- I'll clean up after the cat! And if I get married I'm gonnae take the cat with me!

203

- Your husband'll have something to say about that!
- I'll no marry anybody that doesnae love cats!

Ali cut in:

- And then there's Yasmin.
- What's she up to?
- She wants to go to drama school!
- Drama school!

I start to laugh.

- I told you what would happen if they spent all day watching movies!
- It's not funny. She's a clever girl from a good family. She has to use her brains. Study medicine or law. A serious profession.
- Her head's been turned by glamour. She's got years before she has to decide. Anyway – who knows? Maybe she'll be a big Bollywood star!

Catriona calls us through to the kitchen to eat. As we sit round the table, Ali notices somebody's missing.

- Where's Yasmin?
- Out. (Noor)
- Where? (Ali)
- She said she was going to a cafe. (Noor)
- She should be eating with her family. (Ali)
- She's fourteen. She doesn't want to be always eating with her family. She wants to go out with her friends. (Noor)
- She's gallivanting too much! (Ali)

Catriona hands a bit of chapati to baby Bobby. She wipes the milk moustache from Lena's upper lip.

- Listen, Bina. Your Ammi and I have been talking things over. If it makes it easier the cat can come and live with us.

Bina frowns.

- I want it to be my cat.
- It can still be your cat. Only it'll live in our house. And as long as we're still here you can pop in and see it whenever. (Catriona)
- What do you mean "as long as you're still here?" (Noor)
- If it lives in your house it'll no be my cat! (Bina)
- So are you seriously thinking of moving away? (Ali)

I turn the talk back to cats.

- Just a moment. I didn't hear anybody asking me if I want to share my home with a cat. (Me)
- What kind of person wouldnae want to live with a beautiful wee kitten? With silky fur and big eyes? (Bina)
- Maybe a mouse? (Farooq)
- Anyway, Auntie Catriona's out teachin all day. The cat'll be lonely. We should have it in our house where Ammi can keep it company. (Bina)
- And if Ammi doesn't want to keep it company? (Noor)

We finish our meal. Noor, Catriona and Bina begin clearing the plates. The front door opens and in walks Yasmin. We all stare at her.

- What's that on your face? (Ali)
- She's wearing make-up. (Noor)
- You're only fourteen. Go and wash your face. (Ali)

Yasmin goes over to Ali.

- Baba, I've something to ask you. There's a course I want to go on. But it costs money.
- What kind of course? (Ali)

- A course with the Scottish Youth Theatre. (Yasmin)
- You're a girl from a good family. You're not going on to the stage. (Ali)
- How much money? (Noor)
- £300. (Yasmin)

During the hullabaloo which follows, I catch Bina's eye. She's smiling. I lean over and whisper to her:

- No sense of timing, your sister.
- I'll pick my own moment, Uncle. And you'll see: I'm gonnae get my kitten.

* * *

Lorraine

The phone's battery's run out. I should take it right away to the police. But …

- Angie, pet, can I borrow your phone charger?
- Doesn't fit yours.
- Just want to try something.
- Well, put it back after, OK?

It fits. I leave it cookin and pace about until I force myself to sit down at my computer and get stuck into some reports I've to finish by tomorrow.

* * *

Ewan

It took several Facebook messages. She wasn't keen. But when I Facetimed her, that did it. Face to face I'm persuasive. That's why I'm a good canvasser. So here I am, walking through Alison's front door to visit my sprog.

Her building has similarities to our own. Same vintage.

Same sort of tiling in the close. But it's a corner building and so an off beat shape of floor area. Three flats to a landing. And located in the West End.

Alison's living-room has unusual cornicing: unicorns picked out in gold. Donald's is an abstract tangle of fruit and flowers.

Where our own flat's an easy walk from George Square and Strathclyde University, this one's an easy walk from Byres Road and Glasgow University. And Kelvingrove Park. And the Botanic Gardens. This flat would fetch a pretty penny on the market. More than twice what poor old Donald would get for ours ... for his.

It's my first meeting with Alison since that day, apart from the time I followed her at a distance from the YES Bar. She's plain and neat. Nothing outstanding in her appearance. Not flashy, not dowdy. Not attractive, not repulsive. I can see why she's 40ish and single. I hope the baby takes after me in looks.

I go and admire Calum. Sitting semi-upright in a bouncy chair. My stake in the future. His eyes meet mine. Fat cheeks and snub nose. Tuft of blonde fluff on an otherwise bald head. No indication in his unformed features of how he'll look later. I hold out my finger and he seizes it. Pink clean digits, perfect miniature fingernails. He smiles a gummy smile.

- Fine little fellow.
- He's advanced for his age. He can sit up on his own and he's keen to use his hands.
- Amazing.
- Soon I won't be able to leave him alone in the room for even a minute.
- You've plenty space here. For you and the baby.
- Come and I'll show you this.

She leads me up an internal spiral stair to the side. We emerge into a circular room, with porthole windows around the walls. 360 degree view. Two parks, a river and the gothic university tower. Great Western Road soaring off into the sunset. The higgledy-piggledy unplanned angular slates of Glasgow's West End.

The turret room itself is relatively bare. Unpolished floorboards. An easel. Some frames. A few paintings stacked against the wall. A jumble of paint boxes and tubes in the corner.

Magnificent.

- I always wondered what was inside these top floor turrets! Do you paint?
- Used to. Went to art school.
- Glasgow Art School? Terrible about the fire.

Don't tell her I once applied and got rejected.

- I know. Particularly that it's the library took the brunt. When I was a student that was my very favourite room in the world.
- So how long have you lived here?
- My parents put up the deposit. We thought this turret would be an ideal studio for me with the light and the views. The plan was I would share with a friend who'd help cover the mortgage payments and afterwards it could be an investment.
- And now?
- I've had flatmates off and on down the years. Nobody at the moment.

She smiles.

- Got to get one soon or flit.
- That would be a pity.
- I'll miss the turret. Not that I do much painting anymore. I'm a graphic designer, all computer based. I'm on maternity leave and Willie Winkie takes up

120% of my time.

- Have you advertised for a flatmate?
- I reckon Calum's a turnoff for most of them.
- So what kind of rent would you be looking for from this flatmate?

The sum she mentions is less than I'm paying now to Donald.

- The mortgage payments are low – I bought the place yoinks ago. And my folks put up a sizeable deposit.

We descend again and return to the Moses basket and look down on the sprog. His eyes are blue. Mine are brown.

Alison goes to the kitchen. I try to think of conversation openers suitable for a five-month old infant. By the time she comes back with the coffee I still haven't thought of any.

- How do you know I'm the father?

Alison just looks at me.

- I mean – a one-night stand. Couldn't there be …

Alison sets down the tray, lays out the coffee and biscuits and pulls up two chairs.

- It can only be you. Up till then I'd practised safe sex. I tried to get pregnant that night.
- You didn't even know me …
- I was 39. No partner. Didn't know if I wanted a partner. I was self-sufficient. But I did want a baby.
- Why me?
- You were on the spot. You were … you don't look like a half-chewed caramel. Wouldn't be a total chore.
- Shucks.
- You told me you'd taught English abroad and volunteered in Africa and so you hopefully had some brain and a sense of ethics. You were attending a National Collective event and so maybe had some pretensions to creativity. I'd been long enough with

my employers that they'd have to give me paid
maternity leave.

- Cool decision.
- Then there was the weed.
- Not entirely cool, then.
- Then I asked around about you the next day and
discovered …
- Discovered … what?
- You're gay.

She stares at the table. Looks me in the eye.

- Gay or bi or whatever. And promiscuous.
- Not very promiscuous. Honestly. I'm generally safe
and faithful. You were an aberration.
- Blame it on the boogie?
- Blame it on the referendum.

I pat her on the hand and withdraw it again.

- I get tested at Sandyford Road from time to time and
I've always been clear. Of everything.
- Well, I went there and was clear too. But I'd already
missed a couple of periods by then and they confirmed
I was pregnant.
- What do you want from me?
- I told you. Nothing.
- I mean, just now you're on paid maternity leave. But
when you go back – maybe you'll want to work part-
time or something. Money can be tight for a lone
parent …
- We'll manage. You didn't ask for this. I engineered it.
Are you single?
- I'm in a civil partnership.
- Well, you'll not want your partner finding out about

210

this.

I mentally go through telling Donald.

- Not at the moment. Maybe eventually.
- Do you plan to stay together?
- Ye-e-s. Though …
- Though?
- He's a NO.
- Och, well, that's grounds for divorce!

We both laugh.

Awkwardly.

* * *

Lorraine

The pink phone must be charged by now.

Lots of messages in bold. The owner hasnae checked for some time, either here or elsewhere. Should I open one of them before handin it in to the police?

I suppose I really have to hand it in to the police?

A swarm of Jiminy Crickets surround me:

What are you thinking? Would you want a stranger checking out your messages?

By removing it from Kenny's flat you were possibly disturbing a crime scene!

What if this phone does belong to the missin girl! You're keeping information from Kirsty's family!

If it was your girl, your girl's phone …!

But …

If Kenny has had something to do with this would you want the police to interrogate him before you do?

And … I force myself …

211

If you were to find out that Kenny … would you … will you … turn him in?

Kenny would never … Kenny wouldnae hurt a fly.

The first email message is from somebody called Watcheratyourdoor:

'Kidnapped by aliens? We should be so lucky.'

This from Watcherinthesky:

'So U R missin. Good fuckin riddance. Hope U R lying in a midden wi Ur throat cut.'

Now comes Watcherinyourbed:

'Hope they shag U bandy U wee toerag.'

Well, this paedophile isnae turnin on the charm.

These are messages from just after the date when Kirsty was reported missing.

Those from before her disappearance are different in tone:

'U will no get hame the night with Ur rubbish looks intact. No way Jose!' (Watcherinthesky)

'We know what way you go home. We'll be waiting'. (Watcheratyourdoor)

'U watch Ur back coming out of school.' (Watcherinyourbed)

'Naewhere to hide – Ur ginger nut gies U away.' (Watcherinthesky)

If he's groomin her, he's way past the stage of flattery. Could be a stalker, issuin threats.

Poor Kirsty. All her messages – apart from spam – are from Watcherinthesky, Watcheratyourdoor or Watcherinyourbed.

No friends. Just foes.

Doesnae look like a paedo. More like peer-to-peer bullying. Here's me pontificatin about it to my colleagues and there's a case of it up my own close.

I turn on the phone texts. Threats are now specific. Three different numbers involved, all down as unknown. So poor Kirsty maybe doesnae even know who her enemies are.

> *'When you're on a platform waiting on a train I'll be behind you. One wee shove.'*

> *'Been sharpening up ma Mammy's kitchen knife for U, hen.'*

> *'Hope U R a heavy sleeper. I'm on ma way. Pillow over Ur face.'*

I look at the three unknown numbers. Could one of them be Kenny's? Maybe not the one mentionin Mammy, but one of the others?

In the days of landlines, I knew lots of phone numbers. Didnae have to learn them – they engraved themselves through usage. But now the only mobile number I know is my own.

I get my own phone and bring up Kenny. Mega whew. None of the numbers match his.

Now I know Kenny hasnae been responsible for the threatenin calls I must hand the phone in at the police station.

Where will I say I found it? If I admit I found it in Kenny's house they'll focus their attention on him. With his record, they might try to pin it on him. Maybe plant evidence to hurry things along? How far do I trust the police if there's pressure to clear up a case?

But if I say I found it in the street or on a number 38 bus, I could be sendin them along the wrong track while poor Kirsty is … starvin in a cellar, suffocatin in a grave …

No choice. Have to tell them the truth.

Just before I pop the phone in my bag, I try one last thing. I dial the first unknown number using my own mobile, key in 141 first.

I hear a phone ringin from through the wall.

Angela's name appears on my phone's display.

When her light bright voice answers, I hang up.

* * *

Donald

Down the Ponderosa, they show us the Better Together Referendum Political Broadcast they're considerin puttin out. They want our opinions on it.

Apocalypse Now.

Children walkin along a perilous cliff top. Down below, the UK is physically ripped apart. Girders crackin, oil spurtin out from broken pipes. All the disaster movies ever made condensed into ten minutes.

We're doubtful – bit OTT. I get a mental picture of Ewan laughin himself silly over it. I hope they don't put it on the air. Mind you, it's been an expensive production. Went to town on the special effects. Don't know how the cost compares with a panto at the Pavilion. We could do with more humour at Better Together. But this is the kind of thing people laugh at rather than with.

Back home Ewan girns:

- You BT types don't have the courage of your convictions. We've been trying to arrange debates all over the city. It's impossible. Either the NO side say nobody's available or else they agree and then don't turn up.

- I've an idea. Instead of po-faced hustings, why don't you and I put on a review. A cabaret show. You dance on to the stage, caper about and present an argument for independence and then I dance on and counter it. Maybe we could get it on that Referendum TV internet channel they're runnin during the Edinburgh Festival.

- Ah, the Festival. Would that be the Festival whose director airbrushed the referendum right out of the programme?
- So what did you see on that Fringe Binge you went to last week with the National Collective luvvies? What was it again … the Villains, the Vote and the Black Black Oil; Pure Dead and Brilliant; Scotland's Referendum Fest …
- Thanks to the Fringe's open mic policy. Otherwise they'd have censored it out of that too. Good old Guerrilla Cinema.

When Ewan returns two hours later, sweatin from climbing forty sets of tenement stairs, I announce:

- Eat your heart out, National Collective!

With a flourish I present my script.

Ewan (dressed in Bonny Prince Charlie gear, dancing across stage from left to right) sings to the tune of The Road to Dundee:

'The oil in the North Sea will make us all wealthy; the oil in the North Sea will make us all rich.'

Donald (dressed as Britannia, dancing across stage from right to left) sings:

'If you think there's much oil left you've bats in the belfry; the oil millionaire plan lies dead in the ditch.'

Ewan sings: 'No wars and disorder, no nuclear deterrents.'

Donald sings: 'Behind our new border, fall out with our friends.'

Ewan sings: 'The pound in your pocket will stay there forever.'

Donald: 'Despite your endeavour this is where it ends.'

I search his face for the hint of a chuckle. Or a wry grin.

Anything but a sneer.

- How long did you take thinking this up?
- It's ironic. Like Lady Alba and her "Bad Romance".
- It's not remotely like Lady Alba. Not even on the starting blocks. Better Together relies on a failure of the imagination and this effort proves you're right on message.

He chucks my poor old script on the floor.

When he comes back with a coffee, I try again. I sit on the arm of his chair and slip my arm round his shoulder.

- Ewan, what's happened to us? Where's your sense of humour? Is this referendum going to be the death of us? Of US, I mean.
- Hope not. I really do hope not. But it's hard. I take it more seriously than you do …
- People on the side of change always do.
- … and we live separate lives. Me and my YES events, you and … whatever.
- We have somethin good. I hope it's strong enough …
- I hope so too.

Our eyes meet. Our lips. The trail of rising passion leads us to bed.

Afterwards:

- You say I don't take the campaign as seriously as you do. That's what I've always felt about our relationship.
- I take our relationship more seriously than you do?
- Other way round. Obviously.
- Why's that obvious?

Now, at the wrong time, comes the smile which was missin before. I hate Ewan when he's disingenuous. Forcin me to praise him. His self-esteem at the expense of mine.

- You're younger than I am …
- Sugar-daddy!
- … and better-looking.
- All in the eye of the beholder.
- Full head of hair, smooth skin, flat stomach.

I touch each of Ewan's attributes.

- Shucks.
- Yes – that's your catchphrase when you're complimented. I've never been complimented often enough to develop a catchphrase.
- Poor little lamb!

I put on a petted lip. He kisses it lightly.

- Tell you what. I forgive you for being NO if you forgive me for being YES. Deal?
- Deal.

We can get over this. I know it.

The light from the window dims as we lie there. His head on my arm. My arm gets pins and needles but I keep it there as long as I can.

I'm about to rise and put on my bathrobe when he speaks again.

- Something else. May the accused ask for another offence to be taken into account?
- Of course.

My smile freezes. I slip my arm out from under from his shoulder.

- I've got a son.
- What!

I sit bolt upright. Switch on the bedside lamp. Turn to face him.

- Why d'you no tell me?

217

- Only found out the other day.

I try to think of something which won't sound insanely jealous.

- Come on, Donald. We've never pretended to be maidens.
- Some of us are more maidenly than others.
- You've never shagged a woman?

I hesitate. The early days, in denial.

- No very successfully.
- I told you I'd swung both ways in the past.
- What age is the wee fella?
- Three.
- So it happened …
- Long before us.

'Long' is an exaggeration but I let it go.

- Are you in touch with … ?
- No. Only found out through Facebook.
- So you've never seen …

Ewan seems far away. I nuzzle his ear to bring him back and to pretend I'm not angry.

- Ewan? Have you seen the child?
- No. It was a one-night-stand. She doesn't want interference or support. Wants to keep the baby to herself.
- Surely you're curious …?
- You're enough for me to be curious about.

He caresses the back of my neck, sending a shiver down my spine.

- It's over and done with. You needn't feel threatened.
- Don't feel threatened.

- Yes you do.
- Are you still drawn to women?

Ewan shrugged.

- I was exploring my sexuality.
- You were in denial. You're no still explorin your sexuality in your thirties.

Ewan. Eternal Peter Pan. How can anybody in his mid-thirties look so fresh?

- You'll feel some satisfaction that you've left a gene-pool. Your legacy.
- You're the only legacy I need. You … and … independence.

Sting in the tail.

* * *

Ewan

Less than a month to go and I still haven't canvassed my own street. I send Mike and Caroline to do it. The neighbours will be more honest to strangers.

Coming back home Agnes Morrison opens her close door.

- That you back fae campaignin?
- Yeah. Most nights, now. It's getting close.
- So wis that your fowk roon the doors?
- My team, yes.
- Ye know, Ah cannae make up ma mind. Ah wis Naw, but noo Ah'm no sure. D'ye see yon party political broadcast fur NO the ither day?
- With the housewife?
- Ah wisnae that struck on hur, were you? The wey she wis talkin, women shouldnae bother votin, should

leave it aw tae the men. We should stick to wur
housework.

Take every chance when it presents itself.

- So you haven't made up your mind. Would you like
  somebody to come up and discuss it with you?
- Aye, that wid be great. Ah know ye're awfy busy
  though. Ah'm no waantin tae take up yer time.
- Not at all. Don't be daft. What day would suit you?
- Ah'm free maist o the time. Whitever suits you. Ah'll
  bake a cake an we can huv a wee cuppa tea …

Scene unfolds. Mrs Morrison, me and a home-baked cake.
Having to eat several slices. Listening to her gossip for an
hour or two. Hours that could be spent converting lots of
people, not just one. Or meeting my work deadlines. Or even
watching the box with Donald.

- You mentioned that housewife's patronising attitude.
  Might be better if a woman talks to you about it.
- Whitever ye think. Aw wan tae me.
- Lorraine's the very one.
- Lorraine Murphy? Fae oor close? Och aye – she's a
  nice lady.
- She's been helping us now and then. I'll email her.

I submit the results from my street into the YESMO database.
Interesting when it's people you know.

Up my own close Iain MacLean's not at home. Rarely is.
Works mainly in India, training call centre workers.

Both the Usmanis and the Akrams are happy about it.
Gratitude for the SNP Government letting small businesses
off with their rates? Maybe self-employed people are
predisposed towards independence? Maybe an atavistic folk
memory of the Indian wars of Independence.

I get a surprise with the Czech building workers three up.

I'd assumed that Czechs, with their history, would applaud any country seeking self-government. In the event, they're hostile. Even angry about it. Caroline scribbles on the side of the sheet:

- He said: If you saw the disaster zone Slovakia has become since splitting away from Czech, you wouldn't contemplate it!

How does the rhyme go?

Big fleas have little fleas,
Upon their backs to bite 'em,
And little fleas have lesser fleas,
and so, ad infinitum.

Back home I google Slovakia in case it arises again. Apparently:

Alex Salmond used it to show where there's a will there's a way. He said the formation of the Czech and Slovak republics after a few months of negotiation 'demonstrate that once the popular will is determined constitutional discussions can be concluded in good time'.

By the time of the global financial crisis, Slovakia's economy was growing so fast it was known as the 'central European tiger'. The *New Statesman* hails it as 'one of Europe's quiet successes'. The *Economist* Intelligence Unit has forecast that Slovakia's GDP will grow three and a half times faster than that of the Czech republic. And no one ever talks of reuniting.

The story of Slovakia should be compulsory reading for Unionists.

* * *

Donald

Ewan's just gone out when there's a ring at the door. Iain MacLean from up the stair.

- I need a form for a proxy vote in the referendum. I'm going to be away in Mumbai.
- You can download them online.
- My printer's on the blink. Have you any printed out?
- I don't, but I think Ewan has.

I feel guilty diggin into Ewan's box files of political intel. I suspect he wouldnae be pleased if he knew. I wouldnae be happy about a YES activist lookin through my notes. No that I ever bring intel home.

- I know Ewan's YES. But I heard you're NO. Is that right?
- Yes.
- So am I. I was wondering: would you be my proxy?
- Anybody can be your proxy. Doesnae have to be votin one way or the other.
- Ewan's your partner. Would you trust him to mark the ballot paper the way you want him to?

I consider. In the unlikely event that Ewan asked me to go proxy for him, I would be delighted that he trusted me. I wouldnae consider breakin that trust. It wouldnae be my vote I would be castin. It would be Ewan's. I would never lose sight of that.

But the other way round …

- Let's sit down. We can fill up the forms together.
- I've been talking to my neighbours across the landing.
- The Czech guys?
- Yeah. Jan and Zack. When I'm back in the country we sometimes go for a pint together. They were telling

me what a mess Slovakia's been in since it broke away from the Czech Republic.

After he goes away, I google Slovakia. Interestin light shed on what was at the time hailed as a 'velvet divorce'.

It's as he says. The people were never consulted. In neither Czech nor Slovakia was there a popular majority for independence. Durin the followin decade relations between the two were 'at freezing point'. There was a general loss of influence in the world. The Czech Foreign Minister said the international weight of both republics together was less than that of the former Czechoslovakia. There were economic challenges, particularly for Slovakia, the weaker part. The Director-General of the CBI said Slovakia's independence had 'cost the country 4% of its GDP in the following year'.

The story of Slovakia should be compulsory reading for separatists.

* * *

Agnes

Today's the day Lorraine fae up the stair is comin in to talk to me aboot the referendum.

When Alasdair wis wee Ah used to sometimes bake a cake, but these days a cake widnae get eaten in ma hoose. Ah'd eat a slice the first day and anither the second and mebbe a third the next toasted up wi butter. Then it would be like a brick. Fit fur the birds.

No worth the effort. If Ah want a bit cake the supermarket's doon the road.

But this time doon the supermarket Ah buy ingredients.

Comin back Ah notice the thistle in the Gilchrists' gairden has come intae full bloom. Two foot high wi a purple toorie. Rab musta forgot tae cut it doon. An him such a keen gairdener.

223

Hope it disnae spread its down aw ower ma gairden.

Don't mind a wee sprinklin o wild flowers. Daisies are bonny, especially if they're pink-tipped. Ah've a few speedwells come up and tint the grass in May. Whit's yon famous paintin of a wee lassie: 'The Little Speedwell's Darling Blue'. But jaggy thistles pushin up through ma lawn – no thanks.

Aw the time Ah'm stirrin an kneadin, Ah'm hummin 'If I knew you were coming I'd have baked a cake …'

A chocolate cake, studded wi cherries. Turns oot no bad. At the last minute, I go oot again to the supermarket and buy some icin sugar and pipe YES ? NO across the top. Ma haun shakes a wee bit but ye can read it fine.

Efter the bakin, the place is even mair of a guddle than usual. I spend the next coupla hoors wipin doon the kitchen, hooverin and dustin the livin-room. Sprayin the bathroom where the litter tray's kept.

She'll no be ben the bedrooms.

The kittens huv a rerr terr, pouncin on the feather duster an the flyin bits of oose but runnin away fae the hoover. Unlike me they love hoosework. Pity they cannae dae it fur me.

Ah've been roon aw the neighbours wi the kittens an got a knock-back. But mebbe Lorraine'll change hur mind when she sees their douce wee buttoned-up faces. Ah pick up Bertie. His airms an legs spreadeagle oot tryin tae catch a haud o somethin.

- Yese'll need tae be on yer best behaviour.

Bright eyes, six faces pointin the same way comin oot the mound o their bodies. Pits me in mind o somethin. Somethin many-headed. Film Ah seen or book Ah read. Science fiction or Greek mythology or somethin.

Mebbe she'll want two.

Ah lay the cake on the kitchen table wi a bowl ower it tae keep away the cats. Ah pit oot sugar, sweeteners, wee jug o milk, teaspoons an plates. I pick two mugs – the wan my

224

cousin gied me wi a thistle tae show Ah'm patriotic and the wan Alasdair gied me wi 'Copacabana' tae show Ah'm no parochial. Ah brush ma herr and slap on a daud o lipstick. Ah sit doon and switch on the telly.

Cannae settle.

7.00. Really, tae be fair Ah should invite a NO campaigner tae come roon an pit their side an aw. But Ah don't know ony NO campaigners. Rab Gilchrist thinks Donald up the sterr's involved on the NO side, but surely no when he's livin wi Ewan? Ah've never seen him goin oot on the trail the wey Ewan does aw the time.

7.05. Fowk hardly ever arrive dead on.

7.10. When Ah used tae visit fowk Ah wis always late. Better late than catchin them oan the hop.

7.20. It's no as if she's a long way tae come.

7.30. Don't think Ah've got her phone number. Wonder if she's in the book? Hardly onybody is, nooadays. Maist fowk don't have house phones – jist mobiles.

7.35. Don't think she's got my number either. Ah'm ur in the book, but. Maybe she disnae get a book, if she's no on the phone.

8.00. Should Ah go up an knock her door? Bit pathetic, chasin her up like that. She'll think Ah'm a bored, lonely auld wife.

8.10 Doot she's forgot. Busy dame. Workin aw day and campaignin aw night. Single parent an aw. Ah'll no be number wan in her priorities.

8.20 Or even number wan hundred an forty three.

8.30 Thur absolutely nothin on the telly. Hunners o channels – aw mince.

8.45 Ah pit oan ma outdoor shoes an fix the Yale back on ma close door.

* * *

Lorraine

I go to Angela's bedroom door. Knock and wait. It's locked.
I knock harder.

- OK, OK, OK!

She opens. I shove my foot in the door.

- Well?

How do I tackle this? My trainin deserts me.

- What is it? Your best friend fall under a bus?
- Have you been textin Kirsty Gilchrist?

Her sneer turns into somethin uglier.

- Are you checking up on me? Going through my
  phone?
- No.

I hold out the pink phone.

- Goin through hers.
- Where did you …

She snatches but I'm faster. I push her backwards into the
room and am in myself before she can bar me.

- What about the emails? Which are you: Watcher in
  the Sky? In the Bed …?
- How dare you invade my privacy …
- … This is a girl who's missing. Missing. Children kill
  themselves over online bullyin …
- Then they're idiots.

She sits on the bed. Reaches for her own phone.

- You're just my mother. I'm not one of your cases.
- So what are you? My daughter?

Doesn't look up. Thumbs busy on her phone.

- I don't know you! You're a monster!

She looks up at that.

- Monster? Did you say "monster?" Some social worker you are. What about "Whoever murdered these people needs help?" You'll get drummed out the Brownies.
- Should be drummed out, producin a daughter like you.
- Whatever.

She focuses again on her phone. I chance lowerin mysel into a chair, my back to the door.

- Why, Angela? Tell me why you joined forces with other cowards to torment this poor girl.
- Cowards?
- Three against one. Cowards.

She shrugs.

- What did she do to you?

She shrugs again. Footers with her phone.

Around us are the evolvin crazes of Angela's childhood. My own old Teddy on the bed, eyes missin. Window sill o dusty friends: Furby, Barbie, Tamagotchi. Polly Pocket house with Polly and all the furniture gone AWOL. Dressin table wi today's support systems: rings, ear-rings, bracelets and chains hangin on a miniature coatstand. Colours and scents spillin out o three wee treasure chests. On the bed her laptop, hair straightener and hairdryer.

- Do you realise the trouble you're in? Deletin your own messages won't help. When I hand Kirsty's phone in to the police …

That makes her look up.

- What? Grass us in …?
- Kirsty's missin. Maybe kidnapped. Maybe murdered. This phone's vital evidence. I've no choice.

I rise, turn to the door. Angela hurls herself at me. Throws

227

me to the floor. I land painfully on my elbow but keep a grip on the phone. We wrestle. 50-year-old versus 16-year-old. 11 stone versus 7 stone. She bites my hand till it bleeds. I let go Kirsty's phone.

I rise, chase after her, runnin out the room, runnin out the front door.

* * *

Agnes

Shoutin. They're in. Ah chap the door, softly, then louder. Rattle their knocker.

The door opens. It's the lassie, Angela.

- Yer Mammy said she wis comin roon the night, hen …

- If you want tae talk to her, she's in.

She runs past me, doon the sterr an oot the close.

Next minute Lorraine bursts oot efter her, wild-eyed an starin. She looks at me but disnae see me. She runs halfway doon the sterr.

- Angela! You come back here!

Ah've come at a bad time. Ah go back doon the sterr. In the close, Lorraine an Angela are fightin. Actually brawlin. No ma business. Ah let masel in. Scoopin up Bertie an Stripey, keekin roon for a wee adventure. In the kitchen, Ah lift the bowl and look at the cake. YES?NO. Ah pick up a knife.

* * *

Lorraine

We nearly knock down Agnes Morrison on the stair.

Angela stops at the close door and starts again feverishly deletin messages. I catch up wi her. Another struggle.

228

Marilyn Gilchrist comes out her own close door to see what's goin on. At the sight of her, Angela hides Kirsty's phone behind her back. I manage to retrieve it, make it back up the stair and into my house. I shut the front door on my changeling of a daughter and put the chain on.

I postpone the moment by bathin the bite on my hand in antiseptic, puttin on stickin plaster. I picture Angela up before the Rector, barred from returnin for a fifth year to sit her Highers. I picture Kenny's bewildered face, monstered on all the redtops of the land.

Then I phone the police.

* * *

Malky

Kirsty husnae said onythin tae me, but Ah get the feelin she's soon gonnae gie hursel up.

It's been a magic two month but Ah knew it couldnae last forever.

Ah'm sorry it's comin tae an end an Ah huvnae managed tae make it intae the sack wi hur. We got close a coupla times. Ah think if Ah'd gone right fur it and kept oan at hur she wad hae let me in the end. Fur the sake o peace. But then she'd o thought Ah wis the same as aw the ither boays. Ah waant hur tae see me as somethin special.

On the plus side Ah've landit masel a girlfriend. Ah kin defo think of her like that even though we've no done it. We've shared mair emotional intimacy than aw thae ither cunts at school that are in and oot o wan anither's pants. Intellectual intimacy an aw. We discuss politics, philosophy, psychology, and wan anither's dysfunctional faimilies. Ah'm hur best friend as well as hur lumber. An she's mine an aw.

* * *

229

Agnes

So looks like Lorraine's no gonnae come and discuss the vote wi me. Ah'll huv tae make up ma ain mind.

Ah wis never that bothered aboot politics. If Ah'd time, Ah read the political columns in the papers efter Ah'd finished the news an the features an the letters.

But Ah've ayeways voted. Fowk died fur the right tae vote. Ma granny telt me aboot the Suffragettes. Hur pal Sadie went on the mairches. Ordinary workin weemin got caught up in the fightin, sent tae the jile. Some had their weans taken aff them. Weemin in thae days hud nae rights, no even ower the babies that they gied birth to. If Ah missed ma vote Ah'd be letting weemin like Sadie doon.

It's aye been Labour like everybody else – pairty o the workin man. Never really thought aboot Scotland daein its ain thing. But noo there's this referendum an suddenly it's everywhere.

Ah open the paper. First thing hits my eye: 'A vote for independence would be irrevocable'.

They aw say that. Again and again. Irrevocable. Irreversible. 'No going back'.

Scary word that. Even if it's good, ye haud back if ye think it's irrevocable.

Sign here and the lovely three-piece suite is yours. Only £20 a month.

Eh … is it true Ah get a fortnight tae chinge ma mind?

Gorgeous wee kitten. Right pet meowin up at me. But here, a kitten's no just fur Christmas, it's for life. Eh … no thanks, then.

Ach. Need tae get ma mind aff kittens and on tae referendums.

Haud on a wee minute. Whit wey is votin fur independence irrevocable? The Government doon in London's tryin tae hang on tae us wi aw they've got. Threatenin us wi the

Fower Horsemen o the Apocalypse if we vote YES. They peyed fur this advert aboot how irrevocable it's aw gonnae be if we vote YES. Wi oor taxes.

So if we did vote YES, an it aw went pear-shaped, surely they'd welcome us back wi open airms?

Unprecedented. Anither scary word. Well, Ah'm auld enough tae know it's no unprecedented. Lotsa countries huv won their independence within ma lifetime, fae the UK or fae ither countries. India. Ireland. Ghana. Kenya. French Indo-China, that turnt intae Vietnam and gied the USA a run fur their money.

Sae let's think noo. Whit happened tae the wans that asked tae get took back in?

Ah think.

Cannae come up wi a single country that's asked tae get took back in.

There must be some. Wish Ah wis good wi thon Google cairry-on – Ah could look it up.

Ah've seen a few referendums in ma day. The Common Market wan in 1975. By the time they allowed us tae vote on it we were awready in.

The devolution wan in 1979. Willie an me didnae get tae vote because we wur away on holiday on the Costa del Sol. Wur first foreign holiday – Willie an me an wee Alasdair.

It wis rerr. We got that burnt wi the sun. We hardly even thought aboot the vote. We widnae a been allowed postal votes onywey. In thae days ye could only apply fur a postal vote if ye were sent oot the country fur yer work. Holidays ye jist missed oot.

It wis only efterwards wi aw yon fuss aboot the country votin YES an still no gettin wur Assembly, that Willie an me realised missin the vote pit us in wi the NO camp because o the 40% rule.

In 1997 Ah voted NO onywey. Ah wis aulder then, mair set in ma weys. Ah wis stressed oot at work, lookin forward tae retirin an no sure whit ma pension wis gonnae be. Naebody at work talked aboot the referendum much. Ma boss said it wid jist be an expensive talkin shop. The shop steward – Labour tae his marrow – wis agin it, even though it wis a Labour bill. He telt me in the long run it could be the slippery slope tae independence an that could affect the pensions.

An tae be honest, Ah looked aboot me at ma fellow Scots an reckoned we couldnae run a minodge, never mind a country. Forever fightin amang wursels. Rangers an Celtic. An look at how we run Glasgow City Cooncil – full o corruption.

But here, the vote went tae YES, an we did get wur ain Parliament. An tae ma astonishment they've run it very well. Baith Labour in thur day an noo the SNP.

Brought in benefits they widnae thole in England. Bus passes the length and breadth o the land. Free prescriptions. Free care o the elderly – ma ain mither got the benefit o that in hur final days. They've did away wi student fees at the uni. If wee Emma went tae uni doon in England Alasdair wid huv tae fork oot £9,000 a year fur her. Or she'd huv tae borrow it. That's how he's sendin hur up here.

So now Ah'm no sure whit tae vote. Ma first inclination wis NO, because Labour's fur NO, an Ah'm Labour. But here, the Tories are fur NO an aw, an Ah hate the Tories. An we only get the Tories foisted on us because they keep votin for them doon in England. If Scotland had been independent we'd never huv hud to suffer the Tories.

The phone rings. Alasdair.

- Mum! You never told me the schools go back earlier up there!

- Whit? Och aye, they're well back noo. Aboot a fortnight, I'd say.

- So Emma's missed a bit already? Look we'll have to

send her over right away. I'll see if I can get her a flight for next week. It'll cost a fortune this late, but we can't have her missing all her subject choices, and everything.

It's really happenin. My hert sterts hammerin.

* * *

Donald

Fortunately the high-heid-yins agree with me that the Apocalypse Now political broadcast might incite more ridicule than fear. Unfortunately, they conclude this after spendin fifty grand on the special effects.

Instead, we put a carefully-scripted, carefully-directed, convincingly-acted Political Broadcast specially aimed at women on the air. And it goes down like a lead balloon.

The script was lifted verbatim from focus groups of C2DE women. This really was their prevailin attitude at that time to the referendum. 'It's too early to be discussing politics. Eat your cereal'.

But what's meant to be a mirror comes across as a lamp. Someone somewhere chewed up our innocent RPB and spat it out as an adjunct to women: politics is just nonsense that men get up to and women should stick to cookin and cleanin.

Once this idea takes hold everybody runs wi it. 'Trying to take us back to the 1950s' is one of the kinder comments on social media.

The main character gets the hashtag #PatronisingBTLady and the YES machine churns out cardboard facemasks of her. What this does for the poor actress's career is anybody's guess.

* * *

233

Kenny

Here's me slumped in the chair glowerin across at two police officers. Middle aged man. Youngish woman, pen poised over a notebook.

- Look, dae youse wans never let up? Ah've no done nuthin fur whit – therty year – an Ah'm still yer first fuckin port o call.
- You're not our first port of call. This is one of several lines of enquiry.
- Huvnae spoke tae ma brief in years. Ah think he retired.
- If you feel you need a lawyer we can get you one. You're free to end the interview at any time.
- A wee lassie. Ah've never done nuthin tae a wean in ma life.
- Ye were caught in a public lavatory with a boy.
- Rent boy. His choice.
- He was underage.
- Aye, then he wis underage. He widnae be noo the age has went doon tae 16.
- And two cases of indecent exposure.
- Back in nineteen-canteen. Ah wis a silly boay. Ah learnt ma lesson …
- Nowadays you'd be put on the sex offenders' register. And you still might. How did the pink phone come into your possession?
- Wisnae in ma possession!
- It was on your sofa.
- Ah never saw it till Lorraine found it. Swear on ma mither's grave. Ah never touched it! Did ye find ony o ma prints on it?

- We can't discuss the forensic evidence.
- So ye didnae.
- You could have wiped it.
- … An then jist laid it doon on ma couch fur the warld tae see? Onywey, were there nae other prints on it?
- Maybe Kirsty dropped it herself when she was in your house.
- She wis never in ma fuckin hoose!
- OK, supposing neither you nor Kirsty brought it in. Who did? Who was in your house recently?
- Widnae know this Kirsty fae Mother Theresa but there's been nae wee lassies, that's fur sure.
- So who, then?

Ah wrinkle ma brow. Show them Ah'm pittin in the effort.

- There's no mony make their wey intae ma hoose. Ma sister Lorraine … the meter man … Oh.

The police exchange a glance.

- Who else? Come on. There is somebody.
- Gordo.
- Who? Speak up.
- Gordon Nimmo. Fae up the sterr.

The woman mutters in the ear o the man whose coupon takes on a scunnered look. Normal reaction to a character sketch o Gordo.

- What was Nimmo doing in your house?
- Nuthin.
- Must have been something.
- Naw. Jist comes doon tae pester the fuck oota me. Ah don't waant him. Cunt jist comes aff his ain bat …
- Watch your language. No need for that. So why do you let him in?

235

- Cannae keep him oot.
- So you're havin a carry-on wi him an all?
- Naw! But if Ah wis … Ah'm no, but if Ah wis … he'd be over age an it wid be nane o your fuckin business.
- We won't tell you again. Mind your language.
- Look, Ah'm pissed aff wi aw this. Cannae help it. You wid be an aw. But check fur Gordon Nimmo's prints, gonnae? Bet the phone's covered wi them.

* * *

Lorraine

Four of us round a table down the police station. Angela, me and two police officers. I'm glad Angela's weepin buckets. If she'd withstood the police interrogation there would have been less hope.

Basic facts:

'We trolled her because she grassed in Chantelle'.

'Fight behind the bike sheds couple o months ago – Kirsty went and got a teacher'.

'It was words, just. We never did anything to her. Never even met her outside the classroom'.

'We're no a real gang. Just a wee club. We give each other titles. I'm supposed to be the brains of it, Chantelle's the muscle of it and Kelly-Anne's the beauty of it. It's just a joke'.

'Doesn't mean I make up plans. We don't have any plans and if we ever do anything, it's Chantelle suggests it. I don't see them much after school because we don't stay near each other and I've always got homework'.

'She just made me the brains of it 'cos I'm in top section Maths and English. Really doesn't mean anything. It's a joke!'

236

'I've no idea where Kirsty is. I swear it'.

I believe her, but I'm her mother. Luckily the police appear to believe her too. For the moment.

As we leave, we pass Kelly-Anne and her mother comin in the other direction. The mother avoids makin eye contact. Maybe she's heard I'm a social worker to trade – bit of a barrier. Kelly-Anne looks at Angela impassively. I cannae see Angela's face.

Uh oh. Through an internal window I glimpse somebody looks like Kenny in a room wi two police officers. Don't want to stop and stare. Even if it's no him this time they're bound to pull him in.

Back home we circle each other's taboos.

- Cup of tea, Angie?

- No thanks.

- Coffee? Can I get you anything?

Long pause.

- Want to share a spliff?

I huvnae smoked cannabis – or anythin – in nearly thirty years. Nor till now was I aware that Angela did. I've attended lectures about cannabis openin the door to cocaine, crack, heroin. Professionally, I'm sometimes involved in trying to talk young people off heavy drugs.

- Have you got any?

- I'll see if there's any left.

While she's in her room I recall the last time I smoked a joint. Martin Chalmers's graduation party, I think.

I never was a heavy user – as with cigarettes, I just accepted them to be sociable. Shortly after Martin's night I gave up smokin altogether. I'd caught myself starting to need a fag, starting to want to buy my own supplies.

All the cigarette smokers amongst my clients, when funds

are low, will prioritise ciggies before food. Even before food for their children. We have a dependency on air, water and food. No point fosterin a dependency on yet another external substance. Particularly a harmful substance like nicotine.

Mind you, I know for a fact some of my colleagues are still partial to a joint. When one of them left to go for a new job they even put the sheet round to get him a tin of weed. Dinky wee thing with an embossed leaf of marijuana on the top.

Angela comes back. I prepare to be comradely. Comradely, broad-minded, avuncular, even maternal – whatever it takes.

- Can't find any weed. Just this.

She lays a screw of paper on the table and undoes it. Teaspoonful of yellowish powder.

I keep my expression bland, tone casual.

- What's that?
- Mandy.

I try to recall where mandy comes in the spectrum.

- Who d'ye get it from?
- Somebody I trust.
- How d'ye know what's in it? Could be anything.
- You don't want to take it – you don't have to. No big deal.

Mandy is a party drug. Supposed to make you feel warm and friendly towards strangers. Encourages confiding. Encourages bonding.

- O … kay. Do you take it in water or what?
- It's a bit bitter if you put it straight on to your tongue. What about a mandy shandy? I'll get a bottle of beer from the fridge.

* * *

238

Kenny

Ah'm daunerin through the contorted byways of a vodka-inspired dream. Bogeyman at the end of every passage. Round the last bend, dredged from ma maist distant memories, is Buster McGlinchey, a bully that made a misery o ma tender years. Buster turns grinnin towards me, bunchin his hauns. But insteid o reachin fur me, he sterts to perform the Maori Haka, saucer eyes rollin, nine-inch tongue danglin, legs jumpin, forearms thumpin. Thud, thud, thud …

Ah wake up wi a jump. Thump, thump, thump fae up the sterr. Crockery crashin. Glass smashin. Wean bawlin. Wumman scraichin.

Ah rise, go to ma front door, listen at it, cautiously open it. Ah look up the sterr.

Roon the bend, walkin backwards doon the sterr bracin his right airm on the wa, comes a wee, fat, baldy-heidit bloke. In a minute, roon the bend an aw, comes the reason he's walkin backwards. With his left haun he's draggin by the herr the nameless wumman fae up the sterr. Bubblin, screamin, clutchin blindly at the wa, at the man, she stumbles doon efter him towards me. Behind her, last in line, wailin in terror, toddles the wean.

- Aw, here, noo, whit's gaun oan?

Weak, but aw Ah can think to say.

- Keep oot o it, auld yin, or ye'll be next.

Ah take the bravest action Ah've ever attempted. As they reach ma level Ah grab the man by the shouthers and shake feebly.

- Leave the lassie alane!
- Ah telt ye, keep oot o it! This is ma wife an she's comin hame wi me.

Across the close, Daisy Donnelly opens her door an keeks oot at us. Nosey auld bitch. Hus tae be in on everythin.

Ah shove in atween the man and the wumman. Thur blood pourin doon her face. Ah try to prise the fella's haun aff her herr.

- She disnae waant tae go wi you.
- Will ye keep yer fuckin nose oot o it, ye daft auld cunt!

He lets go of his wife withoot warning and as she staggers forward he fells her wi an uppercut. Turns on me, grabs me by the collar and bangs me up agin the wa. Bunches his fist and draws it back. Ah shut ma eyes.

- Heh, whit's this, eh? Batterin the shite oota lassies an auld men?

Gordo to the rescue, clatterin doon the sterr. He reaches ma assailant, pulls him aff and shoves him in turn agin the wa. Flash o silver in his haun. Gordo's left forearm across the man's throat, the right hand with its flash o silver restin oan his cheek.

- Get oot ma close ye wee bawbag or ye'll be smilin like the Squinty Bridge.

The man shakes him aff. As he opens the street door he turns and points at the wumman and the wean cooried on the flair.

- See you, Cindy? You're deid. Ah'm comin back wi shears. First yer ears, then yer eyes.

Gordo rushes oot the close but the man's harin doon the path and into a motor parked across the road.

Ah help the lassie to her feet. Baith her eyes are near swollen shut and blood's pourin oot a wound on her scalp. Tufts o herr on the sterr. Spittin slivers of teeth.

Uncertainly, Ah haud ma ain door open.

- Ye waant tae come in here till ye get sortit oot?

Daisy's haudin a phone.

- Ah've called the polis. (Daisy)

240

- Naw! Nae polis. (Cindy)
- But look whit he done tae ye! (Daisy)
- He wis threatenin ye. Ye need protection. (Me)
- Ah'll no get it fae the polis. If Ah grass him in, Ah really wull be deid. Caw them aff. Gonnae. (Cindy)
- Ye cannae let him away wi this, hen. Think o the wee fella. It's no good fur him tae … (Daisy).
- Phone the polis back an tell them it's OK! Goannae? (Cindy)

Face streaming tears, snot and blood.

- It's very faur fae OK. (Daisy).
- Ah suppose it's up tae her, but, Daisy … (Me)
- Ah know him. Youse wans daen't. (Cindy)

Gordo comes pechin back in.

- Bastard got away. But he gies you ony mair bother, missus, you chap ma door an ask fur Gordo.
- Thanks …

At the top of the stair, he turns.

- Mind, noo. Gordo's yer man.

The Young Chevalier.

Daisy goes:

- Ye'd better come in here, onywey. Ye cannae go back intae yer ain hoose.
- Uch, it's …
- You are no way gaun back intae yer hoose on yer ain. Is thur onywherr else ye can go?
- Naw …
- Yer maw?
- She disnae … She's goat hur ain worries.
- They cannae be as bad as yours.

- They are. Believe me.
- Brothers or sisters? A pal?
- Naw. Ah'll be OK. Ah've goat a double mortice an a chain on the door. And there's the security on the close.
- He got in afore, but.
- Ah wis daft. Ah'll no be daft again.
- Well, goan an secure yer door the noo an then come away in an let me see tae yer face.

While Cindy's away Daisy goes:

- She cannae stey therr noo he's fun oot wherr she is.
- Whit aboot wan o thae places fur weemin …
- A Refuge.

Cindy returns and Daisy puts it to her.

- Ah've been in wan o them afore. They're aw right – see ye through till ye get yersel sortit. But Ah'm no gonnae find a place this time o the night.

Ah go:

- Ma sister's a social worker. Ah'll phone hur and see whit she can dae.

Daisy leads Cindy and the toddler into her hoose, Cindy repeatin

- Mind an call aff the polis.

Ah go into ma ain hoose and pick up the phone.

* * *

Lorraine

- I'm sorry for being a terrible daughter!
- I'm sorry for callin you a monster.
- I am a monster!

242

- You're just a teenager – that's all.
- I'm sorry for bullying Kirsty. I hope she's all right!
- Let's all hope for that.

Strong stuff, that mandy.

I'm holdin my jaw to stop it gettin out o control. I look at Angela and she's also holdin her jaw. I remember reading once that Tchaikovsky used to conduct orchestras and play piano concertos holdin his head on with his left hand in case it fell off.

Why am I thinkin about Tchaikovsky?

Time, I think, for an external focus for the bonding. A soppy movie? A chick flick. A rom-com. Cannae stand them myself, but Angela used to like them. I'll let her choose and watch it with her. A mother's role.

I check the TV guide to see if there's anythin like that on this evening. So many channels now. At least three of them devoted to movies. Nearly all for teenagers. Romcoms for the lassies and action thrillers for the lads.

- Hey. There's a debate on tonight about the referendum. Have you decided which way you're gonnae vote?

Here's me goin round the doors campaignin and I've never even asked my daughter what she'll be votin. Never dared.

- We'll have a shufty later. Let's dance just now.

I put on the first CD I can find. Retro compilation from the days of my youth. Chirpy Chirpy Tweet Tweet. I like it because it's one of the few pop songs which mentions mothers.

An hour later we're slumped exhausted on the couch. I'm watchin the walls. They've been throbbin but now they're startin to settle. I'm talkin but I'm no sure what I'm sayin. I am sure Angela's no listenin because she's talkin at the same time.

In the middle of it all my phone rings. Kenny of all folk,

243

askin me to fix up an emergency place in a refuge for one of his neighbours.

Kenny takin responsibility for others. Well, that's a first. He doesnae mention whether that was him down the police station. And I don't ask.

No way can I get a place in a refuge tonight. An she's got a wee boy.

- Put them in a taxi and send them over here. They can sleep at mine the night and I'll try to get her a place in a refuge the morra.
- Ye OK?
- What do you mean?
- Yer voice sounds funny.
- Well, I'm no gettin any younger.

For some reason this idea makes me burst out laughin. Christ knows what this woman will make of Angela and me and our madness when she gets here.

But any port in a storm.

* * *

Kirsty

I have to re-enter the real world.

School's back and they'll have plunged into the Higher syllabus. I've missed too much.

And I'm sick of this way of living. Not being able to go to the loo whenever I need. Having to brassneck my way into toilets in cafes I'm not eating in. Constant shortage of water. Constantly feeling unclean. Whenever I get my period it's a nightmare.

I'm still a bit scared of the Watchers but I'm hoping they'll have moved their attention on to some other imaginary grievance by now. Malky keeps saying he'll protect me but I'll believe that when I see it.

Don't have the guts to face the Wrath of Marilyn. She'll screech, Dad'll sorrow and the kids'll knot themselves.

Cara: Just brassneck it. Whatever she does, it'll not be as bad as what my nearest and dearest dish out to me.

I suggest to Malky we go and visit Grandpa in Stirling. My Dad's Dad.

- It's been years since I saw him but when he used to visit us, he was always nice to me. Never got on my case the way Marilyn does. And he still sends me presents – for Christmas and birthdays and …

I stop myself saying Easter Eggs, remembering what Marilyn says about me being too old.

Malky's sad at me going back. I can tell although he suppresses it. All he says is

- Phone him first. Make sure he's in.

* * *

Kenny

Chap at ma door. Mair company. World's fair beatin a path.

Ah keek through the peephole, feart it might be the polis back again. Or thon Nimmo cunt. Or even thon bampot that's efter thon lassie up the sterr.

Daisy Donnelly fae next door.

- Hello Kenny. Thought ye'd like tae know, Cindy an the wee fella's settled intae the Refuge fine.
- That's good.
- Ah visited them yesterday. They don't let men in, otherwise you coulda come wi me.
- That's OK. Ah don't mind.

245

- It wis yer sister sortit it fur her. She's been a great help, yer sister, so she has. Wi aw this cairry-on Cindy missed her appointment at the Benefits Office, so she did, and they sanctioned her.
- As if she husnae enough oan hur plate.
- But yer sister spoke up fur her and they're liftin the sanction. An in the meantime yer sister got her sortit wi a food bank.
- Aye. Lorraine's good at hur job. An she's a great help tae me an aw an that's no even hur job.
- And it wis you that brought yer sister in on it. Cindy said to tell ye thanks.
- Nae problem.

She's still starin at me.

- Wis there onythin else?
- Didnae get roon tae askin ye how ye were. Efter the polis comin roon tae see ye the other day.

Nosey bitch.

- It's OK. Wis jist routine enquiries.
- Routine enquiries? There's no been onythin else happenin roon here, hus there?

She laughed.

- Apart fae Cindy's bampot of a man an the usual jakeys on a Seturday night!
- Naw. Wis nothin. Pure routine.
- They took ye doon the station.
- Just tae make a statement.

She's still starin at me.

- Ah witnessed a car crash the ither day. Nuthin much. Naebody hurt. But the drivers are arguin aboot who tae blame.

246

Will she never stoap gawkin at me?

- Somethin else?
- Aye. See this referendum business?
- Wish Ah could get away fae it. It's never aff the box.
- Ah'd like to discuss it wi somebody afore Ah decide how to vote. You know thur anither debate on this evenin.
- Ah saw somethin in the paper, aye.
- Ah wondered how ye'd like to come next-door and waatch it wi me? It's always better to have somebody to talk to.
- Ah'm gonnae vote NO.
- So am Ah, probably. But still it would be nice to talk it over wi somebody. If ye're hungry, Ah've got a stew in the pot. Enough for two.

* * *

Walter

The phone rings.

- Grandpa? It's Kirsty … Grandpa? … Grandpa! You still there?

Kirsty. She's no deid. She's right here phonin her auld Grandpa as if it wisnae years since we saw wan anither. As if the polis wurnae doon on their hauns an knees combin the land fur clues. As if hur Dad hudnae phoned me the ither night an broke doon greetin.

- Aye. Ah wis jist … Ye took me aback there. D'ye know the polis are oot scourin the country for you? … Kirsty? … Kirsty? Ye still there?
- Yes. But don't tell anybody just yet. Can I come round and see you? Maybe tomorrow?

247

- Ye know ye've caused yer Dad terrible worry … Kirsty? … Ye still there?
- Yes. Look, maybe I'll just go somewhere else.
- Naw, naw, it's OK. Come ower the morra. Or even the day. Ah'll no say a word.
- Promise? Not to anybody at all?
- Aye.
- Can I bring my pal, Malky?
- Sure thing.
- OK, well. We'll get the train around two o'clock from Queen Street tomorrow. Could you tell me how to get to your house from the station?

Ah tell her. She hangs up and Ah get on the phone tae Sylvia.

* * *

Kenny

Daisy an masel are in her hoose watchin the second debate between Alastair Darling an Alex Salmond ower a plate o stovies.

- D'ye think he dyes his eyebrows?
- They've baith got bushy black eyebrows.
- But Alastair Darlin's don't go wi his hair.
- How d'ye know it's no his herr he dyes?
- Naebody dyes their hair white.

For a minute, Ah picture Alastair Darlin wi jet-black herr an snow-white eyebrows. Kinna unnatural. Alien. Ah try tae think tae masel if Ah know onybody wi black herr an white eyebrows.

Thur's a chap at the door. Daisy goes to answer it. Ah turn doon the soond and as soon as Ah hear the voices, Ah know who it is.

248

No again. Wull they never bugger aff an leave me alane? Whit aboot second chances? Ah've peyed ma dues tae society, Ah've kept ma nose clean an ma breeks up for twinty year or mair. And noo they're at Daisy's door. Whit the fuck are they sayin tae hur?

She'll waant nae mair tae dae wi me noo, that's fur sure.

She's away a wee while. Ah man-up an make fur the door. Two o Scotland's finest. Different polis fae last time. Daisy turns as Ah approach.

- This is my next-door neighbour Mr Murphy. Kenny, thae polismen waant to know …

- Thank, you Mrs Donnelly. Could you leave it to us to ask the questions?

- Of course. Would yese like to come in for a wee cuppa tea?

To ma boundless relief they decline. Daisy hovers until wan o them says:

- I think we're finished with you, Mrs Donnelly.

After she's gone, one says:

- We're here about an incident last night at the door of your close.

Jesus God. Whit the fuck are they tryin tae fit me up wi noo? Ah frantically try to think if Ah've an alibi for last night. Depending on when it wis Ah'd be in ma ain hoose on ma tod or in Daisy's hoose. Ah've got in the wey o going across to watch telly wi her efter ma tea. Sometimes she gies me ma tea.

Ah find the telly's mair fun when ye're watchin it alang wi somebody. Even when it's wan o thae soppy soaps she's intae. Ah'd reyther watch a soap alang wi Daisy than watch the snooker on ma tod.

Fitba, noo, that's a different ba game …

- A man was attacked last night just at the close entrance.

At around 11.15pm.

- Ah wis in ma bed. Fast asleep.
- So you didn't hear anything? No scuffling or shouting?
- Nothin.
- Well, maybe you could tell us about an earlier incident. On August 2nd. It was a Saturday. We believe you witnessed a struggle in the close between a young man and another older man. There was a woman involved too.
- Don't remember …
- Could you try to remember, please? Maybe you even knew two of the people involved?
- Naw, sorry. Cannae mind.

Daisy came hurrying through from the living-room.

- Ye must remember, Kenny. We were jist talkin aboot it. Mind Cindy fae up the sterr, an her man comin tae batter hur, an then yon lad fae …
- Please let Mr Murphy tell us in his own words.

Nae help fur it.

- Och aye, Ah mind noo. There wis a wee bit of a rammy …
- Wee bit, Kenny? The lassie's heid wis split right open …
- Please, Mrs Donnelly, could you leave it to Mr Murphy … ?
- This bloke came and wis hurtin the lassie …
- And?
- And she wis greetin an the wean wis greetin …
- And … ? Did somebody else intervene?
- You intervened, Kenny, so ye did.

Daisy turned to the policemen.

- He wis awfy brave, so he wis …
- Ah didnae dae nuthin. Just pullt him aff the lassie a bit …
- We're actually more interested to hear if anybody else intervened.

I hesitate. Too long. Daisy cannae control hersel.

- Ah telt them, Kenny. Thon lad fae up the sterr …
- Mrs Donnelly, would you please go inside and leave it to us to question the witness.

The witness. They want me as a witness, jist. Ma second wave o boundless relief. No that it's a picnic gaun witness for the prosecution. Particularly if the accused is Gordo Nimmo.

- She's right. The boay up the sterr. The eldest. Gordon Nimmo.
- What exactly happened?
- He got the fella an pullt him aff the lassie an chucked him oot the close.
- Did he threaten him with a weapon?

This time there's no hesitation.

- Ah saw nae weapon.
- Nothing at any time? A blade?
- Well, Ah saw nothin, onywey.
- And did he verbally threaten him with stabbing him or slashing him?
- Naw. Didnae hear that either.
- The man who was allegedly attacked last night claims Gordon Nimmo threatened him with a knife on August 2nd. Here in the close. In front of witnesses.
- And is it Gordo that's supposed tae huv stabbed him last night?

- Our enquiries are ongoing.
- Is the fella that got stabbed gonnae be OK?
- We have to wait and see.
- Well, Ah didnae see nothin onywey.

They look at me. Ah look back at them. Eventually they go away.

Back inside Daisy's glued to the telly. I sit doon beside her. She puts in the comments she always does, mainly critical.

- Ah cannae staun thon Salmond.
- Whit's he like? Right up issel, so he is.
- Did ye hear whit he sayed therr? Whit a nerve!
- He wants tae be King o the Scots, that one.

I take in nae mair o the debate. I'm desperate to know whit she's telt the polis – or no telt them. I take my stovies to the kitchenette and reheat them, and eat them in silence.

The theme music comes on and she switches aff.

- Well, that's it. Ah'm definitely votin NO. How aboot you?
- Same here. Listen. See when the polis came tae the door …
- Whit a cairry-on, eh? Sounds like Cindy's man musta come chasin efter hur again last night an Gordo caught him an stabbed him.
- Whit did ye tell the polis?
- Ye heard whit Ah telt them. Jist whit you did. That the fella wis batterin Cindy an Gordo pullt him aff. An that you pullt him aff an aw – ye were very brave, so ye were.

She pats ma airm. Ah look at her and she smiles at me. Ah wonder whit she's really efter.

- Did ye tell them ye saw a knife?

- Think Ah'm aff ma heid? Whit if the fella dies – ye think Ah waant tae go witness in a murder trial?
- Right. Well, Ah feel the same wey …
- Cindy's wan o oors.
- Wan o oors?
- She's fae up oor close. An Gordo's wan o oors an aw. An yon fella hud it comin. Batterin his wife. Durty dog. Noo see here, Kenny, thur a good film comin on at nine on True Entertainment. Ah'll away and pit on the kettle. Ah've bought a Battenberg cake in – yer favourite.

* * *

Kirsty

So here's Malky and me on the Stirling train, the countryside flashing past. If you call the central belt countryside. Malky has his arm lightly round my shoulders. Nice and tender. Protective. I feel the heat from his body and it sends some pleasant tingles. Nothing threatening.

- When we see the Wallace Monument we'll know we're nearly there. Have you ever been up the Wallace Monument, Malky?
- Naw. Never been tae Stirlin.
- They've got Wallace's sword on display there.
- His actual sword? Surely no? Wis he no kickin aboot hunners o years ago?
- Depends how you define his actual sword. The blade was replaced on one occasion and the hilt was replaced on another occasion, but otherwise …
- It's exactly the same sword!

We both laugh.

253

His plooks have faded a bit. Or maybe I don't notice them so much now I'm close up and can see his bone structure. His profile's actually quite refined. He looks a wee bit worried.

- Cheer up, Malky. My Grandpa's a nice old geezer as far as I can … remember.
- It's no that. There's somethin happened at hame.
- What?
- Ah'm feart ye'll think the less o me fur it.
- What have you done?
- Ah've no done nuthin. But ma faimily – well, ye know we're aw neds.

A secret is intriguing. If somebody tells you a secret, they're not only showing they trust you, they're picking you out as somebody more special to them than most of their other friends. That's why nobody's ever told me any secrets.

Malky with a secret? I like Malky for his street knowledge, his ability to hide me, his interesting talk, the fact that he fancies me strongly. But I've never before thought of him as a man of mystery.

- You're not a ned, Malky.
- Still no waantin tae tell ye.
- Look – if you tell me your secret, I'll tell you mine.
- Thur somethin you're no tellin me?
- You're scared I'll think you're from a family of neds. And I'm scared you'll think I'm off my head.
- OK.
- You first.
- It's no really a secret. It's in the public domain, or it's gonnae be. But Ah'm feart you categorise me because of it.
- You're my friend. I'll never categorise you.

He smiles and gives me a quick hug. Reaches to kiss me and

254

I turn and offer him my cheek.

- OK, well. Ma brither Gordo …
- … the neddiest ned out of a family of neds …
- Gordo wis liftit. Last night.
- What for?
- They say he chibbed some bloke.
- In a gang fight?
- Naw – this wis an aulder fella. Some cunt – some guy – in his forties.
- Is the victim – I mean the person that got stabbed – all right?
- He's in the land o the livin. Mebbe he jist got slashed rather than stabbed. But it's still aggravated assault and Gordo's gonnae go doon fur it. How'd ye feel aboot lumberin somebody fae a faimily o jailbirds?
- Do you know why he slashed him?
- Ah heard the fella wis batterin his wife an she'd tae go tae Women's Aid.
- So Gordo's on the side of the angels!
- Ye cannae say a blade-cairryin bam's on the side o the angels. Boays gaun aboot tooled. The crime that ruins lives. Wan deid an the ither banged up.

Jailbirds. Not only do I not know anybody who's been to jail, nobody I know knows anybody who's been to jail. That is, as far as I know. But then, I don't know very many people very well.

I wouldn't say I relate well to my own family. And I hate some of the folk in my class at school. But most of us accept some values. Housebreakers and glue-sniffers and boys that carry blades and run in gangs are neds.

But there have been alternative sets of values. Other times, other places.

- You know what I think about Gordo? And boys like him. They were born the wrong time and place. They should have been born into a pre-literate society …

- Haud on. Gordo's no illiterate. If somebody texts him a plan of action he takes it in at wan glance. An he's great wi figures – keeping track o aw his stashes an loans an debtors an rates o interest. Considerin he hardly ever went tae school …

- No, no. What I mean: our society values people for their level of formal education. But why should we all be judged on written exams? Who's worth more: your brother Stevie helping to get food out to the customers or somebody with loads of qualifications sitting at a computer writing reports that only others like him will ever read?

- Stevie hissel disnae think he's worth as much as a company boss.

- Of course not – he buys into this too. Now if Gordo had been born into some tribal society like the Vikings, he'd be expected to carry a knife. He'd hope one day to carry a sword and if he did, the sword itself would be honoured and kissed and given high status, like with the Wallace sword. He'd be respected for being good at fighting, for useless brave gestures like hanging off the balconies. And the crowd that Gordo hangs out with judge each other by these pre-literate measurements.

- OK – Ah'll get Gordo's brief tae caw ye in as a witness fur the defence! Onywey, whit aboot yer ain secret?

I look out the window. I'd told him I was scared he'd think I was crazy, but that's only part of it. If I tell him our secret I'll be committing an act of betrayal.

Cara: An irreversible step.

- Look Malky! There's the Wallace Monument! We're

256

almost there!

- Naw ye don't! Ye're no getting oot o it that way. C'moan wi the secret.

Cara: Remember the time you ran away? Without me, would you ever have had the guts to stay hidden in these big empty committee rooms? And what about the second time? Who showed you the way into the back of that lorry?

It's true. Whenever I've been in a crisis she's been there for me.

Cara: And will be again. You need me, Kirsty.

I can't picture my future without her.

Cara: Who means more to you? A boy that only wants to shag you or a friend who's stood by you and loved you and advised you all your days?

Women down the ages have done it and lived to regret. Ditched the lifelong BFF for the new boyfriend.

Cara: If you do this, I'll never forgive you.

The man who betrayed Wallace was made a sheriff as a reward. What do I gain by betraying Cara? I only said I'd tell Malky my secret because I was curious about his secret. And his secret turned out to be a damp squib. Not a man of mystery at all. Just a schemie from a ned family.

Cara: I might stick around a while but it will never be the same. I'll never trust you again.

Malky raises his eyes to the window.

- Aw here, we're comin to a station. Wait the noo.

He rises and edges along the aisle, ducking his head, trying to see a sign. He comes back and sits beside me again.

- It's OK. No Stirlin yet.
- Which is it?
- Eh – haud on.

He ducks and dives again. Comes back.

257

- Bridge of Allan.
- That's the station after Stirling!
- Fuck! Shite!

He and I grab our bags from the floor, jackets from the overhead rack, and shove our way up the aisle. Have to stop for people coming the other way. My purse falls out my bag and I have to stop to pick it up. We reach the door just as it closes. The train starts moving. It chugs slowly along the platform. It picks up speed again, heading north.

* * *

Malky

We get aff the train at Dunblane an cross back ower tae the opposite platform.

- So this is wherr Andy Murray comes fae. Scotland's wan hope o sportin domination.
- Tennis. The only sport I sometimes watch. Because I associate it with summer, I suppose.
- Ah wonder if he'll ever come oot wan way or the other for independence. A lot of sportin celebrities say nothing because they're feart o losing their sponsors.
- But Andy Murray's bigger than that now.
- Heh, get a load o aw thae big hooses. Widnae dream of it as a place o mass murder.

Kirsty goes oot to check the timetables. Why do they always put them ootside the platforms, at street level? While she's away, the Glasgow train appears in the distance. I yell at her and she comes pechin back, just in time. By now it's the rush hour. Nae double seats left. We fling wursels intae seats several metres apart fae wan anither. Nae danger o missin the stop again through yatterin on.

258

* * *

Kirsty

Two mugs of tea, a can of Irn-Bru and us round the coffee table.

- Can I stay wi you for a while, Grandpa? I don't like it at home. And from the 18th when I turn sixteen, I can stay where I like.
- Sixteen on the 18th September, eh? That's a significant date to have your birthday. Did ye register to vote?
- You bet. Malky and I are going to vote YES. For a new start. Hope over Fear.
- I see.
- What about it?
- Well, Ah'm gonnae vote NO, and Ah'll tell you why …
- Not the voting. I mean, what about me staying with you for a while.

Grandpa doesn't answer for a moment. I guess he's considering how a teenage girl would affect his daily routine. We teenagers get a bad press. He's imagining loud music day and night. He looks over at Malky. He's thinking about giggly girlfriends and sullen boyfriends. And that there's one of them sitting beside me right now.

- Malky's got a home of his own, by the way. He's not part of the deal. It would just be me.
- Of course ye're welcome to stay here if ye want, hen. But wid ye no consider goin to stay wi your mither?

That I didn't expect. But I don't need to think about it.

- Not her! She abandoned me!
- Naw she didnae …
- Aye she did!

259

- She ran away with you, twice. She broke the law – pit her ain liberty at risk.
- Nobody told me that.
- That's whit happened.

I cast my mind back. Running away with Mummy. Surely I couldn't have forgotten that.

Fragments come floating. An unexpected holiday, coming at the end of one of my visits to Mummy. Getting up early. Bundling ourselves and bags into the car. Then abandoning the car in town and taking the train.

I was pleased at first because I would miss school. I was finding it hard to settle into my new school. There was nobody like Cara there.

On my last day at the old school, at the end of the day, instead of going into the playground to meet our parents, Cara and I hid together in a forgotten storeroom. It was exciting. Our own wee secret den. I thought I could hide there forever and never leave the school. Never leave Cara.

We sat in the dark amongst the dusty boxes. Imagined what was in them. Held hands. Held our breath as much as possible. Spoke in whispers. Planned where we would go and hide once the school closed for the night. Pledged undying love – that even if they did separate us, we'd meet up again once we grew up. Giggled softly.

Then the janny pulled us out and gave us a row. Took us to the heidie's room where Cara's Mummy and Marilyn were waiting. The Wrath of Marilyn was upon me, all the way home. Never saw Cara again. At least …

The new school was different from the old one. Grim-faced, shouty teacher. Hostile children. All already bonded into pairs and tribes. When I tried to attach myself to a group in the playground, one of them told me they would let me spy on them from the corner, but not join them.

So I was glad to be taken away from all that.

- I remember going on a big ship.
- She took you to Ireland.

Ireland. Three images.

A horse pulling an open car with people sitting in it. I wanted a ride but Mummy said it was too dear. We had to save our pennies.

A green pillar box. Mummy said it was a pillar box but had turned green because it would rather be a tree. It didn't look like a tree at all. I wanted to post a letter in it to see whether it was a pillar box or a tree but Mummy said we mustn't post any letters just now.

Sitting in the wee room with Mummy. We only had one room. A bed, a table, a chair and a kettle. I had no toys and no books. Mummy was on her phone the whole time. I was bored. I kept trying to talk to Mummy, trying to get her to tell me stories, trying to play with her. She kept telling me not to interrupt. I missed Cara, missed my toys, missed my old homes, both of them, with their space and familiar furniture.

I begged her to take me back. Homesick. Crying for Cara. Crying for Daddy.

After that, I don't have much memory of my mother. I think I saw her a few times. Never happy occasions.

Then I never saw her any more.

- Why'd she never bother to get in touch? Not once! All it would have taken was a phone call, an email, a wee letter …
- She didnae dare, pet. There wis a court order on it. Her mither had already gone to jail because of her runnin away wi you.
- Nobody told me that either!
- Ended up she was banned fae aw contact till yer 16th birthday. She's been desperate aboot it ever since.

She's kept up wi me because Ah wis a kind of link, through Rab. No that Ah saw much of you in recent years.

- I'm sorry about that. When you're wee you only visit the relations your folks take you to. It'll be different now I'm big. But thanks for keeping sending us presents. Like the Easter eggs last April. Even if I don't get to keep them.

- How's that?

- Marilyn takes from me and gives them to Erin and Benny. She says I'm too big for Easter Eggs. She's been saying that since I turned ten.

- Ah'll no lie tae ye, hen … It's Sylvia buys the presents Ah send you. She buys them for the three o you so it's fair and no suspicious.

- So she is still keeping up with me!

The phone I got two Christmases ago. The laptop on my 15th birthday. All from Sylvia.

- A lesson, hen. Think fur yersel. Question everythin ye're telt. Never take folks' word. Work it oot in yer ain heid.

- Especially now.

- How's that?

- The referendum!

- Aye. Well, onywey. Sylvia's been plannin for years to get in touch wi you. To have you stay with her, if you want to. The interdict runs oot on Thursday.

- Thursday 18th September. A big, big day for me …

Malky speaks:

- … and for Scotland.

* * *

Agnes

Ah open the door. It's Lorraine.

- Sorry I didnae manage over on Monday. Would you be free to talk about the referendum the now?

Ah'm angry. Efter aw my efforts, turning ma hoose into a wee palace for her.

Now the cake's gone to the birds and the hoose is back to its usual shambles and she waants to come in. My first visitor in months – maybe years. And ma knickers hangin ower the radiator, ma hauf-finished tea on the table an three kittens up there lickin the plates clean.

- Ah've been thinkin maybe Ah shouldnae listen tae you, jist. No if Ah cannae huv the same discussion wi a NO person. Widnae be balanced.
- Well, Donald up the stairs campaigns for Better Together …
- Does he? But Ewan …
- His flatmate. Campaigns for YES.
- Flatmate, eh? Here, Ah'm no as green as Ah'm …!

As soon as Ah say that I stop an wish Ah hudnae. An her a social worker. She'll be thinking Ah'm an auld last-century reactionary.

- Whit Ah mean is – it's funny, the perra them. Steyin thegither and wan gaun aw oot fur YES an the ither for NAW.
- Makes you wish you were a fly on their wall!
- Aw right, well, in ye come. Ye huv tae ignore the guddle.
- Sure your house isnae as much of a guddle as mine.

* * *

Walter

I write out Sylvia's address and phone number for Kirsty. She looks at it for a moment.

- The courts awarded custody to my Dad – is that right? From the start?
- That's right.
- Why? Did they think Sylvia was an unfit mother? Did she drink?
- Naw. Nothin like that.

I weigh it up.

- They said Sylvia wis a lesbian. Widnae matter much nooadays but then there was a bit mair stigma. Rab's lawyer suggested bein in an unusual family set-up might get ye bullied at the school.

Kirsty and Malky look at each other. He gies her a lop-sided grin and snorts. A private joke.

- And is my … Sylvia a lesbian?
- She denied it. Swore blind it wisnae true. Then Rab's lawyer pit up a couple o witnesses had seen her wi her lady friend. So it looked to the judge – it looked to all of us – like she wis perjurin hersel. Ah think that's whit went wrang for her. She pit the judge's back up. An he wis an auld-fashioned kinna judge onywey.

The silence grows awkward.

Malky goes:

- Ye said you're gonnae vote NO?
- Let me show ye somethin.

I leave the room.

Kirsty goes:

- You shouldn't mention the referendum.
- How no?

- He's a NO. It'll sour things up.
- Maybe we can turn him.
- An old guy like that? Doubt it.

I return wi ma big black photograph album under my airm.

- Ye don't see thae albums nooadays, do you? Aw your photies are hidden away on your phones.
- They're no exactly hidden. We share them wi wur pals. And sometimes hunners o ithers.
- And how do you locate a picture that was taken 30, 40, 50 year ago?
- We don't want to. We just show folk the photos we took last week.

I turn to the third page. Black and white picture, postcard-sized. Crowd mairchin along the road, led by an exotic-looking figure on horseback.

- This is the Bannockburn Rally of 1934. They used to dae thae mairches through Stirlin every year. Commemoratin the battle. Demonstratin for independence.
- Used to?
- Stopped a few year ago when the SNP took ower the Government. They wurnae the opposition ony mair, see? So whit's the point o a protest mairch?
- They still hudnae won independence, but.
- Naw, and in fact they resurrected the Bannockburn rally this year, for the 700th anniversary. End o June it wis.
- Thur'd be a big turnoot, surely. This bein the year o the indyref an that.
- Naw, it wisnae weel advertised. An thur wis competition. The UK Government held thur Armed Forces Day the very same date – in the very same

265

place!

- Ye're kiddin. Stirlin an aw?
- The auld sodgers mairchin under the Union Jack fae Stirlin Castle doon through the toon, the Red Arrows pourin reid, white n blue smoke through the sky – an us hauf a mile doon the road at Bannockburn reenactin …
- Us? But you said you were a NO.
- See here.

I point at the picture in the album o the 1934 Bannockburn Rally.

- See there – the wee laddie sittin on his dad's shouthers? That's me.
- So yer Da wis aw fur independence way back then?
- You bet. He even got involved in … paramilitary stuff.
- Like the IRA?
- Different times, different methods. He and his pals took tae the hills. Mairched up an doon. Practised their drills. Pretended they were sodgers.
- Blew things up?
- Naw. Faur as Ah know.

I've gien them baith something tae think aboot. They look at ane anither. An back at the photo. The lad jabs his finger at it. I scliff away his manky paw in case he leaves his print.

- Who's the Buffalo Bill clone?
- That's Don Roberto. R.B. Cunninghame-Graham. Author, gaucho, MP and co-founder o baith the Labour Party and the SNP.
- Whit aboot you?
- Whit aboot me?
- You're a NO.

- Listen, son.

I wag my finger at him.

- Don't you stert on at me aboot YES and NO. Ah wis arguin fur Scottish independence afore your Mammy an Daddy were born.
- Arguin for it. But no votin fur it.
- Aye, votin fur it an aw. Ah supported the SNP when naebody else had heard o them. Ah wis a minority o wan again an again arguin fur it in pubs an meetins – onywherr fowk wid listen. Ah wis laughed oota court. Easy enough tae staun up fur independence noo when it's aw the rage.
- But here when the big chance comes at last ye vote NO.
- The Scots dinnae deserve independence! Shower a fearties! Aw thae years when we coulda lived the life o Reilly on the oil money an they let the English Government have it. Gied it tae them wi their richt haun while their left haun held oot a beggin bowl. An were pathetically grateful fur the crumbs. Daft as weel as feart. Noo when thae Better Together fowk say the Scots are too wee, poor an stupit tae rule theirselves Ah couldnae agree mair. Beggin bowl mentality. Benefit Scroungers. Noo they're aw set tae vote doon their wan chance o independence an hell mend them. They'll hae the rest o the century tae reap the whirlwind an maybe wan day they'll realise whit they've done.
- Ah still don't see why ye're helpin them tae vote doon independence.

Kirsty pats Malky's hand.

- Leave it.

Ah pick up the cups.

- Want a refill?

Ah go out to the kitchen.

Malky says

- You know fine well why he's votin "NO". Spite.
- Shush! He'll hear you.
- Ah know his type. Always has to be against the current. Feart fowk'll think he's a follower o fashion.
- Keep your voice down!
- Plus he's chronically angry at the rest o the population for no agreein wi him in the first place.
- Come and we'll not fight about it, eh?
- He's spittin oot his dummy.
- He's my Grandpa. I need his support.
- Pure cuttin aff his nose.
- That's enough.

Ah come in with the mugs of tea.

Kirsty asks Malky for his phone. She turns her back to us and crosses to the window. Stares oot at the autumn street. Looks back doon at the phone and sterts diallin. Neither Malky nor I look at hur but we're baith quiet. Trying tae piece thegither the hauf o the conversation we're no privy tae.

- Could I speak to Sylvia?
- Sylvia? Mummy? It's Kirsty here.
- Yes. That's right.
- I'm up at Grandpa's at the moment.
- I know.
- I'd like to come and visit you.
- Yes, Grandpa's just told me about the interdict. I didn't know …
- But …

- That's right, the 18th.

Short laugh.

- Referendum Day.

She lowers her voice then. Murmurs away. Ah'm strainin but cannae make ony mair oot. This hearing aid's better than ma last one. Ah managed to hear whit the lad wis saying aboot me when Ah wis in the kitchen. But still makes a whistle if ye turn it up. They aw seem tae dae that.

Kirsty hangs up and announces she'll visit Sylvia on the 18th.

- That's good. Keep within the letter o the law. Noo, whit aboot yer poor Dad? He's oot his mind. How aboot handin yersel in the day?
- I'd rather hand myself over to the police than go back home.
- Aw right. You can go to the local police station here.
- Can I? I don't need to go back to Glasgow?
- It's all Police Scotland nooadays.
- Will you come with me, Grandpa?

* * *

Kirsty

Down the police station they ask Grandpa if he'll stay with me in loco parentis. He says he thinks it would be better if my Dad was there. So they give me a cup of tea while they call Dad.

Once Dad arrives, he, Cara, two police officers and I go into a wee room.

They show me two pictures: an old geezer and a young guy. Could the young guy be Gordo? Didn't get a proper look at him that time he drove past – too far away. Looks a wee bit like Malky. Or maybe I'm just telling myself that.

Anyway. I convince them I've never met either of them nor
been in the old geezer's home. I tell them I was hiding the
whole time of my own free will in the derelict Red Road
flats.

- Who was helping you?
- Nobody.
- How did you manage for food?
- OK. I did get some help from friends.
- Who?
- There were several of them.
- Give us some names.
- Don't want to get them into trouble. They only helped
  because I asked them to.
- They won't necessarily get into trouble.

Cara: Aye, right.

- I won't name them.

I look both the police officers in the face. Steadily. Openly.
Pleasantly. As far as I know I haven't committed any crime.

- Have you got a boyfriend?
- No.
- What about Malcolm Nimmo? Is he your boyfriend?
- No.
- Did he help you when you were hiding?
- No.
- Did he have sex with you?
- No.
- If he did have sex with you he was breaking the law.
- I've never had sex with anybody.

Dad interrupts.

- She's surely answered enough. Can we no just get

home now?

The policewoman says

- She's a young person at risk. We must make sure she doesn't run away again.
- I won't run away again. I promise.
- We'll be contacting the Social Work Department …
- No social workers, please.
- That was a pretty daft thing to do. Running away.
- I know.
- Didn't you think about your folks?
- Didn't think they would bother.

Dad reaches for my hand.

- Kirsty, sweetheart, we were crazy with worry!

Cara: Aye, right.

- Really?
- Yes, really!

Dad's eyes are brown and slightly bovine. Bit of tissue paper on his neck where he cut himself shaving. Light dandruff on his shoulders even though he has hardly any hair. The police continue their questioning.

- Anyway, why were you hiding?
- I was scared.
- Who of?
- Doesn't matter.
- It does matter. Your parents?

Dad puts in again.

- You've no need to be scared of us, sweetheart.
- Please let Kirsty answer for herself.
- No. Not my parents.
- Some of the girls at school?

- What makes you think that?
- I don't think anything. You tell me who you were scared of.
- I'm not scared any more.

Cara: Aye, right.

- I've got something to show you.

The policewoman goes out and returns. In her hand is … my wee pink phone, turning up like an old friend after goodness knows what adventures. I reach out in glee. The policewoman draws it back.

- There are messages here which are a bit disturbing.
- I know. From the Watchers.
- Do you know who they are?
- It's all right. I'm not scared of them anymore.

Dad tries again.

- You won't be a clype, pet. The police already know who these girls are.

Cara: This is what the police always say if they want information. That they already know.

- Do you know Angela Murphy, Kelly-Anne Henderson and Chantelle McLean?

Cara: Sing dumb.

- The Glasgow police have already had these girls down the station. And their parents. You'll be getting apologies from them.

Cara: Aye, right.

I reach again for the phone. The policewoman puts it in the drawer.

- You'll get it back when we've finished our enquiries.

All the way back home I'm sick with trepidation. The Wrath of Marilyn full frontal, her eyes staring with rage, her voice shattering all the tumblers. Maybe Angela looking out of her own window, sending hostile vibes at being forced into an insincere apology.

None of these things happen. Angela's nowhere to be seen. Marilyn gives a wry smile.

- Hello stranger!

Erin and Benny, on cue, sidle up and give me hugs. Sweetness and light.

Cara: I give it till Monday.

* * *

Agnes

Come the day. Her flight gets in at 5pm. There's a bus goes by George Square takes you right to the airport.

I baked a cake specially fur her in the mornin. Covered it in pink icin and wrote on it in white icin 'WELCOME EMMA'.

I've tidied the place and made up the bed in the back bedroom. Bought new sheets and pillow cases.

No that I expect a teenager to care about tidiness – but ye never know. Her mither seemed pretty house-proud the times I wis doon there.

The kittens should keep her amused for a bit. They're at their best just now. Exactly like the kittens you get in calendars. When they lie in a tangled heap sleepin, or look up at ye, aw their wee heids thegither an their big eyes starin in the same direction – it pits me in mind o a patch of flowers – they would win a photo competition.

They're ayeways fightin amang themselves. Quite ferocious. They bite and claw wan anither's faces and roll aboot. I'm forever expectin wan o them to lose an eye. But so far they've never even drawn blood on wan anither. Drawn plenty on me, but.

273

There's her tea to think of. Masel – there's nothin like a good fish soup. Ma mither used to make it for me and Sandy a lot – she was brought up on it up in Portknockie. We ayeways called it 'fish soup', jist, but noo it's become fashionable an the posh restaurants are pittin it on the menu as 'Cullen Skink.'

Full o healthy ingredients: fish, onion, leek, milk, an totties.

But Ah know young folk urnae keen on traditional food like that. Whit they like best is burgers. No that Ah wid touch thae greasy things – ye never know whit's in them. But that's probably whit she wad go fur. So yesterday Ah went doon the supermarket and stocked up on burgers an a pizza for the freezer.

The telephone goes. Alasdair.

- That's her gone into the departure lounge now. She'll be arrivin in just over an hour.

My. They're that fast nooadays.

- Ah got burgers in fur her tea – is that aw right?
- Oh – I don't know. I think she's gone vegetarian. I don't really notice what she eats, but I think Sheena mentioned she'd gone vegetarian.

Ah pit my coat on again, thinkin whit Ah could get her. Maybe cauliflower and cheese sauce? No much time to get in the cauliflower. And Ah've still to get ower to the airport to meet her.

As Ah go oot ma ain door Lorraine's lassie Angela wi two of hur pals ur hingin aboot at the close. They don't look at me. Gaun doon the path somebody's doggin ma steps, but. When Ah reach the pavement Ah turn roon. Wan o the pals – the hefty wan – is right at ma back. She steps away fae me wi a mock innocent look on hur face. Angela calls oot

- Lovely weather we're getting, Mrs Morrison!

She disnae say it nice, but. Sorta sarcastic. Jist showin aff tae

274

hur pals, but no very nice.

Ah mumble somethin an turn away again. As Ah hurry on tae the supermarket Ah hear them killin theirsels laughin. Don't know whit that's aw aboot. The hefty wan musta been takin the mickey. Maybe copyin the wey Ah walk? Ah know Ah hirple a bit wi ma sair knees.

No fur the first time, Ah get a stab o fear at whit Ah'm takin on, bringin a teenager intae ma hoose.

Ah buy the cauliflower an a bag o grated cheddar and then take the bus straight up the toon. The cauliflower in the carrier bag on wan airm bumpin against ma leg, my handbag on the ither.

Eventually Ah'm in the airport, waitin ootside 'Arrivals'.

A flow o folk stert coming through. Ah try to find oot from their luggage an fae whit they're wearin if it's fae London.

Ah spot her. Much taller than last time Ah saw her (five year ago), but thinner.

Frayed jeans jist past hur knees, thick socks, tackety boots. A bomber jaicket (is she no awfy cauld in a wee cut-doon jaicket?). Bright orange hair cut short at the back – short as a boay's – but wi a lang fringe hingin into her eyes. She looks like she's wearin her hairdo back to front.

When she comes closer Ah see the ring through her nose.

- Hello, hen.

Ah go up to her, pit my airms roon her. It's awkward wi the cauliflower bouncin atween us. Awkward onywey – don't know if she waants me to hug her. She steys rigid but sorta kisses the air beside ma cheek.

- Hi, Gran.

- Can Ah help ye wi your luggage?

- I'm cool. This is all I've got.

'This' is a backpack. Pretty light-lookin. No a dedicated

follower of fashion. She's comin for at least a month an bringin wi her less than Ah used to take gaun away for a week.

On the bus back Ah ask her how her flight wis, how her Mum and Dad are keepin, whit she's studyin at the school and if she can mind her last visit to Glesca. (She wis five – she cannae). Ah tell her three lassies around her age stey up my close – maybe they could be pals for her. Kirsty, Angela and Yasmin. Ah tell her the kittens are comin on and are all ower the place. Huv tae watch aw the time wherr Ah pit ma feet. Ah tell her Ah've stood on wan accidentally a couple o times an Rosie flew at me and bit me on the ankle.

- But she's no really vicious. Jist defendin her wee anes.

Efter that Ah rin oota things to ask or tell Emma.

She disnae ask me onythin.

In the hoose the kittens are a big hit, but. Loosen her tongue.

- They're gorgeous! Let's keep them all!
- Ah'd love to, hen, but ma hoose is too wee for seven cats. Ah thought Ah'd keep wan, jist. Maybe the wee grey boay. But that's assumin Ah find hames for the rest. It'll be mair difficult noo they're gettin past the baby stage.
- Should be easy enough, Gran. Advertise them on Gumtree.
- But whit if the wrang soarts answer the advert?
- How d'you mean?
- Fowk wantin bait fur dogfights.

She stares at me. No like Ah'm hur Gran. Like Ah'm an object.

- Dogfights! Is that what you get up to in Glasgow?
- No particularly in Glesca. Ye get bad fowk everywhere.
- Well, I've never heard of dogfights in London.

- Ah've lived in Glesca aw ma life an Ah'd never heard o them here either. It wis wan o ma neighbours warned me. She's a social worker.

Emma's hard stare melts into a grin.

- A social worker. Wouldn't take her word. Anyway, I still want to keep them all. What about keeping three? The grey boy and one of the stripeys and the white one with the orange patch?

- Aw, pet, ma hoose is far too wee for fower cats …

- A compromise. Two. We'll keep two kittens.

Three big cats in ma wee hoose. Ah don't want to disappoint hur, but … no on the first day. An no efter thon wee edge o difference we jist had.

- Aw right, well.

Whit um ah lettin masel in fur?

- I've thought of names for them, Gran.

- Well, Ah'd thought Ah might caw the grey boy …

- Let's call him Arsenic. And let's keep the long haired stripey.

- Och, Ah don't know. A lang-haired cat's a lot o work. Needs brushin …

- I'll brush her! And we can call her Cyanide.

In some weys she's still a wee lassie.

I take her to her room.

- This wis your Daddy's bedroom when he wis a wee boay. Thur still a boax o his toys up on the shelf. And some o his books in the press.

She doesnae look like she'd be into Hot Wheels cars or plastic Thundercats, but you never know.

- I'll get the tea on. Yer Dad telt me ye've went vegetarian. Is cauliflower and cheese sauce aw right? I'll toast it up lovely on top.

277

- Oh, Dad got it wrong. I used to be vegetarian but now I'm vegan.
- Vegan? So that's … nae animal products at aw?

I try to picture cauliflower and cheese wi the cheese taken oot. Awfy waattery.

I could maybe put some barley in to thicken it up.

- I can make you up a wee cauliflower and potato broth …
- Don't bother about me. I'm not hungry.
- Ye need somethin for your tea, hen. Did ye get onythin on the plane? Thae cheap flights don't usually gie you ony free food, dae they?
- Yes, I'm really all right. Don't worry. When I'm hungry I'll make myself something.
- Ah've goat a pizza …
- What's it got on it?

My heart sinks.

- Tomato and cheese and … Ah could pick aff the salami …
- I don't need anything, really.

Suddenly I mind.

- Ah baked ye a cake. Come and see. Ah wrote yer name.
- Daddy should have warned you. I never eat cake.
- Never? No even on yer birthday?
- Never touch sugar. Anyway, there would be milk in it.
- Well, will you tell me whit to buy in for you?
- It's OK. I can buy my own food from the allowance Mum and Dad are sending me. And I'll cook it myself too. That's what I do at home.

Ah leave her to unpack and go to phone Alasdair to tell him

she's arrived. It's Sheena who answers.

- Will you make sure she eats properly while she's living with you? I'm worried she eats so little.

* * *

Donald

Watchin the first debate between Darling and Salmond along wi Ewan turned out to be one of my worse ideas.

Salmond was uncharacteristically nervous fae the start. Then when they started argy-bargyin about currency, when Darling asked him what his Plan B was if we couldnae get to use the pound, Salmond had no answer prepared. Just kept repeatin that the UK Government were bluffin, that they didnae really mean it, that they couldnae stop us usin the pound.

It got on folks' wicks. Even Ewan's.

When Salmond started flounderin, Ewan started bawlin at the telly.

- We don't need their stinking pound! Who cares! Get over it! Pick your battles! Go for a new currency! What the hell are you hanging on to this for!

When it was Salmond's turn to attack Darling he fell back on juvenile jokes. He repeated some of the OTT stories Project Fear had allegedly used to scare the horses.

Will we have to drive on the other side of the road after independence? Will we be vulnerable to attack by extra-terrestials?

He missed the chance to present the kind of visionary politics that the YES side is sometimes good at. Darling was a statesman. Salmond the class clown.

Ewan lost it altogether:

- Cut faffing about, dickhead! Nobody's laughing!

So refreshin to have him attackin Salmond. I wondered

whether to join in. Encourage this bout of free-thinkin. I thought too long about it, didnae have the guts.

Didnae save the atmosphere between us. After it ended I kept my triumphant feelings to myself. But he still turned all his bitterness on me. He shouted, eventually I shouted back and then he didnae speak tae me throughout the next day.

So for the return match I decide to watch it in the Better Together HQ, in the company of like-minded people. Victory shared is victory multiplied. And I could do wi some shared triumphalism. I really could.

But this time it all goes wrong. The old cocky Salmond is back – all trace o nerves vanished. Deadpan delivery, cutting steel.

- Do you think having 100,000 children driven into poverty because of welfare reforms is a price worth paying for Westminster Government?

How's Darling – or anybody – to answer that? Have you stopped fiddlin your taxes? Are you still beatin your wife?

The audience duly turn hostile. To Darling.

It's back to that old conundrum for Labour supporters: would you rather be under a Tory Government run from London, or under a Labour Government run from Scotland. I think the YES lot would make faster headway if they concentrated on that side of things instead of bangin on about economics that nobody understands.

Fortunately it hasnae occurred to them. God knows their headway is fast enough.

The sgian dhubh comes out at the end o the debate.

- Name three job-creating powers that the Better Together parties intend to give Scotland.

Alastair Darling cannae come up wi one.

The audience hang him out to dry.

When Darling arrives back at the Ponderosa, he's in a

right state. He blames the makeup of the audience. Most of the audience was selected by a polling company; the BBC selected about 20%. We reckon the polling company is reliable and so he turns his blame on the BBC. The BBC which didnae bother to network his first, triumphant debate with Salmond but this time around has broadcast his humiliation to the world.

When his retinue go back to their hotel the rest of us at Better Together have nothin to say. Still, I'm glad I'm there. Defeat shared is defeat spread thin.

Goin home I cannae get an old song out my head:

'When this lousy war is over, no more soldiering for me
When I get my civvy clothes on, oh how happy I will be.'

* * *

Agnes

That's me hud ma wee conversations noo wi baith Lorraine for the YES side and Donald for the NO side.

Thon's an awfy nice man that Donald. Hud a kinna sad life.

His parents took it awfy hard when they fun oot he wis gay. In thae days thur wis mair stigma. An they were Wee Free or somethin. He steyed in the closet as lang as he could. When he wis twenty-two they fun some gay magazines in his bedroom. Thur wis a big flamin row an then they cut aff aw contact wi him. An him gaun through his university finals at the time. His two brithers mair or less cut aff fae him an aw – he husnae seen them in years.

He'd only hud one lang relationship afore he met Ewan. Lasted 15 year. His partner died five year ago which wis when he sold up an flitted here. Cancer it wis. Ah didnae like tae ask but it didnae seem tae be onythin tae dae wi AIDS.

He telt me he enjoyed ma cake an asked fur the recipe. He

enjoys cookin an says he'd maybe like tae get intae bakin an aw. Ah said Ah wis the opposite: enjoyed bakin but couldnae be annoyed wi day-tae-day cookin. Especially when it's only me eatin it. Ah'm still no clear whit Emma eats. No much onywey. She must be eatin somethin or she'd be deid.

So we've agreed that sometimes he'll bring me doon a bit o whitever he's been cookin fur him and Ewan. An Ah'll sometimes bake a wee cake an take a bit upstairs tae them. It's a neighbourly thing tae dae.

Still, he didnae convince me wi the politics. There wis a kinna fatalism aboot him that Ah didnae get fae Lorraine.

The stuff he liked aboot bein in the UK wis aw aboot past glories. Britain standin alone against the Fascists. The creation o the NHS. Noo, unlike him Ah actually lived through that period. Ah mind eftir Dunkirk hearin ma parents discussin the likelihood of imminent invasion. Ah wis too wee tae know whit it wis aw aboot but their worry spread tae me an Ah wis greetin aboot it. Ah mind the jubilation of VE day. But Ah feel ye huv tae move on. Cannae rest on yer laurels.

When Donald talked aboot the future he'd nothin very positive tae say. He wis pushin yon Project Fear business like the rest o them. Wur oil is runnin oot an we've nae other assets. Wur banks might fail an thur naebody tae pick up the pieces. We might get thrown oot the EU. The security services might no share information wi the Scottish Government and then the terrorists might sneak in an blow us aw up. This might happen; that might happen. We're a nation o beggars that couldnae survive athoot the subsidies the London Government's kind enough tae gie us. He made oot the future wis jist a choice atween managin wur current decline or the Armageddon o the unknown.

But Scotland noo is different fae Scotland in the '50s and '60s. And so is Britain.

The wey Lorraine telt it, the haill Westminster shebang is incurably corrupt. Rich men's club set up fur the benefit o the fowk in it. Set up so the MPs never need tae spend thur big wages on onythin – they get it aw free. Never even need tae show up. When they do, they get flattered: The Honourable This; the Right Honourable That. If they don't rock the boat they go tae the House o Lords. Mair than 800 unelected toadies aw wieldin influence an drawin allowances. She said the maist subsidised pairt o the the UK wis actually London but they fiddled the statistics tae hide the fact. She said the UK sucks up tae America and spends the taxes on wars an weapons o mass destruction jist tae try tae keep up thur delusions o grandeur.

Lorraine made the future under independence seem excitin. An independent Scotland wid huv different priorities. We'd spend the money on developin renewable energy. We've got a coastline the length o China's but we've never went fur developin tidal energy because the Ministry o Defence hogs the West coast fur its practice forays. We've enough wind an waater tae supply hauf o Europe wi energy.

Norway. Saves its oil money fur a rainy day. Spreads its population ower the haill country insteid o crammin them intae slums in the central belt an keepin the Highlands an empty playground fur the rich. We could be like that.

Sounds far too good tae be true.

- So efter Independence Scotland might be a land o milk an honey?
- Nobody on the YES side says that. Independence isnae a panacea. It's a prerequisite. It'll no solve all the problems, but without it we cannae really solve any o them.

Panacea. Prerequisite. Big words I'd never use masel. But Ah know whit they mean. Clever lassie, that Lorraine.

Ah still think it's far too good tae be true. But it's hard no tae be sucked intae hur enthusiasm. Ah'd reyther aim fur a dream we might never win, than make dae wi somethin we know is second-rate. Scotland's grown up and wants the chance tae grow mair. We'll no get it in the UK.

* * *

Lorraine

Tonight Ewan and I and a couple of others are deliverin First-Time-Voters letters. Urgin the teenagers to come out and vote. Long slow business. The letters are all individually addressed and widely scattered the length of every street. A few have been bundled in the wrong order so you have to backtrack.

The FTVs are all born between 1994 and 1998. When I started my trainin in social work I was dealin with elderly folk, assessin them for the level of care they needed. The folk I dealt with were mostly born around the turn of the last century. I somehow regarded the folk born in 1898 or 1899 as a lot frailer than the folk born in 1900 or 1901. Illogical, but I couldnae help it.

If belongin to a dead century is so ageing, what'll it be like belongin to a dead millennium? There'll come a day that the likes o Angela might suffer this date-of-birth stigma. She might one day find hersel subtractin a couple o years to bring hersel completely into the 21st century.

The arrogance o youth, the diffidence of age. Comes to us all.

* * *

Agnes

Emma started at the school on Monday. She girned a bit.

- Back home, school would be out till September.

284

- Aye but the weans here have been oot on holiday since the end o June. Their Mums an Dads'll be burstin tae see the back o them! Onywey, ye're already late – they aw went back a coupla weeks ago.

Ah'm excited the haill day. When she's due back Ah know better than to make her ony dinner or even snacks but Ah pit the kettle on in case she waants a wee green tea or somethin.

She disnae.

- So? How did it go?
- OK.

She shrugs and vanishes into her bedroom and shuts the door. Efter a moment Ah chap the door and efter another minute enter. She's lyin on her bed keyin intae her laptop, wires trailin fae her ears.

- Did ye choose yer subjects fur yer Highers?

Ah huv tae repeat it before she hears me.

- Yeah.

Emma keeps her eyes fixed on the screen.

- So whit did ye go fur?

Again Ah huv tae repeat it.

- I had to take English and Maths. After that Modern Studies. And Computing and Human Biology.
- Nae languages?
- I wanted to go on with my Spanish but the school doesn't offer it. French clashed with Modern Studies. And it's too late to start over with German.
- Did ye make ony pals?

Emma looked up.

- Gran, I have to get on with this. Do you mind?
- Sorry, hen.

Later she emerges, evangelical light in her eyes.

- I want to go out campaigning for YES. Do you know where I can go?

Ah send her upstairs to Ewan MacConachie. She's away for hours. Comes back near the end o River City. Ah turn the sound doon at once.

- Oh Gran!

She birls roon, a wild look on her face.

- I think I'm in love!

Ah don't know whit to say.

- That Ewan – he's absolutely gorgeous, isn't he?

Ah jist staun there. Rabbit in headlamps.

- When he talks about his beliefs, his eyes just glow! And then he flashes a smile and it lights up his whole face. Have you seen his smile?
- Ma eyes are no that good …
- Round the doors he has an answer to absolutely everything. Doesn't ever look anything up on his phone. He's got leaflets for all occasions and he wrote a lot of them himself. Never loses his cool, even with the idiots.
- Idiots?
- Passports and visas brigade.
- Oh, them.
- Do you know what he said to me? He said the more English voices we had on the campaign trail the better. He grew up in Gateshead and I'm from London. Makes a kind of bond between us.

She sits doon and hugs hersel.

- I know what you're thinking, Gran – he's too old for me. He looks – maybe – mid-twenties?

Ah say cautiously:

- Ah think he's a bit aulder than that, hen.

- Don't like boys my own age – they're only interested in sex and football. A girl can dream, can't she? Can't I?

She beams up at me.

- He doesn't seem to have a girlfriend, at least he never mentioned one. And he shares his flat with that older guy – the NO campaigner. I wondered at first if they were father and son, but they've got different surnames and different accents. But after all, I've got a different accent from my parents …
- They're definitely no feyther an son.
- Well, anyway, I'm away to google him. Maybe I can follow him on Twitter, or be his Facebook friend.

She vanishes into her room while Ah go on staunin there like an eedjit.

Chapter 9: September

Opinion Poll *(The Sunday Times)*:
YES 47%   NO 45%   DON'T KNOW 7%

Donald

The headline: *'YES Leads in Scots Poll Shock'.*

Consternation in the Cabinet. Bubbling in Blythswood Square. Trouble at t'mill.

A bad dream. Cannae be happenin. But it is.

Next day the daily papers' front pages catch up on the story. Time to hold back the wave before it becomes tidal. Plug the credibility gap with more promises of devolution.

The *Daily Record*, faithful friend down the decades to the Labour Party, goes into outrage mode over the length o time since the last swatch of extra powers were offered to the Scottish Parliament. A cartoon has the three Unionist leaders as three wise monkeys:

Hear no devo, see no devo, speak no devo.

An unnamed 'senior government minister' 'reveals' to *The Observer* newspaper that Scotland will be offered a historic federal solution before the next election in May. After an impulsive OK from Cameron, Chancellor Osborne confirms this story in an interview the same day with Andrew Marr. He's got no more idea than Andrew Marr himself what truth might develop from the announcement, but any skilled politician can fudge when asked for details.

Richard says:

- So they're leaving it up to the Press to save the day? Not enough. Somebody up there better do something.

- Somebody up there?
- Up there, down there.

Now is the time for all good men to come to the aid of the Party. And indeed, the people down there come up.

The counter-revolution. Britannia at long last rouses from her slumber and brandishes her trident at the snarling Scottish lion. None too soon.

At Westminster, they cancel Prime Minister's Question Time and all three Unionist Party Leaders come gallopin north to shower Scotland with love.

Labour advisers from past and present cross the Border, either physically or digitally.

Ed Milliband leads 104 Labour MPs and MEPs to Glasgow to march up Buchanan Street. It's reminiscent of the launch of the Scottish Parliament when all the new MSPs marched up Edinburgh's Royal Mile in a gesture to the old traditions of the original Three Estates. I cannae get away from work to watch them in the street but that evening on the telly it brings a tear to my eye. The only thing to mar the historic occasion is the bunch of YES supporters who march within their very ranks, chantin slogans and wavin banners.

Never mind. Best of all: here's Gordon Brown in bellowin answer to the call. Over three days he wins back media sympathy for Better Together. He promises the imminent handover of still more powers in a new Scotland Bill. Prime Minister no more; he's still a Big Beast.

Ewan says:

- So a back-bench Labour MP speaks for the Tory Government? Writes their manifesto?

The *Daily Record* comes to the rescue again. Behind the scenes they persuade the leaders of the three main Unionist parties to sign up to a 'Vow' promisin to give Scotland 'extensive new powers' within a fixed timetable. It also announces that the Scottish Parliament is permanent – its continued existence no longer subject to the whim of succeeding UK Prime Ministers.

The Vow, signed by Cameron, Miliband and Clegg takes up the whole front page of the *Record* on September 16th.

Two days left to save the Union.

Last chance saloon.

Although I know about it in advance, I don't tell Ewan. Let him see it for himself when he buys his four newspapers on the Tuesday mornin.

Ewan hurls his copy of the *Record* across the room.

- Entrench the existence of the Scottish Parliament? Without a written constitution, no UK Government can bind a future Government. Extensive new powers your arse. Unspecified promises are worth zilch. And they accuse Salmond of peddling snake oil?

I think, but don't say: if it incenses you this much, maybe we've saved the day.

* * *

Ewan

Tonight I lead the canvassing on a forest road in a part I'd missed. The houses are strung along Gartloch Road or clumped in clearings amongst the trees. I'm humming the Teddy Bears' Picnic as we drive along in convoy.

So close to the vote now; healthy activist turnouts. Nine this time. I split us into lots of two each, sending them in different directions. I go alone. The houses are substantial, new-build. The few who answer the knock are wary, more NO than YES.

The nights are drawing in. A reminder of our proximity to R-day. Knocking on the doors on my particular clachan, I lose track of time. Darkness shrouds the deserted streets, the moon rises and the sky is studded with stars. I gaze in rapture, drinking in the atmosphere. On the horizon the silhouetted ruin of the old lunatic asylum.

'If you go down to the woods tonight ...' Minor key.

A tap on the shoulder makes me jump. Lorraine and Margaret.

- Everybody else is gone.
- We thought we'd been left behind. We were wonderin how we'd get home.
- Thank goodness you're still here.

On the road home we discuss the demonstration outside the BBC by YES activists complaining of bias. We laugh at the Establishment's attempt to portray *the demonstrators* as political censors. I want to stay out, to go on talking to these comrades.

No help for it. I have a home of my own. I let Margaret off in Riddrie and drive on with Lorraine.

Parking in the Drives is a nightmare. Eight flats to a close, and only a couple of spaces per close. When Alexander Dennistoun laid his plans, cars had barely been invented, never mind placed within the reach of ordinary working people. In the Conservation Area the convention is for the residents to park semi-legally: semi-on, semi-off the pavement. In the neat grid of the Drives all four wheels are square on the street. The Drives are like the single-track roads up the Highlands, minus the designated passing places. If one car comes in at the top of the street and another at the bottom somebody has to reverse.

By the time I find a parking space, we're closer to Duke Street, with its pubs, than we are to our own close. Suddenly a pub with Lorraine is more welcoming than home with Donald and his injured love.

So I stand her a pint and then she pays for the next round.

We talk about current revelations. About the UK Treasury orchestrating and leaking the story about the Scottish banks perhaps having to relocate their HQ into England before the boards had even discussed the matter. We talk about BBC bias, about how fairness means exploring a scare story in depth and then giving a YES spokesperson a short slot to defend YES against it.

The political gets personal. We talk about my childhood in the Peace Camps with a hippy mother. About Lorraine's involvement in poll tax demos and in the SSP before it split. She had been the kind of activist who attended demos and similar echo-chambers, safely surrounded by fellow-revolutionaries, rather than confronting the great unconverted.

We skirt around personal issues in the present tense. She scarcely ventures into the effect on my relationship of sharing a home with a NO activist (although she's obviously curious) and I don't ask about her split from a man now interested only in his new family (because I'm not curious).

Although she chatters freely, there's a shyness, a reluctance to look me too lingeringly in the eye. I know this look well. However, we both accept that a fling with a 50-something female whose partner has ditched her for a younger woman is not on my list.

- Are you actually a member of the SNP?
- I'm politically promiscuous. I've been a member of the Greens and the SSP. But just now, to play a full part in the YES campaign at organisational level, it helps to be in the SNP.

Bashfully she passes me a bit of paper. Must have been carrying it about all evening in her pocket. Maybe other evenings too – this is the first time we've been alone together.

- Thought you might like to see a poem I wrote when the SNP first got into power in 2007.

Soond shift

Daunerin oot ae braw mornin in May
The laverock tweetlin in the caller air
The lads in the ba park gien it laldy
A wean stringin gowans through her mither's hair.

Gaun for the morn's paper tae Mr Akram
Passin the time o day wi aul Tam Bain
Scutchin back the bindweed thrapplin the rosebuds
An aw the country's chyngit, but aye gaes on the same.
An the blue earth birlin like a beacon in the sky
An the rain aye scutterin wherr it hits the mochie ground

An nane ae us has broken oot in biles an carbuncles
An naebody has robbed me o five thoosan pound.
And yet a helicopter on the Barra strand
A Lossie loon that hud his wits aboot him on the day
Huv workit noo a sleekit shift in aw wur wey o thinkin
An history will keep in mind this rare mornin in May.

Unnecessarily she says

- It's in Scots. I went to a workshop about writin in Scots.

Maybe explaining about the Scots because she thinks I'm English?

- Your poem's very good. Evocative.

She still looks at me expectantly. What does she want me to say?

- Mind the Labour Party Political Broadcast where they said if the SNP got in it would cost everybody £5000? That's a reference …

- Ah yes. The £5000.

293

I don't remember. But I guess it must have happened.

- Mind all the drama? How the last seat was mistakenly given to Labour …
- I remember.
- It was so dramatic, wasn't it? Don't you remember how dramatic it was?
- Very dramatic. Do you write a lot of poetry?
- Only when I'm feelin passionate.

She goes on looking at me. Pepper-and-salt hair, bags under her eyes and the start of a double chin. Nothing much to look at even in her heyday.

- Ever tried to get them published?
- Don't know how. D'ye no have to be already famous to get into an anthology?
- There are literary magazines. You should check them out on the internet.

She wants further comment. Endorsement. I haven't the time. I hand her back the bit of paper with an encouraging smile.

Back home I eat the dinner Donald lays out for me. Pasta with zucchini blossoms. I try my best to avoid mentioning the anti-BBC demonstrations. I know that Donald won't if I don't. But it's like a scab I can't help picking.

Donald's response is predictable.

- Fair point. Trying to control the political media … that way danger lies.
- It's a complete distortion of the situation! These demonstrators are individual protesters who individually feel strongly about something. If anybody should be compared to Russian State television, it's our own State broadcaster!
- If you'd ever lived in a real totalitarian state you

wouldnae use the phrase "State Broadcaster" so lightly.

- OK – what's the difference? The BBC's funded by the Government. The boss is appointed by a body who are appointed by Government ministers. Their output is biased …

- That's no true.

- And when BBC Scotland a few years ago voted for the right to put on their own news to reflect the workings of their own new Parliament, the Prime Minister galloped up from London and put the kybosh on that.

- Our BBC is the envy of the world. Certainly of all these countries whose news gets filtered through their Government Propaganda Department.

- And ours doesn't?

- Anyway, I wouldnae want my world news comin with a tartan tinge. No "Torry man drowned at sea" for me.

- You Scots despise yourselves, don't you? What a sorry bunch.

- Look Ewan, let's not …

- Fuck off.

As Donald reaches out a conciliatory arm, I shake him away. I hurry into the bedroom and bolt the door. I fling myself on the bed.

Too much for my brain. I'm still working for wages part of every day and yet all these other issues compete for attention.

Compete? Hardly. My current copywriting commission (producing promotional material for wedding planners) comes a poor fourth in my priorities. Ahead of it comes:

The campaign, relentless, day after day. If it's not canvassing it's leafleting. If it's not leafleting it's stalls, organising where to set them up, setting out the materials, seeing that they're adequately staffed by volunteers, staffing them myself. If it's not stalls it's public meetings (unfortunately still with only one side presenting itself: the NOs are always too busy to come and defend their stance).

My relationship with Donald. Getting more and more difficult. He's now trying to keep off the topic. He's retreating into 'for the sake of peace' mode. But it's too late. He irritates me whenever he opens his mouth, even if it's to ask me if I'm ready for my dinner. His 'Naw Thanks' badge is a blue rag to a bull.

The idea of being a father. Increasingly I think I should be pro-active. Calum needs a Dad. Whether I make a good one or a bad one, I'm the only one he's got. It's unfair of Alison to shut me out.

I remember when Mam met Phil and we all moved to Gateshead. Phil was a relief from the relentless femininity of Greenham Common. Phil took me to watch football. To play snooker. He played with me differently from the way Mam did. I'm glad I had that role model. Mam with her meditations and mantras was not enough.

When I first came out to Mam, she uttered all the enlightened words I expected of her. Whatever my preferences, whoever I choose to love etc. etc.. So did Phil.

Later I overheard her weeping in her bedroom. She was not crying about the prejudice I might face. She was crying because she thought she would never be a grandmother.

So there's somebody else who should know about Calum.

* * *

Abdul

We are having breakfast when the postwoman knocks at the door. Letter in her hands. From the UK Border Agency.

As I sign for the letter and watch the postwoman carry on

up the stair, my heart is thudding. I take the letter to the breakfast table and tell Parween

- It's from the UK Border Agency.

Parween looks at me rather than at the letter. I slit the envelope and contemplate the mass of text. I scan down it for familiar words, words which might allow the core of meaning to break through the bureaucratic jargon. Words like 'refugee status'. Or 'deport'. Or 'expired'.

'Refugee status' does not appear. What does leap out at me is 'Fareiba'.

I work my way through the letter

- What is it? Are we being thrown out?
- I don't think so.
- What is it, then?
- I'm not sure.

I glean some meaning but can't be sure. I don't want to tell Parween until I'm certain.

Who can help? The flat across the landing is now empty. I'm reluctant to approach the people upstairs. So I tell Parween to wait and I go downstairs. I knock on Mr Murphy's door.

No one at home. However, the door across the landing opens. Mrs Donnelly looks out. Mr Murphy is behind her.

I hold out the letter. Suddenly I'm tongue-tied. In my excitement I haven't worked out what to say.

- Help me?
- What's this – a letter?
- Official letter. What does it mean?

Mrs Donnelly smiles.

- Bureaucrats. How can they no write ordinary English, eh? Gie's it.

She and Mr Murphy pore over it together.

- Huv yese got a daughter cawed Fareiba?
- Yes! Yes! What does the letter say?
- Has she been missin?
- Yes!
- Well, she seems tae huv turnt up.
- Turnt up?
- They've found hur.

Tears spring to my eyes.

- Is she alive?
- Disnae say …

Mr Murphy nudges Mrs Donnelly.

- It wid mention if she wis deid.
- So it wid. Aye, ye can take it she's alive. She's in Hamburg. Here, that's in Germany. How in the name did she end up there?

I take back the letter. Scrutinise it. Try to draw out more layers of meaning. Mrs Donnelly points.

- Thur a phone number ye can caw for mair information. If yese want Ah kin ring them fur ye.
- Please. But first I tell my wife.

Fareiba is in Hamburg. There's still a maze of red tape, a mountain of documentation to get through before she can come to Scotland or we can go to Germany. Before we can even talk to each other. But she's not in the hands of traffickers or at the bottom of the Aegean Sea. One day we will meet again.

Our joy fills our living-room, soaks into the drapery, swirls around the table, couch and armchair and spills out on to the balcony. It even makes the dragon smile as he squats on his patch of the Australian desert.

* * *

Kirsty

The BBC puts on a huge event in the Hydro in Glasgow. 7,500 of us schoolchildren are assembled for a debate. On the platform are Nicola Sturgeon for the SNP, Patrick Harvie for the Greens, Ruth Davidson for the Tories and, representing the NO side in general, an old geezer in a funny hat. No spokesperson at all for Labour. But Malky googles it and tells me the old geezer is George Galloway who used to be a Labour MP but got kicked out the party. The funny hat is his 'trademark fedora'.

Poser.

Although some of the others round me have attended concerts at the Hydro, I've never been in such a huge auditorium before. It's terribly hot and I'm too shy to ask any questions.

But we're arranged according to our schools. I find myself sitting between Malky and a nice girl called Emma who's new to the area. By sheer coincidence she's living up my old close, staying with her gran. Afterwards we all go for a coffee together. She was bullied at her last school as well. It was when she was going through a Goth phase. But these days she dresses cool. A lot cooler than me. Emma would be a good best mate. Hanging with her would boost my cred. If I move fast I can link up with her before she gets in with another crowd.

* * *

Donald

Ewan announces out the blue

- My mother's coming up to Glasgow.
- What? When?
- Second weekend after the referendum. She'll be staying the Friday till Monday.

299

- So I get to meet her at last!

My heart sings. Introducing me to his mother. Gives the stamp of officialdom to our partnership. Absurd for that to matter at my age. But it does.

- Well, I don't know …
- Would it be best if we give her our bedroom and we can sleep on the futon in the computer room?
- She's booked in at a B&B.
- What? Wouldn't hear of it! We've got that spare room …
- Mam wants to stay at the B&B.
- That's ridiculous …
- She insists.
- Why?

He doesnae answer. I regroup my forces. Pick my battles.

- Anyway, she'll be comin here for her dinner. I'll cook somethin special. What does she like …
- Don't go to any trouble …
- Come on! This is my mother-in-law I'm meeting! I'll be goin all out!

In truth I'm shit-scared. What if she thinks I'm too old for him? I'm nearly as old as she is. He's no said much about her, but she sounds a New-Age type. Maybe she'll think I'm too staid, too conventional. I go over my wardrobe in my head. Can I still get into yon old purple kaftan?

- Is she comin for any reason?
- Not particularly … It's been nearly ten years since she was up here.
- Weekend after next … Is that the September weekend? So I'll be on holiday? Great – we'll organise some trips. What's she not seen yet? Has she been to New Lanark?

- Look – she's basically coming up to see me. She won't be that bothered. Don't organise anything too …
- You were down there just at Christmas, were you no? So this'll be the chance for her and me to get to know one another.

Now I think of it, maybe I gave the kaftan to a charity shop.

- Donald …

Ewan looks like he's gonnae say something else but then he thinks the better of it.

- Have to offski. I'm late.

He gathers up his YES bags and makes his exit.

* * *

Elspeth

Here's me takin the chance tae hang oot ma waashin. Hope it disnae rain. The weather's been good so far.

Here's Wilma Armstrong comin oot tae pit hur ain up. Hope she disnae stert anither fight aboot whose turn it is o the waashin lines. Ah've steyed here five year an Ah'm still no sure if thur really is a rule aboot it or if it's aw in hur heid.

- Hiya, Elspeth!
- Hiya, Wilma.
- Hope this weather keeps up, eh?
- Aye. It's been lovely aw week.

She's in a good mood. Still ye never know the minute. Aggro in ma hoose an aggro roon the back green. Whit Ah'd gie fur a quiet life. Ah've never sterted a fight in ma puff. Why's it ayeways me hus tae tiptoe roon everybody?

Born under an unlucky star.

- Huv you hud thae YES fuckers roon yer door an aw?
- Aye.

301

- Whit a nerve shovin thon shite through wur letterboxes. Ah shoved it right back at them, so Ah did. Telt them tae pit it wherr the sun disnae shine.
- Aye.
- Whit a cairry-on, eh? If it's no the fuckin IRA it's the fuckin SNP.
- Ah know.
- Ur you gonnae go oot tae vote in this farce?
- Don't know.
- We all huv tae. We huv tae keep Scotland British and loyal tae wur Prodestant Queen.
- Aye.
- See if the SNP get powers over immigration, they'll open the floodgates. Let every fuckin towelheid an his uncle in here tae fill up wur schools an wur doctors' waitin rooms.
- Ah know.
- Ah mean whit aboot yon shower doon below me. Whit aboot them gettin thon two bedroom hoose wi jist the wee boy an here you've tae muck in wi aw yer big grown up fellas?
- Ah know.
- Wonder how they worked that?
- A bedroom fur the parents and anither fur the wean ...
- When they're used tae livin in a tent?
- Ah heard there wis originally tae be a lassie wi them ...
- Well she's no therr noo, is she?
- Naw ...
- An it's no jist the hoose. They got aw thur furniture, an computers an everythin laid on. You an me – if we waant a computer, we've tae save up an buy it wursels.

302

- Ah know.
- Me no spikka da English, eh? Smart enough when it comes to gettin somethin fur nuthin.

Talk aboot timin. The door fae the close opens an the Arab wumman comes oot wi a black bag o waashin. She disnae look at us. Sterts hingin it up on wan o the ither lines. Wilma wades intae hur.

- Heh, you!

The wumman turns roon.

- We take turns o the waashin lines here. Turns! No your turn! Take yer waashin back up the sterr!

The wumman looks fae Wilma tae me an back tae Wilma. Wilma picks up the bag o waashin an shoves it back intae the wumman's airms. Grips the wumman by the shouthers an turns hur roon so she's facin back tae the close. Shoves hur back towards the close.

- Aye, that's right. Back tae the hoose. No your turn. Come again anither day.

The wumman humphs her waashin back intae the close.

- That's hur sortit. So ye gonnae turn oot tae vote an keep Scotland British?
- Suppose so …
- Come an we'll go doon thegither? Ah'll chap yer door fur ye. When wid suit ye? Mornin or efternoon?
- Ah don't know. Ah'm workin that day …
- When d'ye finish yer shift?
- 3 o'clock.
- OK, well. Ah'll come roon fur ye at four an we can go doon thegither. Aw right?
- Aw right.

Chapter 10: Going to the Vote

Apprentices at one of the few surviving steel companies had welded the date in steel, tempered in the fire. Gradually welded it as the date was gradually revealed, starting on the right hand side with the year: 2014. An allegorical photo-opportunity for the Depute First Minister: the date itself, bursting through flames, solid and unchanging, the fresh-faced boys and girls a reminder that the seedcorn of our heavy industry survives.

Thursday 18th September 2014.

Ewan and Donald

The day dawns cloudy but dry. Ewan and Donald both rise before the alarm which was set to 6.30am. As they take turns to shower and shave, as they dress and prepare their separate breakfasts, the conversation is safe.

- These your socks? They were in my drawer.
- We're out of decaf.
- Bought some the other day. Look in the pantry.

Over breakfast they silently check the news on their phones. The arty-farties, the self-styled creatives and performing artists have overtly supported YES. Sporting celebrities on the other hand, reliant on UK sponsorship and training facilities, have tended to support NO or, more often, stayed schtum.

However, Scotland's claim to global superstardom, the darling of the tennis courts, Andy Murray, at the eleventh hour opens his lips.

- Let's do this.

Donald and Ewan clatter down the stairs together, overtaking Agnes and her message bag.

- Good morning. Big day fur yese, lads.

They split at the end of the path to head for their separate cars which will take them to their separate hubs to be given their very separate duties of the day.

* * *

Habib

Habib has a holiday from school because of the referendum. After lunch Parween for the first time proposes they go for a walk. Their route takes them past Habib's school. He points to the gate.

- There's the lady who thought my Taki came from Afghanistan!

He runs ahead to where Anne-Marie is standing amongst boxfuls of pens, balloons and leaflets. By the time his parents catch up, Anne-Marie is showing him a picture of herself with her uncle's staffie on her phone.

She asks him to choose a YES balloon. He picks a red one. She gives his parents a YES pen each.

- Be careful – the red on the barrel comes aff on yer hauns. No great quality!

The NO agent gives Abdul a leaflet. He takes it politely while explaining that he and his wife don't have a vote.

Down at Hogganfield Loch, Habib spots a boy from his class with another YES balloon.

- Scott picked a blue one because he supports Rangers!

He runs down to join his friend. Scott's parents are feeding the birds. They give Habib some of their bread and he too throws it into the water. The ducks, swans and geese crowd round, gobbling.

Abdul and Parween sit together on a bench. The sun comes out from behind a cloud. It filters through the trees, turning their leaves light yellow.

- How are you feeling?

She turns to him and smiles.

- Truly happy.
- The world is always more cheerful outdoors.
- Habib can speak very good English. I didn't realise …
- Much better than mine. He's left us behind.
- Left you behind. I'm not even in the race.
- Why don't you come to the English class along with me?
- You said the teacher is a man.
- In my class yes. My class is a mixed class. But there are separate classes for women if you prefer. They can give you access to a computer. You could talk on Skype to Maryam and Jameela.
- Perhaps I will.
- And later to Fareiba.

She turns and smiles. The beautiful smile Abdul remembers so well.

- Then I definitely will.

She leans back, eyes closed. The sun plays on her face the way it rarely did in Afghanistan, where the sun shines every day.

* * *

Ewan

Ewan has arranged to spend the day on Get Out The Vote, to go round with a car reminding identified YES supporters

306

to turn out. However, before he even starts the word comes: Knock-up is cancelled. They don't need reminding: they're turning out in droves. Never seen such a turnout.

The knocker-uppers are redeployed to polling station duty.

Ewan marvels at the friendly smiles, the banter, the old pals routine coming his way from nearly all the voters as they pass through the school gates. However, it's an exchange between the two duty police officers:

- Fingers crossed, eh?
- Oh, I hope so!
- Here, we're supposed to be neutral!
- I'll no tell if you don't tell!

That convinces him YES has won Glasgow.

But what of the rest of Scotland?

* * *

Donald

Donald, after voting at the local school on behalf of himself and Iain, also spends the day outside a polling station. A wretched lump of wire and concrete, more like a prison than a school.

Better Together are short of activists and there are three shifts of YES polling agents to his one. He is always alone while the YES sometimes have each other. The day drags as the voters cold-shoulder him, flashing their grins at the YES agents, accepting their balloons and pens.

Donald consoles himself that the deadpan majority wear no hearts on their sleeves; no badges on their hearts.

YES voters are puppies, he reckons; NO voters are cats. He remembers Lady Purr who shared a home with him and Gerry for fourteen years.

307

Agnes Morrison was handing out kittens the other day. He would have taken one if it hadn't been for Ewan's allergy.

* * *

Walter

At 10am Walter Gilchrist opens his curtains. Across the road: two window posters.

To the right: 'NO thanks' with the cross in the circle of the O. That sign always reminds him of a rabbit's nose.

To the left a square 'Believe in Scotland'.

On the coffee table the album he showed Kirsty and her friend. He opens it again at the picture with R.B. Cunninghame-Graham. The years dissipate.

The view from up on Paw's shoulders: the sea of bunnets, the cloche hats.

Running his fingers through Paw's sandy hair, the slippery strands, the scent of Brylcreem.

Paw's tweedy lapels rough on the undersides of his calves.

Paw's hands gripping his ankles as he tried to kick 'Gee-up!'

Don Roberto: the aristocratic profile, the horse high-stepping: clip-clop.

Paw copying the sound for him, clicking his tongue as he galloped with Walter around the field of Bannockburn. No Robert the Bruce statue then, nor any marker to remind the world of the spot where England's mediaeval might was humiliated by a smaller, poorer but not stupider army.

Maw, spreading a raincoat for them to sit on, getting out the three cakes: pineapple cake, Eiffel tower and fern cake. And the sandwiches and flask of tea and ginger. Letting him have first pick of the cakes after he'd eaten up his sandwich. The taste of the pineapple icing. Artificial cream, but he didn't know that then. Maw wiping the cream off his upper lip and

308

the tip of his nose.

The platform where one speaker after another was going his dinger about grown-up stuff and getting cheered.

Cheering himself whenever Paw cheered.

He shuts his eyes and shakes his head.

   - Sorry Paw. Don't know whit Ah wis thinkin.

In a daze he goes for his jacket. Lets himself out and walks to the school at the corner. There are two people at the gate; they thrust their respective leaflets towards him. A dream walking, he passes them by, plods across the playground sending YES balloons flying to either side of him.

Inside, his voice is so low that the polling clerk has to ask him to repeat his name and address. He takes the ballot paper to the polling booth, reaches for the hanging pencil, looks at it, thinks. Feels in his pocket for a biro. He puts his X squarely in the YES box.

*   *   *

Rab and Marilyn

The phone rings. Walter. Marilyn passes it to Rob.

   - Guess what.

Rob guesses, but chooses not to say.

   - Ah voted YES efter aw.

   - Course ye did. You didnae want Grandpa to get dizzy in his grave.

   - Wisnae that. It's aboot the future, no the past.

   - So you've forgiven Scotland for her years of betrayal.

   - Widnae be able to forgive masel, is mair the point. Whit about you and Marilyn? Huv you voted yet?

   - No yet.

   - So. Whit aboot it?

309

- What about what?
- Ach. Talk to you later.

Rab drives Marilyn and himself to the polling station.

- Should be alright, Rab. The polls are back up again.
- Looks like it.
- I'm really astonished so many have jumped on this bandwagon. I mean how can you set up a new country if you haven't even got agreement on which currency to use?
- Daft.
- When an idea comes into vogue they follow like sheep.
- Peer pressure.

Outside the school gates are two YES agents – teenage boys – and one NO agent – a middle-aged lady.

- Poor soul. Must feel isolated. Pair of neds. Look at the piercings on that one.
- They're all smiles.
- They'll be grinning out the other side of their faces tonight.
- Guess so.
- Well, I'm going to walk past them wearing my NO Thanks badge with pride.

As they approach, one of the grinning YES lads proffers a promotional pen. They body-swerve him. Marilyn nudges the NO representative.

- Chin up. It's going our way.

The lady smiles a wan smile.

Inside, they take their ballot papers into their booths.

Marilyn marks an X against NO.

Rob marks an X against YES.

They come out, folding the papers and slip them into the ballot box.

- Duty done.

Marilyn links arms with Rob.

- Assuming this madness is ended tomorrow, come and we'll celebrate? What about dinner in a restaurant and then on to a movie? Just the two of us. Kirsty can babysit.
- Suits me.
- Greek or Italian?
- Up to you, pet.

He smiles at Marilyn, snuggling in close. Casually he glances back and winks at the YES ned with the piercings.

* * *

The Akram family and the Usmani family

The two families make a day out of it. The last big together event before the Usmani flit to Scotstoun.

The school where Catriona teaches and the schools which Yasmin, Bina and Farooq attend are being used as polling stations. Old Uncle Ibrahim takes charge of Ali's corner shop and Catriona's brother Craig goes behind the counter of Iqbal's computer maintenance stall in the Forge Market. Noor and her children dress in their shiny gear. Ali, Noor, Iqbal and Catriona pile themselves and their five children into their people-carrier and drive off, first to the polling station to vote YES, and then down to Largs to eat Nardini ice-cream, throw YES balloons about, cook a picnic on campstoves on the beach and look at Vikings.

* * *

Stevie

Stevie is sleeping at noon when Gordo, out on bail, breenges into his bedroom along with a few of his heavies.

- Oot yer scratcher, wee man.
- Uch, gonnae gie's peace? Ah didnae get hame last night till …
- Don't waant tae hear it. We're aw gaun oot tae vote!
- Uch, Ah wisnae gonnae bother …

Gordo yanks off the duvet. He and his troops take a limb each and swing Stevie into the air. He lands on the floor wearing only his underpants.

- Get yer gear oan. We'll wait.

Out in the street, although Stevie's legs are about the same length as theirs, he has to put more effort into keeping up. They swagger. Claim the width of the pavement. He scampers. On and off the kerb, in and out the gutter.

It was ever thus.

- So ur we gonnae vote YES or NO?
- Whit dae ye think?

Stevie keeps his gaze on the ground. Get this wrong and it could be another hammering.

- YES?
- Of course, fuckin YES! Ye waant thae millionaire cunts doon in London tae go on treatin us like fuckin losers? Fuckin stealin aw wur oil an giein us crumbs. Pure shady, man!

In the polling station each takes his ballot paper. Gordo slaps Stevie on the back as they head for the polling booths.

- Moment tae remember, eh? Yer first vote.

In the booths Gordo and his three mates vote YES. They come out and put their votes in the ballot box. They wait.

- Ye aw right in therr, wee man?
- Look fur the word stertin wi a "Y"!

Gordo demonstrates with a two-finger salute.

The polling clerk says

- If you've cast your votes, please wait outside.

To Stevie's surprise they obey. As soon as they've made their exit, Stevie puts a cross against 'NO'. He comes out and furtively stuffs it in the ballot box.

* * *

Cindy

The postman at last brings Cindy something good. The keys to a new flat, smaller than the one she had to abandon but near a State nursery school. Although there's a waiting list for the nursery, with Lorraine to speak for her and the support of Women's Aid, she secures a full-time place for Charlie.

She hopes that, once he's in education, with other children to play with and nursery nurses and teachers to stretch his mind and curb his impulses, he'll simmer down, become more biddable. She hopes that soon he'll be trained to hold her hand when crossing the road, to stay near her side in the supermarket. That she'll be able to ditch the buggy at last.

* * *

Agnes

Agnes accepts the leaflet and the pen from the YES agent as she and Emma turn into the school gates.

- Ah'm no daein this for masel. Ah'm daein it for Emma here, ma granddaughter. She's the future, Ah'm the past.

* * *

313

Elspeth

Elspeth has no sooner got in from her shift, hung up her jacket, kicked off her shoes and slumped into a chair than she hears the knock on the door. Wilma has been watching for her.

Wilma has her coat on.

- Comin?

It's not a question.

As they stroll down to the school past all the windows, Wilma gives the finger to every YES poster they pass. A special big one to a poster advertising an old Hope Over Fear rally. For her part Elspeth hopes against the fear that they might run into Malky wearing his YES T-shirt and paraphernalia.

At the gates Wilma offers a last gesture to the two YES agents with their balloons. She and Elspeth pick up their ballot papers, go into the polling booths. Wilma presses so vigorously on her ballot paper she breaks the pencil. Elspeth hesitates a few moments looking down at the ballot paper and then makes her cross, also in the NO box.

Outside in the sunshine Wilma's in happy mood.

- Comin back tae mines fur a cuppa? Maybe a wee bevvy?
- Och, Ah don't …
- Come oan. We waant tae fuckin celebrate. It's no every day we save the Union. Ah'm sayin …

She cups her hand round her mouth and shouts down the street at the top of her voice

- It's no every day we save the Union!

She takes Elspeth's arm, snuggles in to her.

- Och Ah'm terrible, so Ah'm ur. Ye cannae take me naewherr!

* * *

314

Angela

Angela waits until Lorraine comes home from work so they can go to the polling station together. Angela smiles proudly as she accepts her first ever ballot paper. In the polling booth she savours the moment, twirling the pencil, reading the ballot paper over and over before marking her X against YES.

* * *

Kenny and Daisy

Kenny and Daisy go together to the school. Kenny says to the YES agent

- We're no ready for it, hen. Gie us anither twinty year.

They both mark the NO box.

After they come out they go for a stroll. They sit on a bench. The sun streams down. Kenny contemplates the golf course.

- Ye intae golf?
- Ye mean playin it?
- Waatchin it. The Ryder Cup's oan next week.
- Ye waant tae come tae mine tae see it?
- If it's OK. You've got Sky.
- Aw right, well.

Daisy takes out a flask of tea and two cups. They share their sandwiches with a grey squirrel who comes right over from out of the trees.

- Aw, the wee sowel.
- Rat wi good PR.

* * *

315

Malky

Malky feels the hand of history on his shoulder as he stands in the polling booth.

The 1820 Martyrs, Scotland Free or a Desert, hanged for seeking the franchise for Jock Tamson's sons. The Suffragettes, undergoing jail and force-feeding for the women's franchise. Now the teenagers are getting the vote without raising as much as a banner.

He lingers awhile, thinking on these things.

* * *

Kirsty

Kirsty messages Malky to let him know she's setting off to her local polling station. When she sees the crowd milling round the gate, she's embarrassed. Her heart lurches when she sees Angela and her mother coming out of the door towards her. Lorraine says 'Hiya, Kirsty.' Kirsty and Angela exchange faint smiles.

Cara squeezes into the polling booth beside her: If voting changed anything, they would ban it.

It is banned, in many countries.

Cara: Definition of an election: two wolves and a lamb voting about what to have for dinner.

More than two wolves in Scotland. And the lamb is starting to grow teeth.

Cara: And the pigs are starting to grow wings.

When she comes out of the polling station into the sunshine Malky's already waiting for her. They kiss. And go hand-in-hand for the bus to take them to Kirsty's long-lost mother.

* * *

Jan Dvorak and Zack Konicek

The boys finish work for the day on the building site. Afterwards they go with two Polish workmates, Piotr and Karol, to a pub near Piotr's flat. They order beer and vodka. They discuss the World Cup in Brazil, the Commonwealth Games in Glasgow, the state of the pound against the euro, the złoty and the koruna and the developing political crisis in the Ukraine.

Around 7.30 the conversation turns to the referendum. They argue: the Poles plan to vote YES and the Czechs plan to vote NO. Round follows round; the voices grow louder, the argument more heated. As younger generation East Europeans, their lingua franca is English and words fly around, overflowing onto the tables around them: Slovakia; oil; Norway; currency; passports; the nuclear deterrent; the old Soviet Union; the Queen.

The European Union.

- If Scotland becomes independent it'll get kicked out of the EU. And you, you, you and I: we'll all get kicked out of Scotland, my friends. (Zack)
- Why should Scotland get kicked out of the EU? It's already a member. No member has ever been kicked out. (Piotr)
- Scotland is not a member. It's only a bit of a member. Can a leg apply to join a club? (Zack)
- Depends on the leg. What about that pair over by the bar. I'd sign them into any club! (Karol)

Four heads turn to the bar. They gape, chortle and josh. Karol stares at the girl until she spots him. He gives her his most winning smile. She gazes back blankly. A small untidy-looking man with greasy hair shambles out of the Gents' toilet.

- OK hen? We fur aff?

The couple leave together without a backward look. Zack slaps Karol on the back.

- Can't win them all.

- She took him over me! (Karol)

- Maybe when she married him, he was young and good-looking. (Zack)

- But then she would be a child. (Karol)

- Maybe he's her Dad. (Zack)

- Can we get back to the referendum? (Jan)

- Seriously. If they kick Scotland out they surely have to kick England out also. (Piotr)

- Didn't you hear what the big man in Spain said? They'll kick Scotland out but England can remain. And it would be 'extremely difficult if not impossible' for Scotland to get back in. It would have to go to the back of the queue. Behind Turkey. (Zack)

- Maybe the UK itself will leave the EU. Cameron doesn't want to stay in the EU. (Piotr)

- Cameron does want to stay in the EU. (Zack)

- So why is he going to give them a referendum on it? (Karol)

- He's allowing this referendum on Scottish independence. And he doesn't want that. (Jan)

- Cameron is a weak leader. (Karol).

- Cameron might be weak but he's not stupid. This EU referendum will never happen. And if it did they would vote to stay in. (Zack)

During a lull Piotr glances out the window. The street lights are on and the stars are out. He checks the time on his phone. 9.45. Only fifteen minutes till the polls close. Zack and Jan are twenty minutes' trot away from their polling station, or five if they're lucky with a bus. Karol's polling station is two bus trips away. Piotr's is right across the road.

Piotr stands up.

- I'll just go and vote. I'll be right back.

Zack grasps his arm.

- Look, Karol's not going to make it. And Jan and I would have to rush off right now and even then might not make it. What if none of us vote? We'd only cancel each other out anyway.
- Good idea. (Jan)
- I don't like to miss my vote on a historic day like this. Everybody'll be discussing it tomorrow. (Piotr)
- Don't let these NO supporters put you off. You at least can still make it. (Karol).
- Listen. Two options. Option one. We all rush off now to vote. Karol won't make it and you will. If Jan and I are lucky, we'll get in before they close. So there will be two NO votes against one YES vote. Advantage to us. Option two. We all stay here and order another round of drinks. (Zack)

Piotr remains standing for a moment, looking wistfully out the window across to the school until Zack pulls him back down to his seat. He goes on looking over to the school gate, still buzzing into the night with polling agents and YES balloons.

* * *

Kirsty

We ring the street security bell. Glance at each other. Squeeze each other's hands. Somebody presses the enter button without asking who we are. Malky walks faster than me. Leads me up the stair. I would rather reach the door before him but I don't like to tell him. Seems petty.

319

The door is already open and Malky is standing there facing my mother.

What does she see? Gangly youth, grey hoodie, tracky bottoms, trainers, face covered in plooks.

I come peching up behind him.

- Hello, M ... Um. This is my friend Malky.

Malky steps aside.

Thin longish face, faded dyed blonde hair piled atop a greying fringe. Uncertain smile, short upper lip, deep-set eyes. I remember the bone structure, the upward tilted eyebrows, the spirit behind the eyes, the mouth. The wrinkles and hair colour are new. Her hair used to be as red as mine.

Cara: Fairly aged in ten years.

Sylvia breaks into a smile. A tear glistening in her eye. She recognises me.

Expressions are like fingerprints.

My cheeks are thinner, my hair is thicker, coarser and darker, I'm much taller and fatter.

Yet she and I would pick each other out in a line of twenty.

- Come away in, Kirsty dear. This is my friend Pamela.

Hair silver, short back and sides, black top and trousers.

Cara: Typical dyke.

Pamela smiles and holds out her hand.

Cara: Phoney grin if ever I saw one.

In the living-room Malky and I perch on the couch. Facing us, on the wall above the fireplace ...

- The lady in the boat!
- You remember her? The Lady of Shallott.
- The Lady of ... what?
- Shallott. From Tennyson's poem. About the lady who's only allowed to look in a mirror to see who's

passing her window. Did you not get that poem in school?

- No. But … did you maybe read it to me or something? The story's familiar.
- I didn't read you the whole poem because you were too wee – it's long and it would have bored you. But I used to tell you the story. It was one of your favourite bedtime stories when I was tucking you up. What a good memory you've got.
- You still look like the lady on the boat. Even more so. Your hair used to be redder than hers.
- I'm more like her mother, now, maybe?
- Remember Daddy used to say it was you? And I believed him. I used to go to galleries hoping to find that picture. The Art Galleries has pictures of ladies who look a bit like her. But not the same picture.
- They've got other Pre-Raphaelite pictures.
- Pre-Raphaelites. We got told about them in Art. Like Dante Gabriel Rossetti.
- He was the most famous. They painted all their ladies the same style.
- Looking like you.
- The Lady of Shallott is by John Waterhouse. Your Dad bought me that print as an engagement present, because he said it looked like me.
- What a romantic present!
- He apologised at the time. Said he couldn't afford a ring. I told him I'd rather have the picture anyway.

Pamela clears her throat.

- Do you want herbal tea? Or …
- Young people usually prefer cold drinks.

Cara: Down with the kids.

321

- Herbal tea's fine.

Cara: Wee sook.

- Huv ye got Irn-Bru or Coke? (Malky)

Pamela vanishes into the kitchen.

Cara: Watch that one. She spells trouble.

Over dinner the memories ricochet between Sylvia and me. Half-remembered toys (she resurrects Little Miss Chatterbox from a drawer, still scribbled with my artwork), day trips and holidays. Visits to my grandmother, now dead. Songs Sylvia taught me. The fleshly Cara gets a brief mention but I quickly change the subject.

Malky, Pamela and Astral Cara are out of the loop. With the dessert, conversation turns to the political event of the day.

- I haven't been able to think about the referendum. For me, 18th September means only one thing: your birthday and the end of the interdict. (Sylvia)
- When we came here, me an Kirsty were jist efter gaun doon an votin YES. (Malky)
- Then I'll go down before the polls close and vote YES too. (Sylvia)

Cara: Sycophant.

I get up to go to the bathroom. On the way I pass the kitchen and stop and listen. Loading the dishwasher, Pamela mutters

- We discussed this. We were going to vote "NO".
- Can I not change my mind?
- Sylvia, this is really important. Here we are, fine and secure at long last. Two reasonable incomes, manageable mortgage. Why would you want to jeopardise all that?
- Why should it jeopardise it?
- Because we don't know what the future'll bring. Because when you're steering a steady course you

322

don't rock the boat.

- Nothing's more important to me right now than bonding with my daughter.
- It is a secret ballot.
- I won't lie to her.

As I pass I see Sylvia laying her hand on Pamela's arm.

- And I won't lie to you either.

Pamela pulls away and slams the dishwasher shut.

* * *

Donald

They do the Glasgow count down the Emirates. Gaunt place out in the sticks. Looks even more like an aeroplane hangar than the SECC.

I've never been to a count before. Ewan's been to countless. I certainly enjoy this one. I'm happier than I've been all year.

Soon as the Inverclyde vote comes in, that was expected to be a YES but turns out marginally NO, the game's up. Vertical faces on all the Yessers, horizontal faces on us.

I would love to enjoy it along wi Ewan. Or have him congratulate me and me console him. But he avoids me like the plague. We drive separately into the Emirates. He leaves long before me. I stay amongst my comrades for the happy ending. We cheer ourselves hoarse.

The Union is saved. 2,001,926 voted NO; only 1,617,989 YES. Could have been a healthier majority. Up till the last few weeks we expected it to be a much healthier majority. But a majority of one vote is enough. We have a majority of 10%.

Let's hope that's it. Let's hope both sides respect the voice of the people and put this dangerous idea to bed for a long, long time. Salmond said there would be no more referendums for at least a generation. What is a generation? Twenty years? Thirty? Forty? Women are bearing their children later these days. I'll go for forty.

When I get home Ewan's tucked up pretending to be asleep.

* * *

Ewan

Next morning after Donald's left for work, I analyse the results on the internet.

On average, very broadly, the rich, the old, and those born in England, Wales or Northern Ireland reached for the security of NO. The poor, the young, and those born in Scotland grasped at the opportunity of YES. However, within the detail lurk many surprises.

Glasgow: 30 years of solid Labour representation at every level: local, Holyrood, Westminster, the EU. A city where you weighed the Labour votes, where people voted Labour by habit, following the ancestral trail. Across every constituency Glasgow voted YES.

Angus: 30 years of solid SNP representation at every level: local, Holyrood, Westminster, the EU. A constituency where you weighed the SNP votes, where people voted SNP by habit, following the ancestral trail. Angus voted NO.

Stirling: its three main tourist attractions icons of the Wars of Independence. Location for 80 annual Bannockburn Day rallies, with up to 7000 marching through the town centre in honour of Bruce's victory. Stirling voted NO.

Isle of Arran: solid villas, weekend destination for comfortable suburbanites. A council which once tried to evict the anti-Trident Peace Campers because they 'look untidy'. Arran voted YES.

Na h-Eileanan an Iar, last stronghold of the Gaeltachd and of Gàidhlig culture, 40 years of bi-lingual education and many years of increasingly safe SNP representation. The Western Isles voted NO.

Eilean a' Cheò: Gàidhlig-speakers reduced to 31% at the last census, returning Unionist Liberal politicians way back into its eponymous mists of time. The Isle of Skye voted YES.

West Dunbartonshire: closed shipyards and rusting sewing machine factories looking balefully north to the remaining employer: the UK's nuclear deterrent. West Dunbartonshire voted YES.

Perth: self-styled 'Gateway to the Highlands' and an SNP stronghold for 20 years. Perth voted NO.

Inverness: self-styled 'Capital of the Highlands' splitting for decades between the LibDems and the SNP. Inverness voted YES.

Edinburgh: home to unpopular banks and to the largest International Festival in the World, sending 25% of its children to private schools. Edinburgh voted NO.

Leith, home to Hibs FC and dockers, the setting for the druggy novel Trainspotting. Leith voted YES.

Dundee, its journalism slithering behind jute and jam into the grave, voted YES.

Aberdeen, swimming in fish and rich oilies, voted NO.

Fife: scarlet gowns in St Andrews, couthie harbours in the East Neuk and slouching hoodies in Kirkcaldy. The Kingdom of Fife was a microcosm of the Kingdom of Scotland with its 55% NO and 45% YES.

Shetland, haunted by the ghost of the Westminster-initiated Shetland Movement which in the '70s sought to opt Shetland out of devolution, voted NO.

So did Orkney.

Turnout at 84.5% reversed the rise of apathy, smashed all UK records and was one of the highest in the democratic world.

Chapter 11: September 19th

Donald

My colleagues rarely show interest in politics but today there's a wee bit discussion before we settle down to our computers. None of them directly discloses what he voted but the general atmosphere's one of relief.

I work in Finnieston. My car's away gettin its MOT and so I go on public transport and come back on foot. I take a turn through Blythswood Square. Passin the Better Together HQ, I'm surprised to see a senior member of staff manhandlin a flat-screen TV out of the buildin and into a waitin taxi.

It was clear from the start that the HQ was a short-term let, but this rush to loot by individual members of the management does nothin for our dignity.

I carry on along Sauchiehall Street. The sun continues to shine as it has all summer on trees, benches, tarmac. For the first time in months I fully relax. If only we could get a summer like this every year, I wouldnae mind what the sky threw at us in winter. Three separate buskers in the pedestrian zone: a Romanian gypsy on an accordion, a hippy with a guitar and a piper. I give each of them a pound and they thank me politely. I swing to the right by the Buchanan Galleries and the steps of the Royal Concert Hall.

Donald Dewar, our first First Minister up on his plinth, gazes thoughtfully down Buchanan Street. He's as green as an antique coin. Was he always as green or has the metal developed a sheen of vert-de-gris? I cannae mind. Round his base is his famous declaration 'There shall be a Scottish Parliament'.

Seems like yesterday. Yet I read recently that the risin generation no longer remember his name. They call him

'The Green Man'.

Left again into George Square. Music floats out. The swan-songs of YES Scotland.

I listen for a while. Their songs have a wistful quality. Within my bubble of victory, I want to be magnanimous. The end of a dream. That was the point. It was only ever a dream.

Then I spot him. I take off my spectacles, wipe them and put them on again.

Definitely him. Not just him. Them.

* * *

Ewan

Across the square, I'm heading for Queen Street Station when I spot Alison. She's swaying to the rhythm, baby on her arm, right hand resting on the buggy handle.

- Hi there.

She opens her eyes.

- Ewan!

I whisper in her ear

- How are you bearing up?

- Well …

She waves her hand helplessly at the singing, swaying crowd.

- Gutted, obviously. Still …

- Still … ?

- To be honest I didn't think we'd get so close.

Exactly what I've been thinking. All these rookie YES supporters, new to false summits, convinced we were going to walk it. Have a landslide. We oldies knew you have to run up and down a lot of hillocks before you reach the peak. Yesterday much headway was made. So, amongst the public disappointment, a private part of me is content.

- We were 20% at the start of the campaign, 45% at the finish. I call that progress.
- The more folk researched it, the more they converted.
- It's become a mainstream idea.
- And that won't leave them in a hurry.
- Exactly my own take on it.

I'm glad Alison can take comfort from this too.

- I was at the optician's today and when the girls at the reception desk saw my Radical Indy bag one of them started crying.
- What does your bag say?

She looks at it. ANOTHER SCOTLAND IS POSSIBLE.

- Where did you get it? I want one like that.
- Take it.

I slip off my backpack and transfer my shopping from the cotton bag into it. Four different newspapers.

- Every single constituency in Glasgow voted YES. And my own constituency was the Yessiest.
- The Edinburgh bankers let us down.
- Bankers, wankers. D'you see Alex Salmond's resigned?
- Oh Ewan! I've been walking the town all day – haven't seen any news.

Her face, already distressed, falls further. I wonder if I have a clean handkerchief somewhere.

- He made a very good speech. Said the dream would never die.
- Sounds kind of final to me.

A tear rolls down her cheek. Her face crumples.

- Sorry …

The baby starts to howl.

- Can you feel in my bag for me? There's a dummy-tit somewhere …

I fumble in the bag hanging on the buggy handles. Baby bottle full of milk, spare disposable nappy, spare Babygro, bib, carton of wipes, baby cream, teething biscuits. What a life support system you need to leave the house for five minutes with a baby.

- Here you go.

The baby's howls reach a crescendo. I pop the dummy in his mouth. Plugs him like magic. He looks at me, steadily, sucking intensively.

- Would he come to me, do you think?

I've only a couple of times held a baby before. He balances nicely in the crook of my left arm.

My son.

The dummy pops out and I catch it before it hits the ground. Offer it to him again. Like an expert.

Behind us: a familiar voice.

- What d'ye know. A YES family. Not so happy clappy now, eh?

I wheel. Manage not to drop the baby. Everybody must be seeing my flush.

- Alison, this is …
- Donald. Ewan's husband.

Donald asserts this with ringing tones. A couple of people in the crowd turn to look. He shakes Alison's hand. Scrutinises Calum.

- So this is the legacy. Are you not worried about him?

Alison looks from Donald to Calum and back.

- What are you talking about?

She closes her mouth suspiciously.

- Behind in his development, is he no? Most 3 year-olds are up on their feet. And he's still gumsy. Wee runt. I'd get him seen to if I were you.

A flare shoots across the square. A crowd of skinheads collecting in St Vincent Street brandishing Union flags. Shouts, oaths. Some advance across the square towards us YES supporters. A chorus starts up: 'Rule Britannia.'

- Your friends are on song.
- No friends of mine. And neither are you, you lying cunt.

Donald fixes me with a glare which begins to well with tears. He turns and walks away along George Street.

- He's not really my husband. We're not even officially civil partners.
- None of my business what you are. Let's get the wee fellow out of here. No place for a baby.

She takes Calum from me and tucks him back in his buggy. She makes for Buchanan Street subway station. I put on my backpack and follow. We both buy tickets to Kelvinbridge. At the barrier Calum spits out the dummy and starts up again. She takes him out and cuddles him. I pick up the dummy and put it in my pocket. I fold the buggy and put it under my arm.

* * *

Malky

A bang an a hiss wake me. A flame at my elbow. Ah sit up. Musta fell asleep on this bench in George Squerr. Lulled by the music.

Noo thur a big mad bam, foot away, burnin flare in his paw lookin like he's gonnae lub it in ma fizzer. In his ither haun he's trailin a Union flag. He's starin at ma chist. Ah mind that Ah'm still werrin yesterday's YES T-shirt, dotted wi aw the wee badges: YES, Generation YES, How NO? and TAK (Polish for YES).

On ma feet. The auld adrenalin kicks in and Ah'm away, wi him eftir me. Suddenly the squerr is full o polis on horseback, polis on fit, and ranks o Unionists advancin fae the south an east. Wavin Union flags, burnin flares, giein Nazi salutes. Big chorus o God Save the Queen fills the smoky air. The group o YES singers are scatterin in confusion.

Billy the Bam's still on ma tail. He's aff his face wi it, so Ah could outrun him if Ah hud the space. But Ah cannae get across the road fur big limos circling the squerr at speed, streamin Union an Red Hand o Ulster flags. Ah wheel roon to dae anither circuit – an come face tae face wi anither hardguy. This wan's goat a boattle in his mitt.

- YES, is it ye wee cunt? Noo ye're gonnae say YES right across yer fuckin face.

Wherr ur the polis when ye waant them? They're aw across the squerr, formin a ring roon the Unionists wi their screams an flares an Nazi salutes. Kettlin. Thur a man up on a plinth aside some man sittin doon, an he's burnin a Saltire.

Ah kin see why the polis think the south-east corner's the main locus o danger. Too bad me an ma adversaries are in the north-west corner.

Bampot Two smashes his boattle against the plinth o Queen Vicky on a horse. He advances, jabbin the boattle, jaggy end first, at ma face.

- Separatism. Ah'm gonnae separate yer ears fae yer heid.

Then he points it doon.

- Or yer balls fae yer dick? Come on, it's make yer mind up time.

Anither step towards me. Mair screams an bangs an crashes an smoke an chantin fae across the squerr. The clackity clack o horses' hooves.

Fae behind me, Bampot Wan tosses his deid flair an grabs ma wrists.

- Ears or balls? Irreversible choice.

Two people come atween me an the boattle. Two lassies.

- C'moan, Derek, leave ma wee pal alane

Chantelle.

Her pal?

- This is ma wee pal Malky. He fancies Kelly-Anne here, sure ye dae?

I get a riddy, but it's the moment tae agree.

- She disnae fancy him back, but she disnae waant ye tae chib him. Sure ye don't?

Kelly-Anne turns an gies me a big hug. Saft lips against ma ear, she breathes:

- It's OK. She knows him – he goes tae the gemme wi her brither. He'll no chib a lassie. You get the fuck oota here.

I ask ye. Whit kinna bloke rins away, leavin two lassies tae confront his adversaries?

Ma kinna bloke.

As Ah rin like fuck up George Street, Ah'm peelin the T-shirt aff ma back and ower ma heid and stuffin the neck o it doon the back o ma trackies. It flies behind me like a Batman cape at hauf-mast. Bare-chisted, Ah storm up George Street intae Duke Street. Against the current o scores, hunners o ragin hardmen, merchin towards the Squerr wi Union flags, flares, Nazi salutes. Maybe Molotov cocktails, Ah widnae wunner.

The nasal twang o Belfast minglin wi the Weegie till it swamps it.

Back hame Ah follow the riot fae the safety o ma laptop. It goes on till efter sundown. Near midnight they're still rinnin aboot, screamin slogans, burnin flares. On Facebook an Twitter Ah follow it. Blokes boastin that they've pit the heid on somebody, glessed anither, chibbed anither. Polis vowin that they'll arrest those responsible. If necessary chase them back ower the Irish Sea.

Next day Ah read the newspapers online. No much mention in the Scottish papers. The English papers huv mair tae say on the subject although some o them musta been at a different battle. Here's the *London Times* take on it:

'Fighting broke out and a Union Jack was set alight in the centre of Glasgow last night as the tense atmosphere between groups of YES and NO supporters spilled over into violence.

A small group of skinhead, pro-Union Scots were booed and chased out of George Square, which had become a focal point for independence supporters. Chants of 'Rule Britannia' were drowned out by a roar of 'Freedom' and 'Brits out' from YES campaigners as punches were thrown.

Hundreds of YES supporters goaded the Union supporters, who were surrounded by about 30 police officers for their own protection.'

History as written by the victors.

Chapter 12: October

Ewan

Every constituency in Glasgow voted YES. Yessiest of all at 57% was my own constituency. So a couple of days after the vote we activists arrange an evening car cavalcade round the constituency to express our gratitude.

Half a dozen cars snaking in convoy round all the neighbourhoods in turn. Ken's dolorous voice booming out in the gathering shadows:

- This is YES Scotland thanking the people of Barmulloch for voting YES. Thank you, Barmulloch, for voting YES.
- This is YES Scotland thanking the people of Royston for voting YES. Thank you, Royston, for voting YES.
- This is YES Scotland thanking the people of Garthamlock for voting YES. Thank you, Garthamlock, for voting YES.
- This is YES Scotland thanking the people of Easterhouse for voting YES. Thank you, Easterhouse, for voting YES.
- This is YES Scotland thanking the people of Cranhill for voting YES. Thank you, Cranhill, for voting YES.
- This is YES Scotland thanking the people of Riddrie for voting YES. Thank you, Riddrie, for voting YES.
- This is YES Scotland thanking the people of Carntyne for voting YES. Thank you, Carntyne, for voting YES.
- This is YES Scotland thanking the people of Haghill for voting YES. Thank you, Haghill, for voting YES.
- This is YES Scotland thanking the people of Dennistoun, for voting

YES. Thank you, Dennistoun, for voting YES.

Caroline, who is into ceramics, produces a series of mugs all glazed with the statistic 57% and the slogan MOLENDINAR THE BRAVE. It's the first thing I pack when I move out.

* * *

Malky

Goin intae the bedroom – Stevie's an mines – Ah find him greetin. Jist back fae his work – still got his trainers oan.

- Whit's up?
- Gordo's gonnae knock some booze fae Mr Khan's shoap. Waants me tae help him.
- Ye cannae dae that.
- Mr Khan gied me a key.
- He'd know it's you. Ye'd loss yer joab.

Nae brains an faimily o ill-repute. Wee Stevie only landed that joab because Ah done a Sunday paper round wi Mr Khan fur fower year an Ah spoke fur him. An he's managed tae haud the joab doon noo fur a year.

- An maybe worse.

So far, whenever the polis's come chappin at wur door, it's never been aboot Stevie.

- But if Ah don't, Gordo'll gie me a doin.

If Stevie gets intae bother wi Mr Khan Ah could loss ma paper round an aw. An Ah need the dosh.

- Look, Ah'll talk tae him.

See me when ma tongue rins away wi me? Soon as Ah said it Ah regrettit it.

- Aw, wull ye, Malky? Please? Gonnae?
- Aye. Ra morra.

So that's me set tae spend the haill night countin sheep.

* * *

Agnes

The boayfriend Ah hud afore Willie wis a fella cawed Shuggie. Used tae take me tae the jiggin at the Dennistoun Palais. He could fairly jive –the band wid strike up a Bill Haley number and we'd make for the centre o yon great big flair. Patter-merchant o the first order– a right scream so he wis. We might be thegither yet if he hudnae got his call-up papers.

The night afore he had tae leave we were awfy doonhertit. The world wisnae sma the wey it is nooadays. The distance atween Glesca an Singapore wis an unknown chasm. We said we'd keep in touch but in wur herts we knew we'd move on.

So wur faces were trippin us when we went tae see this film 'The Day they Gave Babies Away'. This couple dies o typhoid an their wee boy goes roon aw the neighbours pleadin wi them tae take in his brothers an sisters tae keep them oot the orphanage. We were near greetin as the usherette shawed us intae wur seats. We were bubblin freely as we cam oot an went fur the tram.

Onywey, Ah'm pit in mind o that when they aw come tae claim their kittens. They troop in on a Monday evenin so Emma an masel are there tae see the kittens aff to their forever hames.

First up is a wumman works wi Lorraine. Nice enough dame. Respectable. No the type tae organise dogfights. She's hud cats afore so she knows whit she's lettin hursel in fur. She takes wan o the tiger stripes.

Next is Lorraine hursel. She takes wan o them away tae gie tae a client. Faimily that huv adopted a wee lassie that's got cerebral palsy an hus tae sit in hur wheelchair aw day. She

336

takes away the ither tiger-stripe. I let hur borrow ma cat basket, the wan that wis jail fur the very same cat when Ah wis feedin up his failin brother. Bina an Farooq Akram take away the white long haired wan wi the orange patch. Ah'm fair pleased: this means Ah'll still get tae see hur fae time tae time. So will Rosie, if she's up fur visitation rights.

Last is Kirsty an hur boayfriend Malky. Kirsty's moved in wi hur Mammy noo an wi Emma's help, she's persuaded hur Mammy tae take in the wee marmalade boy.

So that's Emma an me left wi jist the wee grey boy an the kitten wi lang whorly striped hair. Arsenic an Cyanide. Or Bertie an Bonnie as Ah caw them intae masel.

Ah catch Emma wipin a tear oot hur eye. Ah'm near tae bubblin masel. Ah take a scance at Rosie tae see how she's copin wi hur empty nest syndrome.

She's tryin tae open the fridge door. She can smell the fish soup left ower fae ma tea.

* * *

Malky

First Ah approach the auld dear fur some proactive parentin. She's jist in aff hur shift. Ah wait till she's heated up hur dinner an planked hursel in front o the telly. She pits oan the Library on the didgy-boax tae pick oot wan o the reality shows she recorded.

Ah tell her, tersely, afore hur attention gets time tae wander.

- Gordo's oan at Stevie tae help him knock booze affa Mr Khan. He'll batter him saft if he disnae.

Big sigh. She leans back. Closes her eyes. Opens them again. Looks at me. Looks away. Neither body-language nor eye-contact are promisin.

- Uch, son, gonnae you talk tae him? Or get thegither

wi Stevie an the baith o yese talk tae him?

- You're wur mither. He's no as likely tae batter you as he is tae batter us yins.

Honour thy father and thy mother. Gordo's motto. Not.

- He's raised his haun tae me afore.
- D'ye waant Stevie tae loss this joab?

She shrugs.

- Never see much o Stevie's wages. He wastes it aw on thon moped, so he does.
- Look, whit if aw three of us tackle him thegither?
- Uch, Ah don't know …
- If Stevie losses this joab he might never get anither!
- Ah know …
- And whit if the polis come in on it?
- Ah know …
- Is wan criminal in the faimily no enough fur ye?
- Ye're right, son, so ye ur. We'll aw go an talk tae Gordo the morra.
- The night!

However, she goes tae hur bed much earlier than she usually does when she's on the back-shift. By the time Gordo gets hame she's snorin away on hur scratcher in the livin-room wi hur pills in hur belly an hur earplugs in hur ears. Next day whenever he's in, she's oot.

No escape. If Ah wis Popeye Ah'd go an slug a tin o spinach. Ah go an chap Gordo's door wi Stevie at ma back.

He's sittin at his computer daein his accounts. Like a real businessman. Or Shylock, or somethin.

- Gordo. Stevie says ye're waantin him tae knock booze oota Mr Khan's shoap.

Gordo looks up slowly. His expression disnae change.

-   Ye know it's good fur wee Stevie tae huv a joab. An it's been hard fur him tae get wan, and tae haud wan doon …

Gordo rises and strolls over to us. He gets ma heid in an airmlock. With his left haun he nips ma nose atween two knuckles.

-   Ye know whit happens tae nosey-parkers? They get thur noses twistit aff.

He twists ma nose till it sterts tae bleed. It's agony. He gets snot an blood aw ower his haun an wipes it aff on Stevie's jersey as he advances towards him.

-   An even worse things happen tae grasses. Ye telt Malky aboot it. Who else huv ye telt?
-   Naebody, Gordo. God's honest truth …

Gordy belts Stevie across the coupon. A back-hander. Sends him intae orbit. Grabs me by the collar an drags me ower tae wherr Stevie's flat oot on the bed. He grabs Stevie by his collar, hoists him up and cracks baith wur heids thegither. Ah see stars.

But the same time, Ah'm thinkin. This is mad. Thur two of us an only wan o him. We're near as big as he is. This is only happenin because we let it.

So when he lets me go Ah jump wi full force on him. Knock him aff balance. Land on tap o him an stert hammerin him wi baith ma fists an aw ma strength.

-   Help me Stevie! Help me!

Stevie rouses his sleepin cojones an leaps tae join the merry fray. We baith knock lumps oota Gordo as he lies on the ground. Batter his face, his body. Jump on him wi baith feet. Kick him in the balls. till he screams

-   OK! OK! It's a fuckin no-go!'

We climb aff him. He struggles tae his feet, haudin his crotch. Lookin at us wi whit might – or might no – be new respect.

We shauchle oot the room.

Stevie goes

- Thanks, Malky.
- It's a sin fur him, but it's the only language he understauns. If you an me kin keep oot his world we'll be daein well.

* * *

Agnes

Saturday night. All quiet on the Western Front. Here's me, legs stretched oot on the recliner, two kittens on ma lap. Aw three of us waatchin *Scotland Tonight*.

Noo they've voted NAW tae independence, suddenly everybody an his uncle's joinin the SNP. Scorin the winnin goal efter the whistle's blown. It wis aye the Scottish wey.

Emma's oot oan the randan wi wee Kirsty Gilchrist. Ah've always thought Kirsty wis a nice lassie. Always polite tae me – never yon torn-faced wey that teenagers sometimes get. Suitable pal for Emma. Nicer type awthegither than Lorraine's lassie (though Ah'd never tell Lorraine that).

The phone rings and here, is it no Sheena phonin fae London. Ah tell hur Emma's oot. She asks how's she gettin on an Ah say fine; she's made a new pal in hur class at the school. Then Sheena comes tae the point.

- It's really you I want to talk to. How's Emma coming on with her eating?
- Eatin?
- Remember I asked you to keep an eye on it.
- Aye. Well, wi hur bein vegan an that, Ah jist leave hur tae dae fur herself.
- That's what I was afraid of. Listen: could you go and check while she's out – see what food she's bought in

340

for herself?

- Ah can tell ye right aff: there's nothin in the fridge that belangs tae hur.
- Could you check her bedroom?

Ah don't like sneakin in an oot hur room behind hur back. She's nearly seventeen an Ah'm no hur mither. But Ah can see Sheena's worried an Ah suppose Ah'm in loco parentis whether Ah waant tae be or no.

- Nothin much in hur room. Hauf-finished packet o chocolate biscuits an a full mug o waater.
- Just as I thought. Binge-eating rubbish and starving herself the rest of the time.
- She telt me she never touches sugar.
- She says more than her prayers. Look, I don't like asking you to confront her about this …

And that's jist whit she's gonnae ask me to dae.

- But could you get her to tell you what she's been eating?
- Whit if she'll no tell me?
- Then say you want to go with her the next time she's shopping for food.

Ah envisage the scene. No a happy wan. So far Ah've got on fine wi Emma, mainly by goin alang wi everythin she suggests; the kitten names an that. This is shapin up tae be a major hitch in wur relationship.

- Huv there been problems afore wi hur eatin?
- You bet. Shouting matches every time we want her to eat with us at the table.
- Wis that why …
- Wasn't the only reason she wanted to come and stay with you. The referendum gave her the idea. And what Alasdair told you was right, about the house prices

341

and us wanting to move back up ourselves.

- But it did come intae it.
- Into her own reasons for wanting to move away from home. The general friction …

So Ah'm supposed tae cope wi somethin they cannae handle?

- I'm sorry. We should have told you.
- Aye. So ye should.
- Teenagers are always difficult.

Ah mind Alasdair bein a handful. Runnin aboot wi a wild crowd, underage drinkin. But he wis mair intae self-indulgence than self-denial.

He turnt oot aw right in the end. Of course, Ah hud Willie therr tae share the burden.

Emma comes rollin hame at wan in the morning. Wherr dae Ah start?

- Emma, pet, Ah've been wonderin …
- What, Gran dear?

Thinner than ever, face flushed, daft grin, bevvy on hur breath.

- Ah know ye're vegan, an Ah respect that …

Hur face loses the grin.

- Whit is it ye're actually eatin? Ah've hardly ever seen ye eatin …
- You've been talking to my mother!

This is an Emma Ah huvnae seen afore. The torn-faced teen wi hur voice up in a scraich.

- I knew she'd be on to you …
- She's worried aboot ye, hen …
- Well, you can tell her she needn't worry. I'm an adult now, perfectly able to take responsibility for my own meals …

- It's just that Ah've never seen ye eatin …
- Of course I'm eating! I've been here a month! If I wasn't eating …
- Or even buyin food.
- Tell my mother to get off my case! And that goes for you too!

She storms into hur bedroom and slams the door. Ah know Ah ought tae follow hur in, huv it oot wi hur. That's whit Ah'd dae if Ah wis hur mither. But Ah'm hur granny, an Ah hardly even know hur.

Whit Ah need is wan o thae assertiveness courses. An assertiveness course fur grannies.

Ah get oot the medical dictionary that saw me through Alasdair's chickenpox an glue ear. Ah look up 'anorexia'. Thur jist a paragraph aboot it, describin the symptoms. No eatin, gettin thin. Nothin Ah didnae know. Disnae tell ye how tae treat it.

If Ah could go the computer, Ah could look up Google. If Ah thought Ah could learn the computer ,Ah wid buy masel wan. Maybe the course Ah need is wan o thae computin courses specially fur aulder folk. Silver surfin, Ah think they caw it.

In bed that night Ah huv a wee greet tae masel. Whit's worse: loneliness or strife? An guilt. Ah pit aw thon energy intae savin ma failin kittens an noo Ah'm tae watch ma grandwean starvin tae death an me feart tae wade in.

But here, at eleven in the mornin, jist when Ah'm worryin aboot how tae approach Emma and pittin aff getting up, does she no come in hursel wi a wee breakfast tray. Cuppa tea an bilet egg wi toast sodgers fur me, black coffee an muesli fur hursel. She pours soya milk ower the muesli.

Ah don't keep either muesli or soya milk in the hoose. She musta been oot tae the supermarket. At this hour o the morning an efter a night's underage drinkin.

- I'm sorry for fighting with you, Gran. I know you just want what's best for me.
- That's right, hen.

Ah struggle tae hoist masel up. She pits the two pillows in place behind ma back an helps tae heave me intae position.

- I thought we could have breakfast together. So you can see there's no problem.
- That's awfy nice o ye.
- Shall we have breakfast together every Sunday morning? Is it a date?

Whit aboot the ither days o the week? An the ither mealtimes? But Ah quell this thought. Bringin me ma breakfast in bed every Sunday. It's a start.

In some weys teenage lassies are easier than teenage boays. Maybe.

* * *

Malky

So here we ur. Kirsty fully flitted in wi her auld dear and Pamela. Sylvia an Kirsty seem happy as Larry wi the set-up – don't know aboot Pamela.

Onywey the two o them are still oot at work an Kirsty an me are in hur bed. We've jist been pettin but she pits the hems on me fae gaun below the waist. Tae calm masel doon, Ah look roon the room. Still Sylvia's choice o wallpaper – cream background wi gold Chinese hieroglyphics – but Kirsty has moved in a lot of hur ain stuff. Hur claes in the wardrobe an hung ower the chair. Hur books an DVDs in the cupboard. It's aw stertin tae turn intae Kirsty.

- How are you findin the commute fae here to the school?

- It's long. A train and a bus, an hour and a quarter. If it wasn't for the fact I've started doing my subjects for Highers, I would move to a school near here.
- Well Ah'm glad ye didnae. Move schools Ah mean. Then ye widnae be in my class.
- But I might have made some friends in the new school.
- Ye don't need ither mates. Ye've got me.

Soon as Ah say it, Ah wish Ah hudnae. So tae cover up Ah ask

- Huv ye never had ony mates there?
- I hate that school. And the primary I was in before. In my first primary I had a really good friend. Cara. She was lovely – long brown hair that curled in like ringlets. Always neat and clean and polite. Full of ideas for games. I went to her house and she came to mine. We were never apart. We sang songs together. We even developed our own language that only we knew!

Ah stert tae take a scunner tae Cara.

- An naebody understood whit ye were sayin?
- Well, that's a wee bit of exaggeration. We invented words and wrote them in a jotter and tried to use them in conversation with each other.
- So when did you last see her?
- When my parents split up and I moved schools.
- No try tae keep up?
- Difficult when you're only seven. You don't have control of anything. Didn't have my own phone or computer – my Dad and Marilyn kept theirs in their own bedroom – and to write a note I'd have to ask for an envelope and stamp. Also, I had other things on my mind: the separation, my mother … But we had a great romantic farewell, Cara and me. We pledged our

345

undying love for each other.

- Never try to track her doon on Facebook?
- I deleted my Facebook account. I was getting trolled. Guess I'm the type that attracts enemies and stalkers rather than Friends and Followers.
- Uch away! Don't faw intae that trap. You're the victim here.
- Anyway, don't know what she'd be like now. Scared it would shatter all my dreams.
- Well, at least you had a BFF the wance. Ah never hud naebody.
- Malky-no-mates.

Don't like that. Waant her tae bond wi me as a fellow non-conformist. No pity me as a reject.

- Nane o thae hangers-on ur of interest tae me.
- What about your brothers? Stevie?
- Ach.

I think. Huvnae thought aboot Stevie since thon time we defeated Gordo. Disnae batter his wey into yer mind like Gordo.

- Stevie's OK. The auld dear used tae say he knew how tae keep his heid doon.
- Might keep him out of trouble. Though not necessarily get him far in life.
- He never made much o school. Gordo wis never therr – when he wisnae suspended he wis doggin it. Stevie went but got naewherr. A for effort, E for achievement.

Kirsty giggles.

- That's harsh.
- At least he's goat a job. Cairryin crates in at Mr Khan's coarner shop. Whenever Mr Khan needs him.
- Zero hour contract.

346

- If there ever wis a contract Ah guess ye could caw it zero hours.
- So how come you ended up so much more academic than your brothers?

Ah kiss hur fur sayin that. Lingeringly on the lips. But she disnae waant tae go doon that wey an so Ah turn an lie on ma back wi ma airms under ma heid. Ah hope she can see ma biceps which are fairly comin on.

- Ah'm no exactly Stephen Hawking. Jist doon fur fower Highers.
- Have your brothers even heard of Stephen Hawking?
- Gordo – defo. Stevie – he can surprise ye, sometimes. No often but.

Ah've mebbe no been fair tae Gordo an Stevie. Giein hur the wrang idea. Gordo's no exactly a ned – he's mair managerial than that. An wee Stevie got the auld dear a cake fur hur last birthday.

- If Ah've goat brains Ah musta goat them fae ma Da. The auld dear's an airheid.
- And the others missed out?
- Different Da.

Soon as Ah say it Ah regret it. Ah've joked aboot us aw bein neds an aboot Maw bein an airheid an aboot Gordo dissin the law. But Ah waant tae present Gordo as a swashbucklin type an the ithers as steadfastly confrontin the poverty trap. Don't waant her thinking we tick aw the boxes. Maw on the game; no heard o contraception; weans aw wi unknown Dads.

She's no sayin nothin. Ah can hear masel an ma faimily rattlin doon the escalator of hur estimation.

- Maw wis mairried tae the Dad o Gordo an Stevie. Craig Nimmo. Doon the Co-op she worked the checkouts, he stacked shelves. When she got pregnant wi Gordo he mairried hur. But when she wis up the spout wi Stevie she caught him in bed wi her best friend Rita.

- What a dick.

- They made it up. But when Stevie wis a year auld Craig finally walked oot on them aw. Ditched hur fur Rita. Walked oota hur world an doon tae London. Never sent ony dosh fur the weans nor nothin.

- She could have put the Child Support Agency on his trail.

- The auld dear's no the type tae pit onybody on onybody's trail. An the Child Support Agency ur only interested aff thur ain bat if the maw's claimin full benefits. Ma maw's always worked. She still works shifts on the checkouts.

- So how did you come about?

- When she fun hursel on her ain wi two weans she got depressed. Tae cheer hursel up she went oot on a hen night wi a bunch of hur mates fae work. She got wellied an ended up wi anither bun in the oven. But this time tae a total stranger.

- She never found out who he was?

- Only two things Ah know aboot ma Da: Furst name's Jimmy ...

- Doesn't narrow it down ...

- An he wis a student at Glasgow Callie University. That's why Ah think Ah maybe got ma brains fae him.

- What was he studying?

- He telt ma maw at the time. Somethin wi a lang name. She cannae mind.

- Not much for Sherlock Holmes to go on.

- So she goes tae droon hur sorrows aboot bein dumped wi two weans an ends up wi three. Whit did Ah say

348

aboot airheid?

- At least she went ahead and had you.
- Probably didnae organise hersel in time fur an abortion.
- Have you thought of contacting Jeremy Kyle?

Uh oh. Here we go again. In hur mind Ah wis back tickin aw the boxes. Ah try tae think up somethin tae redeem ma honour.

- Ah'm thinkin o gaun tae night school tae learn Gaelic.

Ah wisnae till noo, huv tae say, but it's aw Ah kin come up wi. Blots oot the image o me an the auld dear on the benches at the Jeremy Kyle show.

- Are you interested in Gaelic?
- It's wur ain lingo that got banned. We should know it.
- So you're a bit of a cultural nationalist?
- Thur still a lot ye don't know aboot me, Kirsty.

Man o mystery. Aura of enigma. Jist the ticket.

- Ciamar a tha thu?
- Whit?
- Gaelic for "How are you". My Dad told me.
- Right.
- You did do French for a while, did you not?

Uh oh. Don't want to go there.

- Ah've ayeways been better on the Maths / Science side than in languages. But Ah'd pit mair effort in at the Gaelic. Wi it bein wur ain suppressed original language an that.
- Come and we'll go together, Malky? I'll check out the classes and we can enrol next autumn. If we both do all right in the Highers this time we'll have a nice easy Sixth Year with lots of free periods. We can study

Gaelic together in the common room.

- Fine. Okaydoke.

Ah try tae sound keen but tae be honest there's loads of ither things Ah'd reyther get up to in the common room wi Kirsty.

* * *

Kirsty

I don't get my phone back until two weeks after the vote. The police phone me and say I can collect it.

Back with my mother and logged into her wifi, I check my messages. There are hundreds, because it's been weeks. But it's nearly all spam.

From Watcherinthesky:

'Sorry A scared U, Wee Wan. When A see U we'll huv a group hug and a poka chips! Ma treat! ☺X♥X☺♥'

From Watcherinyourbed:

'Sorry.'

From Watcheratyourdoor:

'I'm so sorry, Kirsty. I hate myself for getting into this. I'm having nothing to do with the other two from now on. I hope you and I can be friends, since we stay up the same close. Come up to mine and we can watch a DVD together.'

Cara: You're well out of that close, anyway.

From Watcherinyourbed, however, an earlier message. A line from an old ballad we got in the English class:

'Ye but wear my auld sheen, ye but wear ma auld sheen, Ask Malky about the Valentine.'

* * *

350

Malky

When I chap at Sylvia's door Kirsty lets me in. Sylvia and Pamela are away to the theatre.

Face like fizz.

- You sent a Valentine to Kelly-Anne!
- Long ago.
- Eight months ago. I know when St Valentine's Day is.
- So it was long before …
- A few weeks before you decided to make do with me.
- Wisnae like that.
- Kelly-Anne's my enemy!
- Ah didnae know whit she wis like …
- But you fancy her.
- Look, efter the wey she's treated you … fuck it, efter the wey she spoke tae me … Ah widnae fancy hur if she took aff aw hur claes an lay on a duvet wi hur legs open.
- Oft-visited fantasy, eh? She's prettier than me, right?
- Jist in a stereotypical wey …
- Bottle blonde. Skinny … D'you know she bokes up her food?
- Whit?
- I've heard her. In the toilets. Picture her. Kneeling down on the stinky wet floor, putting up the seat …

Ah join in tae show whit side Ah'm on.

- Heid doon the lavvy pan, fingers doon hur thrapple …
- Holding up her hair to stop it trailing into the vomit.
- Openin hur geggie an … whoosh!

Ah face Kirsty, haud her shouthers, pull her to me. She wriggles slightly.

- Close up, ye're much mair beautiful than Kelly-Anne. Ah love yer flaming rid herr …

Ah kiss her on the tap of her heid.

- Yer tasty wee row of freckles jist therr.

Ah kiss her on the bridge of the nose

- Yer big grey eyes.

Ah kiss her on each of her eyelids

- And your lovely soft rose-petal lips.

As Ah kiss her there Ah feel a surge of … okay, lust, but mingled with the kind o tenderness Ah've never felt for naebody, no even ma maw. Ah need her, want to be with her always, think Ah'll die if she dumps me. Ah love her.

Efter a moment she goes

- In novels the redheads usually have emerald green eyes. But I've never seen anybody with bright green eyes, have you? I don't think human eyes come in green.
- Grey eyes are faur an away superior to green.
- My Dad told me Athena the goddess of wisdom had clear grey eyes.

She's fishin. And Ah'm no wan tae disappoint.

- And ye're the wisest person Ah've ever met. The wisest since Solomon tae walk on the planet.

For a while she gazes with her clear grey eyes intae ma … soarta pale turquoisey wi broon flecks … I see ma image reflected in hers and suppose she must be seein hersel in mine.

- 18th September. Why was it a big day?
- The referendum?
- And?
- We baith got to vote for the furst time.

- And?
- Your birthday.
- And?
- Ye got permission to meet up wi yer auld dear.
- And?

Another thought strikes me but Ah don't know if that's in her mind and so Ah stey schtum. Then she says it fur me.

- I'm now over the age of consent.

Mair gazin intae wan anither's eyes. A thrill runs doon ma haill body. Then she takes ma haun and leads me towards her bedroom.

Is it the discovery that she might have a rival in Kelly-Anne? Nothin like an element of insecurity to make the hert grow fonder.

Mebbe she feels grown-up and waants a rite o passage. She'd know Chantelle an thon crew have been at it like rabbits since they wur aboot 14 an mebbe she disnae waant tae be left behind in the experience stakes. That's important tae boays though wi lassies thur mair o the swings an roundabouts aboot it.

Mebbe it's just that wur relationship has reached that stage.

Whitever it is, Ah'm no wan tae look a gift horse. Ah mumble somethin alang the lines o

- Are ye quite sure aboot this?

But then it's Taps aff! Bottoms aff! For the sake o romance Ah take hers aff and she takes mines aff … And straight under the duvet.

Furst time fur baith of us.

That's apposed tae make it mair romantic, like, mair Romeo an Juliet. In actual fact it makes it mair difficult. Mair footery. She surprises me right fae the start by rummlin aboot in her handbag and comin up wi a johnny! Ah says nothin but it

353

gies me pause for thought.

No much pause. Aboot a nanosecond.

Ah'm ower-eager but no sure whit to pit wherr. She's mair idea o the theory but is a bit feart o the practice. Disnae say much but gies wee squeals. Whether pain or ecstasy? Ah ask nae questions, get nae lies.

Wherr thur's a will thur's a wey. We manage in the end. Ah feel like a million dollars though Ah'm no sure aboot her.

Ah'm feart tae ask onythin alang the lines of 'How was it for you darling?' and so Ah jist jump up and say Ah'll make us baith a cuppa tea.

Ginger is for weans. We're grown up noo.

Ah peel the johnny aff an take a swatch at the next generation daein their breaststroke afore Ah flush them doon the lavvy. Pits me in mind o a Woody Allan film Ah saw wance. Cannae mind its name.

Some jakeys pit it aw ower Facebook when they get tae bang a lassie. No me. Some things ur no meant tae be broadcast tae the world. Onywey, pittin it oot like that tells everybody it's yer first time. An here's me nearly 17.

By the time Ah'm back wi the tea she's back in her claes. By the time Sylvia and Pamela come hame we're sittin watchin a DVD. The cartoon Brave. We've seen it afore but we like it. Ah tell Kirsty the wee lassie's a dead ringer fur her.

Chapter 13: November

Lorraine

Don't see much of Angela these days. She's out nearly every evenin. Phones me around midnight to come and pick her up from some dive.

I'm no gonnae harp on about underage drinkin. I'd rather be included in her world than never know where she is. Besides, she's been more pleasant to live with since thon time we got high together. There's a fragile bond which I mustn't jeopardise. Must accept that she's growin up.

All the same she should be givin more thought to her study with the Higher prelims comin right after Christmas. And these girls are still hangin about with her – the ones that got her into trouble before. One of them big, gallus, givin you cheek and the other a sleekit wee bizzum. Wouldnae trust either of them the length of my nose. But criticism would be a sure way to endear them to Angela.

The last few times I went to see Kenny he was in his neighbour's house. Then last Saturday she was in his. She was hooverin his bedroom. Looked quite at home. The dishwasher I installed for him a couple o months ago had completed its cycle. When I went to empty it I didnae recognise most o the dishes.

His bathroom's still a woman-free zone. Shavin soap an razors, no make-up or hand cream. But she stays just across fae him so she doesnae need to move her gear in.

If she's takin over the upkeep of Kenny then that's one less worry for me. More free time in the week. Suppose I should be pleased at that.

* * *

Kirsty

So many public discussion groups about independence. Something on every week. Just when the homework's piling on because of the Highers coming up. The prelims are right after the Christmas holidays.

But it's a good way of making friends. I hang out with Emma a lot now. She's new to Glasgow and I've been taking her round the scene. Or maybe she's taking me – she's more up on alternative culture than I am.

Still go to my old close to visit my Dad and now I go to visit Emma too. Last time I went there, I ran into Chantelle and Kelly-Anne. They were at the close door pressin the security bell to go up and see Angela. So much for her vow to have nothing more to do with that pair.

But I don't care. They don't bother me any more. In fact Chantelle sort of grunted 'Hi' as I opened the door with my key and let them in. Kelly-Anne just looked the other way.

With me having a best friend that everybody can see and hear, Cara's fading out the picture a bit. She's just not there as often. If I'm stressed out, I text Emma or Malky or talk to my mother.

Mum (I call her that now) is always ready to listen. Drops everything.

All this makes Cara mad. She slags Emma off. I know it's jealousy. I should feel sorry for her. I need her less because I've moved on and have other friends. But who does Cara have apart from me?

So here's me and Malky lying cuddling in bed. We've just finished having it off.

- Mind yon time you said you had a secret? You never telt me whit it wis.

Cara's in with us at once: Think hard, Kirsty. Think before you do something irreversible.

I ignore her.

- Mind I told you about Cara?
- Aye.
- We still hang out. Me and Cara.
- Ah thought yese wurnae in touch.
- We're not, directly.
- Ye mean through social media?
- No.

How can I explain this? Without sounding crazy.

Cara: You've said enough. If you go on he'll be sending for the white coats.

- I mean she still talks to me. Not as much as she used to but still now and again.
- In yer heid?

I hesitate.

Cara: Hell mend you.

- I'm not sure.
- Is she here now?
- Yes.
- Wherr?
- Thereabouts. That is, she was, but she's fading now.

Malky looks wildly around. Mixture of fear and curiosity.

- Do ye actually see and hear her?
- It's complicated. Anyway, she's gone for the moment.

Malky pulls away from me.

- Will she be back?
- She doesn't come as often now.

Malky's intrigued.

- Maybe she's deid and it's her ghost?

I have wondered that sometimes. But I don't think so. She

tells me her family treat her very badly at home. Starved for days on end, put outside to sleep in a shed, beaten to an inch of her life. If she was a ghost she wouldn't have a home and family.

I shouldn't be pleased that a friend is badly treated but it does give me comfort. No matter how forlorn I sometimes feel with my own family, they're never as bad as that.

- It's been ten years. Does she still look like a wean?
- I sense she's the same height as me.
- You sense …?
- But still the same face and hair as she had all these years ago. Lovely ringlets, tied in blue ribbons.
- Baby face an ringlets on a 16 year auld? She'll be a right target at the school.

I laugh. Malky doesn't.

- How did it start?
- The first time I experienced the Wrath of Marilyn. Huge row.
- Whit aboot?
- Doesn't matter. I was wee at the time. Anyway Marilyn sent me to bed in disgrace without any supper and I lay in bed crying for a bit and then I thought it would be nice if I could dream about Cara. Well, I did. In the dream she said she would never leave me again and when I woke up next day she was still there!
- How still there?
- Just like I said. Still there. And she's been there off and on, ever since.

I was wrong. He's not intrigued after all. He's terrified. Edging away from me. Luckily I know how to sort it.

- Don't worry, Malky. I've googled schizophrenia and I don't have all the symptoms.

I roll on top of him and kiss him. That always eases his mind. Especially when we're naked in bed and still a free hour before dinner.

Chapter 14: December

Agnes

Emma an masel are gaun doon tae Alasdair's fae Xmas Eve till the 2nd January. They're huvin a crowd – Sheena's folks doon fae Inverness, an us fae Glesca. Sheena's daein the cookin. She said that last Christmas up in Inverness Emma ate a nut cutlet no bother at aw – cleaned hur plate. So here's hopin.

Pets are aye a worry when ye're gaun away. Lorraine looked efter the cat Ah hud afore Rosie when Ah went doon tae Alasdair's. But Ah don't like tae ask hur tae take three.

But thon nice Donald Gillies offered tae take the ither two athoot me even mentionin. Soon as Ah telt him we were gaun.

Turns oot he used tae huv a cat and he still has the litter tray an everythin. They'll be company fur him. Ah'm aye sorry fur fowk spendin Christmas on their tod. Been in that situation masel, often enough.

* * *

Kirsty

Dad wanted me to come back to his for Christmas dinner. I felt kind of rotten turning him down. It's symbolic: defining my new primary family. But of course he also defined his long ago. Marilyn won't shed tears at having washed that girl right out of her hair. And what's symbolic in a sad way for Dad is symbolic in a happy way for Mum.

* * *

Ewan

I've never spent a Christmas in the stereotypical way. Growing up, there was only my mother and Phil and their minimalism. I never hung up stockings nor was lied to about a man flying through the sky. As an adult I spent Christmases in countries with no snow, amongst people with different feast days.

Alison knows the Christmas card stereotype is a lie. In the 19th century only the rich in England (not Scotland) had turkey, figgy pudding and Christmas trees. And nobody had blazing lights until the invention of electricity.

However, she still intends Calum to buy into this. To live for a while in the enchanted world. So she hangs up a stocking and fills it with rattles, picture books and blocks. Credits them all to Santa. Calum doesn't take it on board. But in a year or two he will.

My mother and Phil come to Glasgow for the festive season. Alison puts them up in her turret. On Christmas Day we all troop over to Alison's parents for dinner.

Alison's parents are the opposite to my mother. Dad shirt and tie. Mum a church organist.

They've broadened their minds and now welcome Alison's deliberately having a baby out of wedlock. My mother and Phil broaden their own minds and accept singing Christmas carols round the piano while Alison's mother plays. Profound adjustment all round.

My status in Alison's home is undefined. I'm down as her new flatmate, paying her rent and sharing the bills but not her bed. However, the fact that I'm Calum's Dad muddies the waters. For her parents at any rate.

Nobody mentions sexuality.

* * *

Elspeth

Gordo sprang a surprise. He booked a posh restaurant fur us all fur Christmas lunch.

The lunch menu's cheaper than the evenin wan but aw the same, Ah'm surprised he wis feelin that flush. Street price o smack musta went up.

His case is comin up in the new year so mebbe this wis his last chance tae splash oot. Last chance of a faimily getthegither. No like Gordo tae be sentimental but therr ye go.

Here we were roon the table. The fowk at the ither tables aw that laid back. Up tae the nines in a casual wey. Ah pit oan ma best pink top but ye could still tell it's oot a charity shoap. Loast thon new look. Too many wee bobbles tae pick aff.

Waiters hoverin roon. Ah drapped ma fork an afore Ah could find it in amang the feet, a fresh wan wis on the table. Wi every course a waiter wid appear and ask us if it wis aw right. Furst time Ah stertit up aboot how the sauce wis a bit wersh fur me an how Ah wisnae wan fur aw thae green vegetables. The fella asked if Ah waantit them fur tae replace it wi somethin else. Ah didnae know whit tae say. Aw Ah waantit wis fur tae apologise fur no cleanin ma plate. But Gordo kicked me under the table – quite a sair kick – an said the food wis OK.

Stevie an Malky didnae finish theirs either but Gordo polished it aff. Wine an aw. Seemed quite at hame. Maybe he goes tae posh restaurants regular. Ah couldnae tell ye onythin aboot his habits except that they're maist o them illegal.

Onywey, hur next door chapped at mine the day an invited me tae hur Hogmanay do. She ayeways hus a big crowd roon at the Bells – Ah've heard them an so's the haill scheme.

Ah'll mebbe go fur a wee while. Ah'm no wan fur the bevvy. Day o the referendum, efter we votit, Wilma an me sat oot

362

on hur balcony drinkin Bacardi an coke. Ah managed the first wan but Ah didnae waant a second. An eftir the third Ah wis fleein.

Used tae like a wee sing-song, but. Hogmanays up at ma granny's hoose wi ma aunties an uncles. Us aw daein turns. Ma pairty piece wis 'Nobody's Child' that ma mammy learnt me. But that's too aul-fashioned fur noo.

Hope it's no gonnae be aw thae Orange songs, but. Ah'm ayeways feart a fight breks oot.

Epilogue

Jinty

Those who can't remember the past are condemned to repeat it. My experiences in Scotland in the '80s turned me into a nomadic activist.

Back in 1979, it became clear that the UK Government would ignore the weak YES vote to devolution. The rewind began.

Foreign correspondents crowded the departure lounges of Scotland's airports, their minds already in Iran, at Three-Mile Island, in the Falklands. The UK media switched their attention to the new darlings, the Social Democratic Party, a group of right-wing Labour dissidents with undefined policies and excellent PR. Starved of the oxygen of publicity, the SNP wilted and shrank.

The Scottish electorate voted Labour with increasing desperation. The Tories were returned with increasing majorities. The Tory Secretaries of State appointed by the UK Prime Ministers to govern Scotland still had power to overrule every elected body in the land.

The Scots marched weekend after weekend against the poll tax. Only when it was applied in England and banners were raised there did the Government react.

They put the sheet round for the striking miners. The Government closed all the mines. Industrialists asset-stripped and closed their Scottish branches, laughing off suggestions of repaying their original grants. Throughout the '80s Thatcher and her cohorts galloped unchallenged over the land north of the Tweed, spending the North Sea riches on the army of unemployed.

I gave up on Scotland. Soon as my son Ewan could toddle,

we took to the road. Greenham Common was the new Bastille. Later Germany, France; wherever angry people waved banners, shouted and sang. In a coffee house in Amsterdam, I got in with Phil. He was older than me and wearying of endless revolution. I had a young son who needed a settled home and regular schooling. So we followed Phil to Gateshead.

In 2014 I fully expected a NO victory. I know my fellow-countrymen and women. Their low self-esteem. Their pessimism. Their cringe. My Dad's old French teacher, Oliver Brown, once summed it up: "A shudder went through the Scottish MPs frantically looking for a spine to run up." So during the independence campaign, I stayed away. Followed closely at a distance. Bulletins from Ewan, blogs and postings.

I'm surprised by the narrowness of the result. My country people have changed beyond recognition. I sit up and start paying attention.

Still. The demoralisation of the 1980s happened in Scotland after a small YES majority. My own fear this time is that after an actual NO victory, the past will repeat itself.

World attention will slide away to some more ambitious minority, in Catalunya, Flanders or the Basque country. The dead weight of apathy will crush down again upon the crowns of the Scottish electorate. The Westminster Government with no votes to lose will punish the Scots for their audacity; teach us a lesson we will never forget.

In fact, the opposite happens. The spark which became a flicker is now a flame, eating its way through the Unionist support. The spirit which inspired the old Martyrs, Radicals and Suffragettes is wide awake. The Unicorn tosses its mane, paws the ground, tugs at its chain.

The very day after the victorious NO vote, joining a pro-independence party comes into vogue. The effect, overwhelming everywhere, is strongest in the wastelands of tumbleweed and poverty.

The SNP confounds all prophets, shreds the record books. Day by day mobs flock to sign up. The party can't churn out enough membership cards to meet demand. Within the first week membership doubles from 26,000 to 52,000. The surge becomes a torrent: 80,000, 120,000. Branches which used to hold their meetings round one table in a snug, now book halls and still can't cram everybody in. Admission to the Party's National Conference has to be limited as there's no venue in all Scotland large enough to accommodate the delegates.

Other pro-independence groups reap the benefit. Within a few weeks of the referendum, membership of the Scottish Greens rises from 1,700 to 8,500. Radical Independence Campaign hold local conferences, packing them into halls. They book the Glasgow SECC (until the construction of the nearby Hydro, one of the biggest venues in Scotland) for a conference and stuff it to capacity.

Inadvertently or by design the SNP books the Hydro (capacity 12,000) next to the SECC for the same day. This is the culmination of new leader Nicola Sturgeon's inaugural trip round Scotland. Again, standing room only. Nicola Sturgeon, a forty-something female politician, gets the frenzied reception generally granted to A-list boy bands. So many queue for a selfie with her that her cheeks hurt.

This mass adoration is reserved for pro-independence parties. The story with Labour and the LibDems couldn't be more different.

Labour has, for decades, straddled Scotland like a Colossus, dominating every Parliament, council chamber, quango, ALEO, and tenants' hall. Now it melts at the edges, sags in the centre. They elect their seventh leader since the coming of devolution. Each successive Scottish leader has been granted more power from London Central Office even as Labour's real power has waned all over the land.

The LibDems, with little left to lose except the major party status accredited by the media, continue their plunge towards the seabed.

Interest in politics remains high. Some councils use the 97% level of voter registration to track down poll tax defaulters from 20 years ago but the Scottish Government hurriedly writes off these debts.

At the UK elections the following May, the SNP break the BBC swingometer; burst the boundaries of their own optimism. Of 59 Scottish seats, the SNP take 56, leaving one each for Labour, the Tories and the LibDems.

These 56 MPs, 50 of them rookies, surge onto the startled green benches of the House of Commons. Not knowing any better, they treat governing the country like a full-time job.

The House of Commons has been run since time immemorial as a private club. The expectation is that members will attend only when they're in the mood or when the Whips order them in. There has never been enough room to accommodate all the MPs at once.

The SNP MPs turn up early to be sure of getting a seat. Finding the Opposition Front Benches deserted they occupy them, forcing those Labour and LibDem MPs who eventually appear to sit behind them or stand.

They compound this show of ignorance by clapping to show approval, the way the hoi-polloi do in theatres the world over. For this, the Speaker reprimands them, pointing out that the acceptable expression of approval in the House of Commons is to bellow 'Heah Heah!' The SNP members accept this chastisement and try to do better in future.

Lots of water, lots of bridges. Rivers in spate. By the time I've outlined the sea changes in the past three years, we'll have racked up another half dozen.

During 2014 Scotland reeled on to the world stage, birled its partner and reeled off.

In 2016 there will be a much shorter Act Two. Here England will take central stage. Prime Minister Cameron will have another go at the roulette with a referendum on EU membership. This time his luck runs out and England, leaderless, will dance out of the chorus line.

The SNP were re-elected into the Scottish Government in 2016 on a mandate to hold a second independence referendum if there should be a material change 'such as Scotland being taken out of the EU against its wishes.'

In the EU referendum, England will vote LEAVE. In Scotland, where emigration rather than immigration is the problem, every single constituency will vote REMAIN.

Nicola Sturgeon will suggest various halfway houses which could keep Scotland in the single market, or with powers over immigration. The new Prime Minister, Theresa May, will say it must be the same 'hard' BREXIT for every part of the UK. No single market, no customs union.

The Scottish Parliament will pass a motion asking the UK Government for permission to hold a second referendum on independence in two years' time, when the terms of BREXIT will be known but before Scotland has been fully uncoupled from the EU. The UK Government will announce that it will block any such referendum until after the UK has appropriated all the EU powers. Even then there will be no referendum until there's 'public consent' for one. Requests to define 'public consent' are ignored.

The unstoppable force of Scotland's First Minister will meet the immoveable object of the UK Prime Minister. Self-determination? Which self is more determined?

If the independence question is put again Scotland will face a dilemma. To Remain in the EU and Leave the UK, or Remain in the UK and Leave the EU. Heads or tails? Wolf in the pack or Tail on the Lone Wolf? Two Project Fears facing each other down.

The resolution of this dilemma will be Act Three.

On September 18th 2015, the first anniversary of the Independence Referendum, I tie my own label on to the fresh wish tree blossoming in Buchanan Street. Red, yellow, blue, green: the wishes of the common weal for a new Scotland flutter in the autumn breeze.

Hoping, one day, to trump fear.

Some other books from Ringwood Publishing

All titles are available from the Ringwood website
(including first edition signed copies) and from usual
outlets.
Also available as e-books
www.ringwoodpublishing.com

A Subtle Sadness

Sandy Jamieson

A Subtle Sadness is a rigorous exploration of
Scottish Identity and the impact on it of the key
Scottish obsessions of politics, football, religion,
sex and alcohol. It focuses on the family and
personal history of Frank Hunter, a sad Scotsman
with a self-destruct streak enormous even by
normal West of Scotland male standards.

A Subtle Sadness covers a century of Scottish
social, political and football highlights, with
disasters and triumphs aplenty, including the
impact of Thatcherism on Scotland's industrial
base.

ISBN: 978-1-901514-04-9   £9.99

Checking Out of the Hotel Euthanasia

Gerard Graham

Checking Out of the Hotel Euthanasia is
an always funny, often farcical, sometimes
scabrous take on a serious subject, assisted
dying. Swiftian in style, approach, and content,
it relentlessly assaults the hypocrisies and
muddled arguments around both sides of
the euthanasia debate with a challenging
combination of dispassionate calm and
outrageous humour. It will offend many, amuse
even more, and leave no-one untouched. It is a
major contribution to the political and ethical
debate already underway about the best
response to a growing clamour for the legal right to end one's life on
one's own terms

ISBN: 978-1-901514-40-7   £9.99

Memoirs of a Feminist Mother

Carol Fox

As a committed feminist, Carol Fox has achieved success for very many women, but her greatest battle described in this book was very personal. Following serious fertility problems, Carol made the positive decision to become a single parent by choice, to have a child while she still could. Refused access to fertility treatment in Scotland she had no choice but to move to London.

Through sheer determination and tenacity, Carol obtained treatment in England in the early 1990s and her daughter was born in 1992, following extensive fertility treatment and battles against judgemental attitudes which appear almost vindictive to us some 25 years later.

Written as a memoir addressed to her only daughter, the story has been, and continues to be, of interest to a wider audience of women, young and old, mothers and non-mothers, as the chapters record the changing social attitudes towards single parents.

Carol is been a lawyer specialising in equality and discrimination law, best known in Scotland for successfully fighting mass equal pay cases for low paid women and playing an active part in the Referendum Campaign.

ISBN: 978-1-901514-21-6   £9.99

The Gori's Daughter

Shazia Hobbs

The Gori's Daughter is the story of Aisha, a young mixed race woman, daughter of a Kashmiri father and a Glasgow mother. Her life is a struggle against rejection and hostility in Glasgow's white and Asian communities.

The book documents her fight to give her own daughter a culture and tradition that she can accept with pride. The tale is often harrowing but is ultimately a victory for decency over bigotry and discrimination.

"The Gori's Daughter is quite possibly the most compelling novel based on a true story that you will ever read" - **Dr Wanette Tuinstra - Golden Room**

ISBN: 978-1-901514-12-4   £9.99

The Volunteer

Charles P. Sharkey

The Volunteer is a powerful and thought-provoking examination of the Troubles that plagued Northern Ireland for almost three decades. It follows the struggles of two Belfast families from opposite sides of the sectarian divide. This revealing novel will lead the reader to a greater understanding of the events that led from the Civil Rights marches in the late Sixties, through the years of unbridled violence that followed, until the Good Friday Agreement of the late Nineties.

Born in the same hospital, within hours of each other, Danny Duffy and William Morrison would never meet again, but their lives, and the lives of their families, would be tragically intertwined by politics, secrets and blood.

While William Morrison shuns the violence that engulfs West Belfast, Danny Duffy finds himself standing in front of a panel of IRA men, ready to take up arms as a Volunteer; but what is he fighting for and how far is he willing to go?

ISBN: 978-1-901514-36-0   £9.99

Millennial Munros

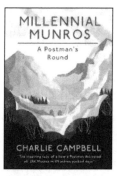

Charlie Campbell

"The inspiring tale of a how a postman delivered all 284 Munros in 49 action-packed days."

Millennial Munros is the inspirational story of an ordinary bloke doing an ordinary job, who did something extra-ordinary. With the help of his mum and some mates, he got motivated, got fit and completed an unprecedented endurance event, in breaking the world record for a continuous self-propelled round of all the Munros, Scotland's 284 mountains over 3000 feet in height.

He averaged nearly six Munros every day, and cycled or swam between them. Anyone who has done just one Munro in a day will know how big a deal this was. Charlie's entertaining account of his adventures comes complete with maps, routes and other details to help inspire others to tackle these mountains, but perhaps in a more relaxed manner!

ISBN: 978-1-901514-33-9   £9.99

Between Two Bridges

Brian McHugh

New York, 1933:

Prohibition is coming to an end, but not everyone is celebrating. A few astute businessmen realise that by legally importing liquor before the Volstead Act is repealed, they can net themselves a small fortune. Charlie McKenna, an Irishman who spent time in Glasgow during the Great War, is sent to complete the deal with Denholm Distillers in their St Enoch Square office.

Glasgow, Present Day:

Still reeling from the murder of their friend, three old friends are once again knocked off-course by the resurfacing of a battered diary. It soon leads them back into their investigation of Julie's grandfather, Charlie McKenna. More troubling tales of war, gold and gangsters soon begin to surface.

ISBN: 978-1-901514-35-3   £9.99

The Activist

Alec Connon

Unfulfilled by student life, Thomas Durant and two friends decide to cycle the length of Britain during their summer holidays, dressed as superheroes. The experience of their short trip is enough to whet Thomas's appetite for further travel and set in motion his decision to drop out of uni and see the world for himself.

Influenced by a burgeoning interest in marine conservation, what begins as a typical gap year develops into over decade's worth of involvement and participation in animal rights activism. The story follows Thomas, from his first tentative steps into the life of an activist in Vancouver, to his battles with the Japanese whaling fleet in the Southern Ocean.

"The enthralling tale presents the plight of the natural world – and its relationship with the human race – with an intimacy that is unlike anything I've ever seen in a novel." Peter Mountford, Washington State Book Aware Winner.

ISBN:978-1-901514-25-4   £9.99

Ringwood Referendum Roadshow

Over 2017 and 2018 Ringwood Publishing will be reviving its Ringwood Referendum Roadshow, and taking it round the country to provide opportunities for Scots of all political persuasions to take part in an evening of political discussion and reflection.

Mary McCabe author of this *Two Closes and a Referendum* and Sandy Jamieson, author of *A Subtle Sadness* (about 100 years of Scottish political and social history, encompassing the 1979 Referendum) will be the standard speakers, often joined by other writers and artists who have commentated on Scottish politics.

Previous Ringwood Referendum Roadshow events have proved stimulating, thought-provoking and productive; with past events analysed, myths deconstructed and future directions explored.

If you, your friends or your organisation would like the Referendum Roadshow to visit your area, contact Ringwood on mail@ringwoodpublishing.com